The Child Bride

Wang Ying

FOREIGN LANGUAGES PRESS   BEIJING

First Edition 1989
Second Printing 1993

English text edited by Monica Faulkner

ISBN 0-8351-2220-4
ISBN 7-119-00402-6

©1989 by Foreign Languages Press, Beijing, China

Published by Foreign Languages Press
24 Baiwanzhuang Road, Beijing, China

Printed by Foreign Languages Printing House
19 West Chegongzhuang Road, Beijing, China

Distributed by China International Book Trading Corporation
(Guoji Shudian), P.O. Box 399, Beijing, China

Printed in the People's Republic of China

WANG YING—HEROINE IN TROUBLED TIMES

THE publication of the English translation of *The Child Bride* by the late actress and progressive writer Wang Ying is a major event for all who want to gain a deeper understanding of the sufferings and struggles of women in early 20th-century China.

The Child Bride is an autobiographical novel that very nearly is a memoir of Wang Ying's childhood and adolescence in the China of the first two decades of the twentieth century, when that nation was still in the final throes of feudalism. It was a world dominated by men, and her story shows why so many Chinese women joined the burgeoning revolutionary movement —to gain their own emancipation.

Because it is a novel, there is some blurring between Wang Ying's narrative and my brief description of her life. Most notable will be her names, her age when some incidents occurred, details of her education and her kinship to those who helped her in her quest for freedom.

Sections of the original Chinese version of the book were first published in 1981 in *Harvest*, a literary bi-monthly edited by the well-known writer Ba Jin. The book appeared in 1982, published by China Youth Press, and received favorable comments throughout the nation. It received special praise from women writers who regarded the book as a vivid, true-to-life depiction of the abuses of feudalism. All 120,000 copies of the *Harvest* issue and the entire 110,800-copy first printing of the book sold out rapidly.

Wang Ying was born in Wuhu, a major industrial and commercial center about 60 miles south of Nanjing on the Yangtze River in Anhui Province, on March 8, 1915. Her original name was Yu Zhihua ("Dedication to China").

Her father, Yu Youren, had been raised as a Christian and had been an outstanding student at Wenhua University, an American-run missionary school also known as Boone University. It was located in Wuchang, which, along with Hankou and

Hanyang, makes up Wuhan, the capital of Hubei Province. He later became an assistant manager of Asia Petroleum Co., a branch of the Royal Dutch Shell Trust, in Nanjing.

Wang Ying's mother, Wang Xiumei ("Beautiful Winter Plum") graduated from a missionary high school in Hankou and worked as a music teacher in primary and high schools. She was a choir accompanist, and one of Wang Ying's uncles on her father's side was an actor, so the little girl's love of the arts and literature was passed on to her from both sides of her family.

Wang Ying's unusual abilities were apparent even during her childhood. Her memory was good and she displayed a natural talent for music and performing. She was quick to learn hymns and folksongs, as well as popular tunes she picked up from the street singers of Wuhu. When she was five, her parents' neighbors nicknamed her "Our Little Songbird."

However, her parents' marriage was apparently not a happy one. Her father was given to the extravagances recounted in the present book, and when Wang Ying was only 10, her mother died after a lengthy stomach illness. Her father had no trouble finding another wife and soon remarried, but Wang Ying's stepmother had no affection for the little girl and she was soon packed off to a convent boarding school near her father's parents' home in Wuhu.

A few years later, her father found himself deeply in debt because of his extravagances. He and his second wife therefore decided to pass the 12-year-old girl off as 14 and sold her as a "child bride" for the son of a wealthy Wuhu merchant named Xue, the head of the "Shao" family in the present book. Xue paid Yu 5,000 Chinese dollars for Wang Ying. This was a huge sum at the time because girls were usually sold for 100 to 200 dollars in feudal China.

"Child brides" or "child daughters-in-law" were a common institution in feudal China. Parents would betroth a daughter to the son of another family in exchange for money, but the actual marriage might not take place for several years. In the meantime the young girl would live in her in-law's home. Often she was reduced to being little more than a slave to her mother-in-law.

This was what happened to Wang Ying. After enduring more than a year of physical mistreatment and mental torture at her mother-in-law's hands she decided to run away—a courageous decision for so young a girl, especially during that period of Chinese history.

She fled first to her maternal grandmother and then to Hankou and Changsha, where her mother's sister, the principal of a middle school, took her in. She gave up her father's name, adopted her mother's family name of Wang, and took on a new first name, "Keqin" ("able to work hard"). Then, before her fourteenth birthday, she enrolled in the nursing training course offered as part of Yale University's "Yale in China" program, at Xiangya Medical College Hospital.

It was at about this time that she began reading the books and periodicals that were being published under the influence of the May Fourth Movement of 1919, a patriotic student movement inspired by outrage over the Versailles Treaty which transferred Qingdao and other possessions seized by the Germans in China to Japan instead of returning them to China. The movement sparked a cultural renaissance, under the slogan "Democracy and Science."

The years from 1919 to 1927 were tumultuous ones in China: the founding of the Communist Party of China in 1921; labor strikes; the first Kuomintang-Communist United Front from 1924 to 1927; and finally, Chiang Kai-shek's massacre of the Communists in Shanghai on April 12, 1927. A time of terror began, and the rest of 1927 was full of upheavals in south and central China. This was the time of the Northern Expedition and the suppression by the Kuomintang of the workers' and peasants' movements in and around Wuhan.

Wang Ying recounted her experiences during this period in the final section of the Chinese edition *The Child Bride*, but the English book ends without her describing her own role in the growing revolutionary movement.

In 1928, she began helping the Communist Party by becoming an information courier. The Kuomintang soon learned about her activities and sent agents out to arrest her, but her fellow students learned about their plans and warned her.

She managed to get out of Changsha and made her way to Shanghai via Nanjing. There, with the help of some progressive friends, she wrote a letter exposing and condemning the Kuomintang as criminals who were killing revolutionary workers, peasants, and students of Hunan. The letter also denounced He Jian, the provincial governor of Hunan, as a brutal warlord.

She sent the letter to He Jian and also to the students and staff of Xiangya Hospital. The letter was reprinted as a leaflet and smuggled into Changsha, where it was widely distributed.

The letter infuriated He Jian. He reprimanded the hospital director and also ordered Wang Ying's arrest, but she was out of reach in Shanghai. For safety's sake, she changed her name to Wang Ying. She first joined a relief society linked to the Communist Party and later went to teach Chinese and arithmetic at a primary school in the town of Hengmian, near Shanghai.

In 1929, she joined the Shanghai Artistic Theater Troupe and starred in "Coal Miners." In 1930, she became a member of the Communist Youth League and the Chinese Communist Party. When the League of Left-Wing Writers was organized that same year, she entered its College of Arts, but the school was soon closed by the Kuomintang authorities.

Between 1930 and 1932, she studied at the China Academy, a junior-college level school, and then at Fudan University, where she entered the literature department. She began reading Western writers such as Shakespeare, Tolstoy, Turgenev, Dickens, de Maupassant, and Gorky as well as classical Chinese works. She also became interested in contemporary Chinese drama and became a member of the Fudan University Drama Club.

The growth of her political consciousness paralleled her intellectual development. She took an active part in the movement against the Japanese invasion of Manchuria (September 18, 1931) and for democratic rights at home. With other students, professors and intellectuals, she often took part in demonstrations that ended in clashes during which the Kuomintang police turned water hoses on the demonstrators. During this period, the Kuomintang authorities arrested her on four different occasions. Her courage was widely recognized.

Starting in 1932, Wang Ying joined several progressive theater groups, including the Art and Union theaters, and made several films at the Mingxing and Diantong film studios. Her theater work included roles in "Storm on the Border," "Lay Down Your Whip," "The Imperial Commissioner," "The Goddess of Liberty," "The Common Enemy," "The Battle of Tai'erzhuang," and "The First Wife." Most of these works had anti-feudal and anti-imperialist themes which called on the Chinese people to take up arms to resist Japanese aggression.

One of her most important roles was "Sai Jinhua," in which she played the title role of a cultured, patriotic prostitute who lived in Beijing during the Boxer Movement of 1900-1901. She persuaded Count Alfred von Waldersee, the commander-in-chief of the Allied troops, not to kill the people of the city or to loot.

Her patriotism was in sharp contrast to the Qing officials who kowtowed to the foreign invaders to save their own skins.

As performed in the early 1930s, however, the play was obviously a satire on Chiang Kai-shek's regime and its attempts to wipe out the Communists at home while kowtowing to the Japanese invaders. The play was a sensation and attracted sellout audiences who often had to wait in line all night for tickets.

Irked by the play's success, the Kuomintang authorities sent a group of plainclothesmen led by a propaganda official to the theater to disrupt the performance one night. The gang threw bottles and spittoons at the stage, shouted at the performers to stop, and even jumped up onto the stage to attack the actors and actresses, but Wang Ying and the rest of the cast ignored the uproar, and the audience finally drove out the intruders.

During this period, Wang Ying starred in four films. In "Tears Under the Tax Burden," she portrayed a country girl who broke the shackles of feudalism by fighting against a tyrannical landlord who was levying heavy taxes on the peasants on the pretext that the money would be used to buy guns to protect the peasants from bandits. In "A Woman's Outcry" she was a slave laborer struggling to free herself from a Shanghai sweatshop. In the film version of "The Common Enemy," she called on the people to unite against the Japanese. And in the film version of "The Goddess of Liberty," she portrayed a young woman who leaves home to go to Shanghai, where she matured as a result of the struggles that followed the May Fourth Movement.

All of these films were very popular and expressed strong support for the liberation of women as well as resistance against Japan. Unlike older films, which drew on legends or ghost stories or depicted the pleasure-seeking leisure class, the new films dealt with the real social and political problems facing China. During this time, Wang Ying also began writing essays, travel notes, and film reviews which appeared in leading newspapers and magazines.

However, she became increasingly disgusted by the decadent lifestyle of the Shanghai's film community, which indulged in excessive drinking, gambling, and sex. Wang Ying was a non-smoker and non-drinker who drank only orange juice at her wedding in New York in February 1950. So in 1934, she gave up her stardom and wealth and decided to go to Japan to study drama and the literature being turned out by progressive Japanese writers opposed to their nation's aggression in China.

Soon after she arrived, however, a leading motion picture company asked her to make some films promoting "friendly cooperation" between Japan and China. Wang Ying rejected the lucrative offer and gradually began making contacts among progressive Japanese intellectuals. She studied Japanese assiduously and soon gained a good grasp of the language. But Japanese police and plainclothesmen often followed and harassed her. In 1935, she decided to return to Shanghai and resume her acting career.

Once back in China, she had to deal with the Kuomintang authorities, who jailed her again in an attempt to force her to reveal where film pioneer Xia Yan could be found. But she refused to give her teacher away.

After Japan attacked China in 1937, the Kuomintang and the Communists joined together to drive out the invaders and to preserve China's independence.

Wang Ying donated all her jewelry, valuables, and savings to the war effort and joined the Shanghai National Salvation Theater Group No. 2. She and her colleagues traveled, often on foot, to 15 provinces and regions and covered more than 10,000 kilometers giving morale-raising performances for the troops and the peasants in small towns and mountain villages.

Besides offering entertainment, they also helped the rural residents organize more than 40 local theater groups to enrich their cultural life. They also brought war news with them and taught the people how to put up wall newspapers to spread the news.

Around the beginning of 1939, the group was reorganized as the New China Theater, with Wang Ying as the leading star and deputy director. The company set out on what became a two-year tour of Hongkong and Southeast Asia to rally support and money for the war effort from Chinese people outside the mainland. Their performances were very successful and raised US$ 30 million, as well as large quantities of supplies, in less than two years.

Busy though she was, Wang Ying found time to become a special correspondent for Singapore's leading Chinese newspaper, the *Nanyang Shangbao* (*South Sea Commercial Daily News*).

Her articles included reports on the company's tour and performances and her impressions of life and sights in the cities she visited. The articles also kept the war cause before the eyes of her readers. She became known as "Our Darling" by Chinese readers in Singapore and other parts of Southeast Asia.

In June, 1941, Wang Ying flew back to Chongqing, the wartime capital, to report to Zhou Enlai, who at the time was the Chinese Communist Party's representative to the Kuomintang government. His judgment of her was that she was "an outstanding young talent."

The start of the Pacific War, which followed the Japanese sneak attack on Pearl Harbor in December, 1941, brought new changes to Wang Ying's life. She was unwilling to live in Hongkong because it was under Japanese control, so she disguised herself as a nun and escaped to Guangzhou in a sampan with some other writers and artists. She finally returned to Chongqing.

In May, 1942, the Kuomintang sent her and her fiance, Xie Hegeng (Hsieh Hokeng), to the United States for further studies. She was to study drama and writing, and Xie was to study municipal government. The move was made possible in no small part by Owen Lattimore, Chiang Kai-shek's political advisor, who found himself hiding in the same cave as the Guangxi Province warlord Bai Chongxi, whose secretary at the time was Xie. Bai told Lattimore that he wanted Xie to study government in the United States, and the American promised to line up financial support for the young man. Lattimore also helped Wang Ying with her educational plans.

Soon after she arrived in the States, Wang Ying attended the World Student Conference as a representative of China in August 1942. She and representatives from the Soviet Union, Britain, and the Netherlands then took part in a one-and-a-half-month nationwide round of wartime rallies at which she explained the situation in China.

At one rally, at the Ford airplane plant in Detroit, Michigan, 50,000 workers gave her an ovation and Henry Ford gave a dinner in her honor.

After the tour, Wang Ying enrolled at Goucher College in Baltimore, Maryland, and concentrated on studying English. She then received a scholarship, funded in part by writer Pearl Buck and her friends, to Bryn Mawr College near Philadelphia. There, she studied drama and writing. In the meantime, Xie Hegeng received a Quaker scholarship to study government at nearby Haverford College. Later, she went to Yale University in New Haven, Connecticut, where she studied in the literature department. She also studied modern dance at the Isadora Duncan Dance School, also in New Haven.

On March 15, 1945, Wang Ying was invited to the White

House to act in a performance of "Lay Down Your Whip," a drama about the sufferings of the people of northeastern China during the Japanese occupation. She also sang some anti-Japanese songs and folksongs. President Franklin D. Roosevelt, who was to die less than a month later, his family, Vice-President Henry Wallace, and many Washington dignitaries were in the audience. A photograph taken that day of Wang Ying and Mrs. Roosevelt is included in this book.

Wang Ying became a member of the board of directors of the East-West Association, founded by Pearl Buck and her husband to foster cultural relations between Eastern and Western nations. Eugene O'Neill, Ernest Hemingway, and many other noted American writers and artists were also on the board of directors.

Wang Ying served as director of the association's Chinese Drama Department and was the founder and leader of its China Theater Group, which presented modern Chinese plays, Beijing and local Chinese operas, dance groups, and other performances. She and the company traveled to many American cities to perform anti-Japanese plays at factories and college campuses. Her starring roles earned her the nickname "the Helen Hayes of China" in some newspaper reviews.

It was at about the time World War II ended that Pearl Buck suggested that Wang Ying write her own life story in the form of a novel. Wang Ying took her friend's advice and began writing *The Child Bride* in 1946. She also worked with the well-known translator Ida Pruitt, also her good friend, on translating it into English.

However, she was very worried about the resumption of civil war in China and between 1948 and 1952 wrote articles and editorials, advocating a coalition government between the Communists and the Kuomintang to bring democracy and prosperity to China, for the *Overseas Chinese Daily News* and *Niuyue Xinbao* (*New York Daily News*), two progressive Chinese newspapers.

She also helped journalist Agnes Smedley write *The Great Road*, her biography of Zhu De (Chu Teḥ), commander-in-chief of the Chinese People's Liberation Army.

However, Roosevelt's death ended an era of political liberalism in the United States. Under President Harry S. Truman, a wave of reaction against the Soviet Union and fear of the "Communist menace" swept the land.

So the victory of the Chinese revolution and the defeat of

Chiang Kai-shek in 1949 were regarded as tragedies by the United States, and McCarthyism soon threatened anyone who sympathized with New China.

Wang Ying and her husband, who had gotten married on February 22, 1950, therefore decided not to ask to become permanent residents or citizens of the United States, as American immigration authorities had persistently suggested, and said they wished to return to their homeland.

In early 1952, Wang Ying and Xie bought boat tickets to London as part of a plan to return to China. When American immigration officials eventually learned of their plans, they decided to prevent them from leaving the United States. In 1954, the couple were taken in for interrogation and urged to become American citizens rather than returning to "Communist China." They refused and were jailed, Wang Ying in the New York State Prison for Women and Xie in the New York City Jail.

Their imprisonment aroused indignation among their friends and acquaintances at Bryn Mawr and Haverford and among Xie's superiors and coworkers at the Columbia University Library, where he had been working with United Nations materials.

A lawyer working on their behalf filed a petition asking for voluntary departure from the United States, but this was denied. Their friends, including Pearl Buck, formed a rescue committee to help them, organized a letter-writing campaign and picketed the US Justice Department in Washington D.C., and the immigration offices in New York. Buck also wrote a letter of protest to the *New York Times*, and debates about the case and how the United States was treating Chinese students were held on national television.

In late 1954, after two months in jail, they were secretly deported—but not to Taiwan, where they would probably have been killed by the Kuomintang authorities. Instead, they were sent to a small village, now Shenzhen, near Hongkong. From there it was easy for them to return to the mainland.

In June 1956, she was assigned to work as a writer at the Beijing Film Studio, where she started on the screenplay "U.S. President Wilson." It depicts the patriotic spirit and activities of many overseas Chinese students and workers who supported the People's Republic of China and helped building it into a new modern nation. Xie Hegeng became an editor at the World Affairs Press.

But it was not long before misfortunes befell them again. In the Chinese Communist Party's 1957 rectification campaign, Xie was accused of being a "Rightist" opposed to the Party's leadership because he had suggested building modernized halls for the Central Government and Party headquarters as well as good apartment houses for the leaders, and then restore Zhongnanhai as a public park as soon as possible. Zhongnanhai became a park for the people in 1929, while the nearby Beihai Park had been created in 1925. The two parks were linked together, people could take small boats and row from one to the other under the stone bridge now called the Beihai Bridge. Xie also suggested that all famous scenic spots, historical relics, as well as big mansions and gardens which formerly belonged to the emperors, nobles and warlords be used by the public, especially the youths and children for recreational activities, and high officials should move out from these buildings as soon as possible.

Like thousands of other intellectuals accused of similar "offences," Xie was sent to reclaim land in the remote border regions near the Soviet Union.

Wang Ying, left alone in Beijing and shunned by friends afraid to associate with her, moved to a farmhouse in the city's western hills. There, she made friends with nearby farmers and their families. She often invited the children to play in her garden and arranged song-and-dance program for them on festive occasions. The children called her "Auntie Wang."

Xie Hegeng returned to Beijing in July, 1959. His health had been damaged by his exile but his spirit remained unbroken. The couple began working together on amending and improving the manuscript of *The Child Bride*, in both Chinese and English versions, and Wang Ying began writing *Two Kinds of Americans*, a report of her experiences in the United States. In it, she argued that the McCarthyites were only a handful of reactionaries, while most Americans had been hoodwinked into terror of the "Red Menace."

Both manuscripts were completed five years later, in the spring of 1964. Xie Hegeng then began assembling the multitude of materials they had collected on the condition of Chinese workers in the States and interviews with black leaders and scholars in preparation for future writings, while Wang Ying began writing a sequel to *The Child Bride*.

But in May 1966, the "cultural revolution" broke out like a thunderstorm over China and derailed Wang Ying's life. Young Red Guards broke into the homes of writers, artists, professors, teachers, and scientists, and destroyed anything they considered "counter-revolutionary." Intellectuals were forced to endure criticisms in open meetings and jailed for being "reactionary authorities" or "foreign agents."

Wang Ying's hillside home was also searched, and many of her valuable possessions, including books, papers, famous calligraphies and paintings were confiscated. The sequel to *The Child Bride* was seized and never seen again. More than a dozen people were stationed in her house to watch her and her husband, and they were both placed under house arrest. They also had to undergo questioning for hours each day. This ruined her physical and mental health.

On July 1, 1967, both she and her husband were arrested and jailed on charges of having been members of the "black gang," a faction of the Communist Party that had opposed Mao Zedong's leadership in the 1930s. They were also accused of working as American spies.

Wang Ying was kept in solitary confinement. At the beginning of 1970, she became paralyzed and lost her power to speak, but her jailors refused to give her any medical treatment until November 1972, when she was finally sent to a hospital.

She died of heart failure on March 3, 1974 after having been interrogated for several days and nights without stopping. She was a victim of Jiang Qing's venom; Wang Ying knew too much about Jiang Qing's sordid life in Shanghai in the 1930s; she had gotten the role of "Sai Jinhua" instead of Jiang Qing; and she supported her husband's suggestion that Party leaders should move out of Zhongnanhai.

Wang Ying's body was cremated that day, before her family, relatives or work organization were notified. So no one could pay their respects to her remains.

Xie Hegeng was released on July 15, 1975, after eight years of imprisonment. He was suffering from physical and nervous ailments which took a long time to cure. It was only after his release that he learned of his wife's death. The death certificate given to him by the authorities did not even include her name. All it had was her prison identification number, 6742.

After the "cultural revolution" ended, Wang Ying was exonerated by the Chinese Government and the Communist Party. Xie was determined to publish his late wife's works, and both *The Child Bride* and *Two Kinds of Americans* were published in Chinese between 1980 and 1982. *The Child Bride* sold about 240,000 copies and *Two Kinds of Americans* sold about 300,000 copies. Many magazines and newspapers had also published excerpts from the books.

I first met Wang Ying and Xie Hegeng in the 1940s in Philadelphia, where I was executive secretary of that city's branch of the China Aid Council. They learned about me from their Chinese friends and American Quakers, and we became very good friends. They visited our home many times and Xie even served as our babysitter.

We were all good friends and ardent supporters of the Chinese revolution, and I learned much from them about the revolutionary leaders and the progressive writers and artists of the period. After we all returned to China, we remained friends, helping and encouraging one another in our work.

So I am honored to have the privilege of writing this brief biography of Wang Ying. I hope this English edition of *The Child Bride* will reach many foreign readers and that its story of the sufferings of a young girl in the old semi-feudal, semi-colonial China will help them understand the China of today.

Su Kaiming
Beijing, China
September 1987

BOOK I

Grandmother, Mother, and I
—We of the Three Generations

Wang Ying (*right*) at ten with her cousin in Hankou.

Wang Ying at seventeen in Shanghai, 1931.

Wang Ying in the play "Young Mistress' Fan" in Shanghai, 1930.

In Shanghai before sailing for Japan to study, 1934.

Wang Ying (*front left*) as a guest in the home of Mr. Wujaku Akita (*center*), famous Japanese writer and dramatist, 1934.

In the play "Sai Jinhua," 1936.

飾賽金花的王瑩

Wang Ying and Chinese painter Xu Beihong in Singapore with his oil painting of a scene from "Lay Down Your Whip," October 1939.

Wang Ying in 1939, just arrived in Singapore with the New China Theater group on the boat at her back.

Wang Ying (*left*) in the play "Storm on the Border." This picture was taken during her performing tour to Hongkong and Southeast Asia between 1939 and 1941.

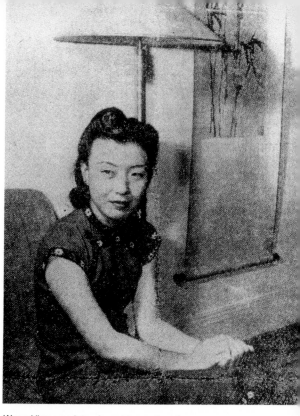

Wang Ying was interviewed by an American reporter at the home of author Lin Yutang in the summer of 1942.

As a representative from China, Wang Ying attended the World Student Conference in Washington in 1942. In this picture, taken after the welcoming session in New York City, she is with delegates from the Soviet Union, Britain and Holland.

Wang Ying and a Russian woman delegate to the conference with American industrialist Henry Ford in his office.

Wang Ying (*fourth from right*) and other delegates to the conference visited the Ford Motor Co. in August 1942, where this picture was taken with the Ford family.

As a student at Bryn Mawr College near Philadelphia, 1943.

Wang Ying, performed in the plays "Lay Down Your Whip" (**upper**) and "The First Wife" in the White House, Washington, March 1945.

With Eleanor Roosevelt after her White House performance, 1945.

Wang Ying and her husband, Xie Hegeng, in Central Park, New York, 1948.

With the children of a Haverford College professor in Philadelphia, 1951.

Wang Ying and Pearl Buck at her home, 1953.

At Pearl Buck's home in suburban Philadelphia, 1952.

From left to right: Wang Ying, with Pearl Buck's husband and Su Kaiming, author of "Wang Ying—Heroine in Troubled Times" and long time friend, July 1953.

Wang Ying (*right*) and her husband (not in photo) were invited, with Ida Pruitt (*back to camera*), to May Day dinner with Helen Foster Snow (*facing camera*) in Connecticut, 1954.

Back in China and at the Great Wall, 1956.

Wang Ying and Xie Hegeng at Beihai Park, Beijing, 1956.

Wang Ying working on her book in her new home at the foot of the Fragrant Hills in Beijing suburbs, 1956.

At the Fragrant Hills, 1961.

A birthday party for a friend in front of Wang Ying's Fragrant Hills home, July 1963. Wang Ying and Xie Hegeng are first and third from right.

Wang Ying practising *Tai Ji Quan* near her home. Xie Hegeng, behind her, is busy with planting. Four years later in 1967 the couple were arrested and jailed. Wang Ying died in prison during the "cultural revolution" in 1974 and Xie was released in 1975 after eight years' imprisonment.

Chapter 1

The pomegranate blooms and the leaves are green,
I embroider a pair of shoes for my mother.
In the ten months she carried me,
Was there one she didn't worry?

A son is born with joy,
A daughter, with rage.
Oh Mother, boys and girls alike are born.
Why must parents have different feelings for them?

THIS story happened long ago and far away. But these events
are as alive and fresh in my memory as if they happened
yesterday, even though, like the years and the months, they have
disappeared without sound or smell, without shadow or trace.

I was born in Wuhu, a small city on the lower reaches of the
Yangtze River, but I was told that my ancestors came from a large
sand-swept plain north of the Yellow River and that they settled
in Wuhu in my great-grandfather's time. My family had for
several generations been a middle-class "scholarly family," but had
gradually become poorer and poorer.

When I was born, in 1915, our ancient and feudal society,
many thousands of years old, was in the midst of trying to work
towards the new while also protecting the old. China was between
two tides which pushed and crashed and rolled against each
other. All was movement, with nothing settled. For more than
half a century, the fortunes of the Chinese nation had been
declining day after day. From an independent country, it had
become semi-colonial, subject to the aggression and control of
foreign powers. Except for the very, very high officials, the men
who conducted big business, the men who managed the huge
export-import trade, and the big landlords—none of whom felt
the effects of these changes, but on the contrary became even
wealthier and more prosperous—the lives of the people became

ever more difficult. Soon before my birth, the "Little Emperor" of the Qing Dynasty, Pu Yi, left his throne and the empire was overthrown. China was to reform, becoming a modern republic governed by a constitution.

Wuhu was very small and, unlike great and famous cities, did not have exceptional prosperity or ancient relics or modern ways. But because of its location on the river it had become a fairly important port and business center. Its products were many, including rice, tea, bean curd, scissors, knives, and fruit and vegetables of all four seasons. Also, the fish and shrimp that came from the river year round were famous all over the country.

Every day, from as far back as I can remember, my grandmother would tie my hair at the roots with red woolen yarn and braid it into two stiff, curved plaits that stood out like water-buffalo horns on either side of my head. On summer evenings, Grandfather would often put on a long white linen gown and, carrying his fan of folded paper and sandalwood slats in one hand and holding my hand in his other, together we would go out for a stroll on Main Street and Long Street. When I was small, these excursions were what I looked forward to most. In those days, Main Street and Long Street were not desolate, as they are now. They were the gayest and most prosperous business streets in the whole city. Each evening, as darkness drew near, their lanterns and lamps were lit and all would be luminous and bright. The shop signs on both sides of the streets were like the kites that flew in the heavens during Spring Festival, of every color and shape. Long and short, round and square, of silk and cloth, of wood and metal, ingenious and intriguing, they beckoned and waved to passers-by. The one that always caught my eye, the most interesting one, I remember, was a pair of huge scissors, the sign for the city's oldest scissors and knife shop. This sign was two or three times as big as I was. From far off, as soon as we set foot on Long Street, I could see it hanging there with its two blades open wide. It dominated the street and was so lifelike that I was never comfortable when we walked under it. I was always frightened that something untoward would happen, that it would fall down and swallow me in its great jaws.

Whenever my mother learned that Grandfather wanted to take me out for a walk, she would hasten to comb my hair carefully and wash my face before dinner. She would change all my clothes and dress me in my second-best suit, of flowered cotton. The coat and trousers smelled of the clean, dry fragrance of the sun. From

4

the button under my arm she would hang a leek-green or pink flowered silk kerchief. Sometimes she would sprinkle the kerchief with a few drops of the toilet water she used in her bath and for mosquito bites. Then she would dip the end of her long, red, bone hair-parter into rouge and make a small red dot, or a little heart-shaped decorative mole, between my eyebrows. When my dressing-up was completed, Grandmother, Mother, and I would go together to the porch for dinner.

I would sit quietly and with dignity on my little stool, fearing that if I moved once too often I would wrinkle my pretty, gay clothes, but in my heart I wished that I could leap with one bound through the main gate. How could they expect me to eat anything? How difficult it was to wait until Grandfather slowly put down his chopsticks and bowl! Then I had to wait even longer while, sip after sip, he drank a big cup of tea.

As we were about to leave, Grandmother would draw me aside and in an anxious whisper warn me, "Little one, in a short time you will be on Long Street. Remember, you are not to ask Grandfather to buy every pretty toy you see. Do we not call your stroll 'sightseeing on the boulevard'?" And she would smile so broadly that her eyes almost closed, touch her finger to the little red heart on my forehead, and say, "Main Street is a place to look around. Is it reasonable to want to buy a thing just because you see it? Just think how much money that would take!"

I would nod impatiently the whole time she was speaking, and then walk with Grandfather down the two flights of wooden steps and across the stone-paved courtyard. But just as we were about to step over the first wooden threshold of the main gate, we would hear Grandmother call to us from the lattice window upstairs. "Grandfather, be careful. Don't let her soil her new shoes. Don't let her lose her silk kerchief."

Grandfather would not turn his head. Drawing the words out slowly, he would answer, "I ... know."

After going out between the two doors of the big, black-lacquered gate, Grandfather and I would make our way along the bumpy little streets and lanes, which were paved with pebble-stones. The light evening breezes of summer blew, cool and caressing, on our heads and faces and carried the fragrance of gardenias and honeysuckle to us from our neighbors' courtyards. Most of the people who lived near us at that time had small businesses like little shops that sold peanuts or bean curd. There were also cobblers and blacksmiths, and peddlers who walked

5

along residential streets shaking little rattles or sold their wares in stalls. There were also two families who made their livings working for foreign missionaries. At this time of the evening, most of the neighbors would be sitting at their gates on bamboo cots and chairs, waving fans and trying to cool off.

"Well, well, Xiao Baogu (Little Treasure), you certainly know how to make yourself pretty, all dressed up like that to go out walking." They would see me from a long way off, coming along with my grandfather, and would smile and call to me. "Dressed up so prettily! Where are you going? Are you going out for a stroll along the big streets with your grandfather?"

"Of course! Every few days I have to take her out for a walk," Grandfather would reply.

"Walk carefully when you cross the Bridge of Lions. Don't let the lions carry her away."

"Don't ... worry ... She'll ... be ... safe ... It will not happen...." Grandfather's slow, drawn-out words would take us past them all.

After turning two more corners, we would reach the Bridge of Lions. At each end stood two big carved-stone lions, one on each side of the road. They were plump and alert-looking, and whenever they saw me coming or going across the bridge they seemed to open their mouths and smile at me. The bridge, of stone slabs, was neither long nor wide, and in a few steps we were across. People said water used to run under it a long time ago, but now the stream bed was filled with refuse and dirt. People also said that the stone lions on the bridge had absorbed the essential elements from the long years of sunshine, moonlight, rain, and dew that had touched them during the hundreds or thousands of years they had stood there, and that they had now turned into elemental spirits themselves—spirits that could fend off evil, especially whenever any of the children of the families in the neighborhood were ill with chills and fever. The mothers of sick children would go to the Bridge of Lions at dusk to call back their children's souls from the evil spirits who were believed to have seized them and caused the illness.

The mother would walk in front and the grandmother would follow. Both would be carrying rice in their apron-skirts. All along the way they would call and answer, and as they walked they would spill the rice, spilling it to protect their children against harmful demons and spirits.

"Xiao Long (Little Dragon), of our family, Xiao Long, come home now," the mother would call to her child.

"I'm coming home, I'm coming home," the grandmother would reply, pretending to be the child.

"Xiao Long, don't be afraid. Your grandmother and mother are here."

"Oh, I'm not afraid."

The low, moaning sounds of their voices, especially in the dark of night, would bring sadness to the heart, as if Xiao Long's soul really had become lost somewhere and would never return.

The entrance to Long Street was not far from the Bridge of Lions. Immediately, our eyes were struck by the lights. There were things everywhere, of every color, green and blue and red. There were shop signs, and many, many people.

Grandfather liked to look at the shop windows, which displayed goods from Suzhou and Hangzhou, at the lights, and at the people. I liked to look at the toy stands on both sides of the street. The toys filled the stands and hung above them—big tigers covered with yellow-and-black striped fur, long-bearded old men who could not be knocked over even if you punched them because they rocked on heavy round bottoms, big roosters with red combs and white feathers, trumpets in every color of the rainbow, skillfully-made figurines depicting all the characters from the famous operas. I would loiter at the stands and look. The longer I stood, the more I loved the toys and the less I wanted to leave. Grandfather would call once, and then again. Seeing that I would not listen, he would take my hand and gently pull me along. I would tug away, trying to go back. Then Grandfather would say, "We must go on. There are many other good things to see. We'll buy something further on." When we had gone the whole length of Long Street and I began to realize there was no hope, I would turn around and try to go back. But Grandfather would take my hand again and say, "It's getting dark. Be good and listen to me. Grandmother is at home waiting for us to come back and eat lotus-root soup cooked with rock sugar. Next time we come out, we'll buy a toy."

After we had been out walking five or six times, Grandfather could no longer deny this persistent little girl. He finally took some coins out of his pouch and bought me the smallest and cheapest clay rooster whistle. This was the utmost delight—a toy in my childhood was an almost unattainable joy. Very carefully, I held it in both hands with its tail against my lips. All the way home, using all my strength, I crowed. "Koo-koo-koo ..." when Grandmother and Mother saw it, they laughed and said, "Look how clever she is! This evening she finally wheedled some money out of her grandfather and got him to buy her a gift."

However, we no longer lived as well as we had in the past. Each summer, Grandfather would buy me a couple of toys, and sometimes he would buy Grandmother a packet of locally-grown "shredded leather" tobacco, which got its name from its appearance. It was the special water-pipe tobacco my grandmother liked to smoke best. On early mornings during the summer months, when we heard the high, shrill voices of the women flower sellers passing by our house, Grandfather would hurry downstairs and buy several tiny jasmine flowers, with their light fragrance, or orchids for Mother. He would also buy some large gardenias for Grandmother. This was one of the rare occasions when he would spend money. When Grandmother saw the little white flowers lying on the long table that stood against the wall, she would tell Mother in a happy, gentle voice, "Daughter-in-law, come and see. Grandfather has again bought flowers for us."

With great care, Mother would tuck the flowers into her knot of hair or hang them from the shoulder button of her gown. Then, smiling, she would go to Grandfather and say, "Grandfather, how fragrant these flowers are!"

"Um...." Grandfather's eyes would have a little smile in them and he would nod his head slightly, as if to say, "If you like them, I'm happy." But the only sound he would make was that "Um...," in the back of his throat.

In later years, Grandmother would often say that of all four of his daughters-in-law Grandfather liked my mother best. When Mother was out of hearing, Grandmother would quote his praise of her to others: "The wife of our eldest son is loyal and serious, gentle, and cares very much for her family." But when he was around my mother, he would never say much to her.

My mother was nineteen when she married into my father's family. I was their first child. Grandmother told me that when I first came out of the womb and into the world, I opened my mouth and cried loudly. The midwife caught me with both hands and said over and over, "What a happy event! This distinguished family has added a thousand gold."* I was told that when the family heard these words, "a thousand gold," no one frowned or

---

*"A thousand gold." A term of respect that refers to other families' daughters. The original term is "a thousand catties of gold"; a catty equals about 1.1 pounds or 500 grams.

showed any disappointment, or uttered a word of criticism that I was not born a boy. Instead, a feeling of happiness spread throughout the house as my mother and I lay quiet and safe under our warm quilts.

When I was old enough to understand what she was saying, I often heard Grandmother tell the neighbors, "We of the Zhou family have lacked nothing except daughters. So you can understand why the whole family was so happy when Xiao Baogu was born. This is not strange—the proverb is right, 'What is lacking becomes all the more valued.' In our family, ever since her great-great-grandfather's generation," and she would count them off on her fingers, "one generation, two generations, three generations, and to the time of her father, four generations—there were many sons but no daughters. And now, not only is she the first child of this generation to be born, she is also the first daughter in five generations. You can see why we love her so much and why her grandfather was so quick to name her Xiao Baogu, Little Treasure.

"On the third day, we began dyeing more than a hundred eggs red. When we sent out the invitations for her First-Month Feast, we invited almost a hundred people.[*] It was in the middle of April and the weather was warm. Her grandfather, wanting everything to be gay and happy, thought up a new decoration. In front of each guest's wine cup, he placed a fresh red cherry blossom. Could a First-Month Feast for a son have been done any more handsomely?"

As Grandmother talked, she would look at me sideways through her white-copper-framed reading glasses, and the neighbors would look at me enviously. In those early years, I could not control the happiness I felt when I heard my grandmother's words. I thought it was really as she said, that I was truly rare and very precious.

During my early years, my father was often gone for a whole year at a time. He was teaching school in a little county city several hundred *li*[**] away, separated from us by mountains and rivers. My two oldest uncles, his younger brothers, were working in other provinces. Because they had not yet had any children, their wives, my aunts, were also with them. My third uncle was

---

[*] Red eggs were given out as gifts at a child's First-Month Feast, held about thirty days after birth.

[**] One *li* equals half a kilometer, or about a third of a mile.

in a boarding school in a province in the upper reaches of the Yangtse. Only my youngest uncle, who was still attending day school, was living at home with us. My mother, who was teaching music in a small school nearby, left home in the morning and came back at night, so I never saw her during the day. It was very quiet at home, where there were only Grandfather, Grandmother and I to pass the days.

Chapter 2

OUR family lived in the eastern part of Wuhu in an old-fashioned "racetrack" house with a gallery of rooms and apartments running all around a central courtyard. The wide round windows that opened onto the courtyard from all four sides had carved wooden lattices. We could put our heads out the windows and see the sky overhead. A few small brick-framed windows on the outside walls gave us a view far over the city. The thick brick walls had originally been white, but the whitewash had weathered to many colors and flaked off, so the walls were now yellowish-grey. On the east and west ends of the roof stood two big yellow-and-green bats of glazed tile. Their outspread wings protected many little bats of different colors. It was said that the bats would ward off misfortune and bring good luck to the people who lived under them. But the paint on their bodies and wings, like the whitewash on the walls, had flaked and faded until it could be scarcely seen.

In the past, the house and courtyard must have had an air of dignity, but after enduring many years of wind, rain, and sunshine, and because the landlord refused to make repairs, it was now old and run-down. It was fine in the summer, cool and airy when the latticed windows were open on all four sides and the air could circulate. But in the winter it was impossible to stop the drafts, especially when the rain came down and the north wind blew. The latticed windows were covered with patched layers of "leather paper," soft, thick, yellow rice paper painted with brush-and-ink pictures of flowers that trembled and shivered under the attack of the cold winds which galloped like horses around the house.

The rooms on the ground floor were bigger and better than the ones upstairs. On the ground floor the gallery of rooms around the courtyard was not continuous, as it was above, but was cut into two parts by the front and back gates. Three families, as well as a family who lived in a little addition at the side of the courtyard, lived downstairs. Upstairs, in the half opposite where

11

we lived, the landlord had stored some of his own belongings. Our half included three big main rooms and a little room at the end where old Mr. and Mrs. Jin lived. Every day when they went in or out, they had to go through our living room, so they saw us and talked with us more than they did with the other families.

Of everyone who lived in the house, I remember the Jins most clearly. Mr. Jin was tall and thin, like a long bamboo pole. Mrs. Jin was short and small, like a thin bamboo leaf. Mr. Jin looked to be over fifty and Mrs. Jin looked perhaps twenty years younger. It was said that Mr. Jin had been a teacher in a traditional school under the feudal system, but had fallen into difficulties and now held down a minor office job in the foundling home in the northern part of the city. Because he was a scholar, everyone very politely called him "Mr. Jin" to his face. But behind his back they gave him another name, "Old Bookworm." Every evening when he came back from work, he would greet my grandfather and grandmother with a smile as he passed through our living room —if he was not depressed. Once he reached his own little room, he would grind ink and write poetry, or paint pictures of stones or orchids. Sometimes he would teach his wife poetry. His quavering voice would linger and circle around and draw out the last word of each line.

They would start out singing together under their breath, but as they sang they would forget themselves, open their mouths wide, and sing at the top of their lungs. Mr. Jin's voice was tired and harsh, like a broken gong. Mrs. Jin's voice was brittle and sharp, like a small flat iron bell. They did not harmonize together, but everyone in the house had become accustomed to them, and no one minded. Moreover, singing was much better than anger and beatings.

Things were very different when Mr. Jin was depressed. He would not greet my grandparents, but would go straight to his room with his head turned away, his eyes averted, and his anger wrapped around him. On those evenings, he would not write poetry or paint pictures or teach poetry to his wife. Instead, he would pick up a copy of the Three Character Classic* and test his wife in her studies.

When Mrs. Jin recited the lesson, her voice was not brittle and

_____

*"Three Character Classic." The first book used in the Chinese educational system.

12

sharp, but breathless, as if she had no air in her lungs to push out the words. She would recite two lines and then cough twice.

"In the beginning
Man is good," (cough, cough)
"Habits take hold
Character changes." (cough, cough)

While she was coughing and repeating what she had memorized, we would suddenly hear old Mr. Jin shout, "What's this? What's happened to your memory tonight? You've been working on those few little lines all day and still don't know them. I know that if I don't beat you, you won't try your hardest. Where's my ruler? Bring it here!"

"No, no, Teacher, no, no! I'm trying! I'm trying with all my might!"

By this time everyone in the house would be listening. We all knew that Mr. Jin was going to beat Mrs. Jin on the palms. The grownups wanted to watch, but were ashamed to go and look. However, we children could not resist going to see whatever excitement there was. With quick feet, and buzzing like a hive of bees, we would run to the Jins' door and peep through the cracks. We could see Mr. Jin, wearing a pair of small, yellow copper-framed eyeglasses and sitting in a high-backed chair. In one upraised hand, he would be holding a ruler more than a foot long. Mrs. Jin, her head drooping, would be standing by the square table reluctantly holding out one hand.

Pam, pam, pam, pam!

"Now will you try or not?"

"I will try! Oh!"

Pam, pam, pam, pam....

When I was small I often had strange dreams. On nights when I spied on Mr. Jin beating his wife on her palms, my dreams would be even stranger. Tigers and lions, or strange creatures from the mountains or the sea would appear before me. Each one would be wearing a pair of small, yellow copper-framed eyeglasses like Mr. Jin's and brandishing a ruler as it chased after me. I would spend all night running away from them and pummelling and kicking them. My poor grandmother, who slept beside me! How could she get any sleep at all with me kicking her all night long?

By the next morning, however, these dreams would be all but forgotten. We young children, separated by a night's sleep from the events of the previous evening, would set them aside and not mention them when we saw Mrs. Jin, her hair uncombed and her face unwashed, go down to the kitchen early with a big white kettle to boil water for her husband's morning tea. The interest of the mischievous boys had not diminished, however. Half-joking and half-teasing, one would greet her with, "Well, well, Mrs. Jin, you're out early!" Another would say, "Oh, dear—my palms hurt! They were beaten again last night."

Mrs. Jin would keep her face expressionless and pretend not to hear, but as she sat by the kitchen stove lighting the fire and adding wood and facing the shrine of the kitchen god* she could not keep from wiping her nose and weeping over her troubles. In a small secret voice, she would mutter, "You, you disgusting old criminal, you old devil! I think you're just going to get older and older and never die...."

I had heard the grown-ups say that, because she was plain and even a bit stupid-looking, her family had not been able to marry her off. When she reached the age of twenty-eight, her father and mother became impatient. It happened that at that time Mr. Jin was living in their household, teaching their son to read the classics. Although he was much older than she was and his family was poor, he had never been married, so her father and mother half-forced and half-gave their old-maid daughter into Mr. Jin's hands.

The grownups also said that Mr. Jin really cared for his wife. He knew that she was used to a comfortable life and that she had trouble shopping because she could not add and subtract very well, so every morning before he went to work he would carry a basket to market and buy the vegetables for her. And though he seldom ate any meat when he dined out, he would always buy a few ounces of meat and bring it home for her on the first and fifteenth of every month when he was paid.

Speaking of eating meat, I remember that except for the three

---

* "The shrine of the kitchen god." Also known as the god of the stove or the hearth. His main duties were to determine how long each member of the family would live, to distribute wealth and poverty in the family, and to record good and bad acts. He would fly up to heaven at the end of each year to report on the family, which would offer his image sweets and honey so he would say only good things. Each year his image, which hung above the stove, was burned and replaced with a new one. His departure and return were saluted with firecrackers and celebrations.

major festivals* of the year, birthdays, or happy events like weddings, we and the families living in the courtyard could very seldom afford to buy meat. Grandmother often said, "Prices keep going up every day, and it's harder to get by. Meat is too expensive. We can't afford it. Green vegetables and tofu are our staples. They keep us alive."

The eldest son of Mrs. Zhang, who lived with his family in the little addition at the side of the courtyard, had been working in a Japanese spinning factory until he developed lung trouble. He was in special need of good food to restore his health. But his mother could not afford even a whiff of fish or meat for him except on paydays, the first and the fifteenth of each month. She would take it to him when she could keep her younger son and her little granddaughter from seeing her. Mrs. Zhang often said, "It doesn't matter if the rest of the family has no meat to eat, but it won't do for my eldest son. He is not strong and everyone in our family depends on him for food. He supports us all. If he should fail, our whole family, old and young, would have nothing but the northwest wind to fill our open mouths."

Only the Zhaos, who lived in the three main rooms on the ground floor, always had meat or fish on their table, so we said they celebrated the New Year and festivals every day. Mrs. Zhao was a widow. I heard that her husband had been a secretary and writer of legal briefs in the county's district court. Others who lived in the courtyard often said when talking about her, "District court secretaries are almost always contemptible. Their pens are like swords and the money they get comes from the misfortunes of others." However, of all the families, only Madam Zhao's had

---

*"The three major festivals" include the Chinese New Year (also known as Spring Festival), Dragon-Boat Festival, and Mid-Autumn, or Moon, Festival. Their dates vary each year, depending on the lunar calendar. The New Year celebration starts on the first day of the first month, sometime in late January to mid-February. The festival season lasts until Lantern Festival, which takes place fifteen days later on the night of the first full moon of the new year. Dragon-Boat Festival falls on the fifth day of the fifth lunar month, in late May to mid-June. It commemorates the patriotic poet Qu Yuan, who drowned himself after a wartime defeat in 278 B.C. It is marked by races in boats decorated with dragon heads and tails, in memory of the search for his body. Mid-Autumn Festival falls on the fifteenth day of the eighth lunar month, or on the night of the full moon in late August to mid-September. Originally it was marked by sacrifices to the moon, which is usually at its most brilliant at that time of year. Now, the eating of "moon cake" pastries while gazing at the moon is a reminder of family unity and solidarity.

any money. Her son, Xiao Gouzi (Little Puppy), sometimes came and played with us. But at other times he showed a different face. He would stand with his legs apart and point his finger at the rest of us and say," Ha-ha! My family is not like yours, eating tofu leavings. My mother says that tofu leavings are pig slop."

When I was small, however, everyone in my family liked to eat the bean sediment from the making of tofu. Grandmother was a good cook. She would mix the leavings with spices and condiments, tiny fresh shrimp, the juicy pulp of mashed red peppers, chopped fresh scallions, and would add a few drops of fragrant sesame oil to the bowl. The fragrance that rose from those small circles of pungent oil made my mouth water.

Xiao Gouzi was eight or nine and had a flat face, like a pancake. He had a small braid on one side of his head. Xiao Gouzi was his milk name.* His appearance was anything but attractive, but because he was the son of a rich family he was very conceited. He often liked to tease us little girls. Without provocation, when he saw us, he would wrinkle his nose, raise his eyes to heaven, stick out his chest and strut back and forth, saying, "Yellow-haired maidens** are not rare, yellow-haired maidens are everywhere." Then, before we could all chase him, he would turn and run into his own home and hide in the far corner of the living room. He would turn around, thump his chest and tell us, "A real man doesn't fight women. A real dog doesn't fight chickens."

If Mrs. Zhao heard us, she would raise her voice and say in her Yangzhou accent, "Xiao Gouzi, you've been fighting with those little girls again! Why won't you behave? Do you want to be spanked again?"

Ordinarily, although we all lived so close together, it was only we children who sometimes bickered among ourselves; the grown-ups all lived peacefully and pleasantly with each other.

The most comfortable seasons in our region were around the times of the spring and autumn festivals, when the weather was

---

*"Milk name," Chinese children were usually given pet names, often with the diminutive "Xiao," shortly after birth. These names would be used mainly by family members and close relatives. When children reached school age, they would receive a more formal name for record-keeping purposes. They might also receive nicknames from classmates or friends.

**"Yellow-haired maidens," a derogatery term meaning "silly little girls." It refers to the fact that Chinese girls' hair sometimes remained sparse, thin and yellowish until puberty, when hormonal changes made it grow thicker and darker.

neither too hot nor too cold. In the afternoons, when there was no housework to do, Grandmother would fetch her water-pipe, which was about a foot high and mounted with carved silver, and her yellow straw mending basket, and would sit by the door of the balcony to enjoy the sunshine, mend clothes and smoke. I would set my little stool at her feet and sit facing her. Grandmother would take out all the bits of cotton thread that were too short to use for sewing and ask me to help her by twisting them into twine. Then, bending her head, she would sew slowly, one stitch at a time. I would sit up straight and gradually twist the twine, one thread after another. When Grandmother's hands were numb from sewing and her back began to ache, she would put down her needle and thread, take up the water-pipe, light a paper spill, and smoke a pinch of tobacco. And while she smoked and rested to recover from her weariness, she would tell stories about our family.

"You—" Grandmother would point at me with the paper spill and say, "—the moment you were born, you were as you are now, an explosive little thing. You cried every night, so much that no one in the family could sleep."

I would put down my cotton threads and sit waiting for her to go on talking, but after a couple of words she would inhale, making the water-pipe gurgle, and would not be able to talk. I would pull at her sleeve, "Grandmother, talk."

"Talk? Talk about what?" She would pull the little bowl out of her water-pipe and, with a sudden strong puff, blow the wad of tobacco ash halfway across the porch.

"Then what happened?"

"Happened? You were a real nuisance! Your poor mother ran around like a chicken with its head cut off, not knowing whether you were hungry or too full or whether you hurt or itched. She was so exhausted by your crying that all she could do was sit by your side and weep. So I had a talk with your grandfather. I said, 'I'm afraid the little one has colic. Run and find a sheet of red paper, cut it into strips and write the words on them. Ask our third son to paste them on the walls in the streets, so those passing by will read them and she can get well.' Your grandfather did as I suggested. He wrote on all the strips. There must have been eighteen or twenty of them. Then he had our second and third sons go out in the evening and paste them all up."

"After they were pasted up, did I still cry?"

"Did you still cry?" Grandmother considered for a moment.

"Yes, you still cried. But compared to what it had been, it was better."

"Grandmother, what did Grandfather write on the red paper?"

"Little one, don't annoy me. Let Grandmother smoke her pipe in peace."

But as Grandmother said, I was someone who always wanted to get to the bottom of things. How could I let things alone until I understood them? I would creep from my little stool and climb into her lap. "Grandmother, tell me, what did Grandfather write on the pieces of red paper? Really, truly!"

"Really, truly, you are a nuisance! Haven't I told you a hundred times?" Grandmother would bend her head and her pair of old metal-framed reading glasses would slide down her nose. Her gaze would follow the glasses down.

"Tell me again, Grandmother, tell me again!"

"Oh, sit still! Stop twisting like an eel in my lap. Look—you almost knocked over my water-pipe!" Grandmother would pinch out the flame of the paper spill and set the water-pipe on the floor. Then she would pat me on the back and begin singing:

> Emperor of Heaven, oh,
> Emperor of Earth.
> A young lord is disturbing the nights in our home.
> Gentlemen passing by, please read, oh,
> That he may sleep until the day dawns.
> Emperor of Heaven, oh,
> Emperor of Earth.

When Grandmother talked, her voice was gentle and pleasing, but when she sang she was a little off-key and lulled me to sleep. Mother's voice was clear and sweet, and when she sang it was round and smooth. People said her singing was like pearls rolling around and around on a jade plate. They said they could listen to her a hundred times without getting bored. Mother could sing new songs and local ballads as well. When she was home I lost interest in hearing Grandmother sing, but when she was not there, Grandmother's unusual and off-key tunes were pleasing to me.

Sometimes Mrs. Jin would join us. But now her hair would be combed, smooth, and shiny, and she would be wearing a thick coat of powder on her face. She would come out with a water-pipe in her left hand and one of Mr. Jin's thick, cotton-soled shoes in her right, to sew with Grandmother and talk idly of everything under the sun. The bride of the Zhang family's sick eldest son would bring her husband's brothers' and sisters' shoes, socks, and clothes upstairs too. And so the whole afternoon would slip by.

The sun was warm as it moved across the sky. First it would pass the old locust tree which reached up towards heaven from beside our porch. Then it would creep past the round and slender wooden porch railing. Then, at last, it would reach the door, and, leaf by leaf, the fine, delicate locust leaves, moving gently in the breeze, would cast their shadows on Grandmother's greying hair and on her double-thick coat of blue cotton, on Mrs. Jin's white-powdered face and on her shining, scanty hair, on the bride's silver earrings, and on my face and my flowered green trousers. The shadows of the locust leaves, coming and going, kept company with the warmth that crept lazily through us and made us feel peaceful and drowsy.

This was neither a time to talk of sad things nor a time to talk gaily about happy things. Rather, these were hours for quiet reflective talk, for thoughts of the past, and for hopes for the future. Everyone's life, no matter how bitter or flavorless, has at least some events worth remembering.

For example, people said Mrs. Jin was so stupid that she could barely count to ten. The life she was leading may have seemed humdrum, but in her own heart she carried memories that could not be forgotten. She would sew and sew and then, putting down the thick cloth shoe sole she was holding, she would look out beyond the porch and up at the clear blue heavens, sigh, and say, "Ever since I was thirteen, when I had that serious illness, my health has never been the same. There were many daughters in my family. Behind our house was a little garden, and my sisters loved to pick fresh flowers for their hair all year round. I was the only one whose hair was thin and sparse. It all fell out during my illness and never grew thick again. Whenever I picked a flower, even before I could put it in my hair, everyone would laugh at me. They would say, 'A person without beauty trying to make a show.' My sisters were all married when they were seventeen or eighteen. Each one of them was carried away to her new home in a joyful daytime celebration and seated in a sedan chair decorated with red embroidery to the blowing of trumpets and the beating of drums. I was the only one to be carried away in the twilight, in a little bamboo sedan chair, with two red paper lanterns, and without any music or merrymaking. As soon as I was in the chair, before I could even open my mouth, my family warned, 'Be quiet! Don't laugh and don't cry! What would the neighbors think if they heard you?' ... I was the only one—" Whenever Mrs. Jin spoke of the past she felt sad, and there was sorrow in her voice.

"Oh, dear!" The bride lifted up her pretty face, as oval as an apricot seed and with that pair of long autumn-leaf earrings swinging against each cheek. She seemed not to have heard Mrs. Jin's words, but murmured the thoughts in her own heart. "When I think of the past, before I was married, when I was a girl at home, I had so many hopes and dreams. Once I was married, I don't understand why, all hopes seem to have grown wings and day by day fly further away."

"You young people have many years ahead of you. You must take the long view and look beyond your nose," said Grandmother, trying to comfort her. "You are now carrying a new life in your body. We hope that next year you will bear a son and that your husband's illness will soon be over. It is certain that you will have a fortunate life."

"Oh ..." There was no way to comfort the young bride, and she sighed again. "I think that, after all, it's best to be the age of Xiao Baogu. She doesn't have to worry about food or what to wear, and her whole family treats her like a precious possession. She has her whole life ahead of her. Whether she will be happy or sad no one can tell clearly now, but as for me, oh, you could say my life is already half over."

"We all hope that when she grows up Xiao Baogu will marry into a wealthy family," Mrs. Jin said carelessly, "with no evil mother-in-law to mistreat her and no sharp-tongued sisters-in-law to criticize her. That would be a real blessing."

When I was small I ignored it when others called me a silly little girl because I heard it so often, but whenever I heard the words "evil mother-in-law," I did not know why but they rang harshly in my ears and made me feel anxious. When I heard Mrs. Jin say that, I quickly asked, "Grandmother, who is this evil mother-in-law?"

"Evil mother-in-law?" It was as if my question had stopped Grandmother cold and she could not come up with an answer.

The bride stepped in and said, "Just an evil mother-in-law, who else?"

"This evil mother-in-law, why is she so terrible?"

"It's strange that you should ask," Grandmother answered casually. "Haven't you heard the saying that from ancient times till now, ninety-nine out of every hundred mothers-in-law on this earth are terrible?"

I thought about this for a while. "Grandmother, will I marry and be given away to another home when I grow up?"

"Of course you will. When a girl grows up she must always marry and become a member of another family. It isn't right to spend your whole life with your own family."

I thought again. "But what about them?"

"Who?"

"My youngest uncle, and the Zhang family's Xiao Fuzi, (Little Prosperity) and Xiao Gouzi (Little Puppy) ... will they be given away to other families?"

Grandmother, the bride, and even Mrs. Jin smiled. Grandmother suppressed her smile and said, "They're sons. Sons and daughters aren't the same. The more sons, the better. They're kept at home to carry on the family name. Some families pray for sons year after year until they became bitter, but don't get them. How could they send them to other homes?"

"Then I want to stay at home. I want to be like them, to carry on our name ..."

Seeing that tears were standing in my eyes, they all spoke in turn to reassure me.

The bride said, "Yes, yes, of course you can stay at home until you are old. Your grandmother was only frightening you to tease you. Do you really think she'd give you away to another family? Mrs. Jin, you talk too much. Look at the trouble you've caused."

Mrs. Jin said, "Xiao Baogu, I was only teasing. You mustn't pay any attention. A while ago, when we were talking, you were the only contented one here—and now, look, your eyes are full of tears."

Grandmother said, "Who said I was going to give her away? I wouldn't give her away, not even to the wealthiest family. I'll keep her at home until she's old, to keep house for us. She'll be our happiness pill—whenever our hearts are heavy we'll take a pill and not be depressed any longer."

When I heard Grandmother talk that way I felt consoled and, rubbing my eyes with the back of my hand, listened to them chat about other things.

They talked and sewed and smoked their water-pipes while the sun slowly sank in the west and the light crept across the roof tiles of the house across the street. Far away in the military barracks, the bugle blew for the supper. The air was no longer as warm on our bodies as it had been. The three women began to fold up their sewing. They stood up, brushed off the loose threads and tobacco clinging to their clothes, and then went downstairs to the big communal kitchen to prepare dinner.

Chapter 3

IT was on such tranquil afternoons that Grandmother, while sewing, taught me as she had been taught by her own grandmother in her own childhood. She would say, "Daughters cannot compare with sons. No matter how treasured they are at home, when they grow up and marry into another family, their lives are not their own. Anyone who has not learned manners and the right way to act will find it difficult to live even for one day in her new home.

"Daughters must know how to behave properly—they should know the right way to sit, the correct way to stand, and the correct way to eat. They should not talk while eating. Sons may fall upon their food like tigers, but daughters must eat as if counting each grain of rice. Sons may box and kick each other and throw bricks, but daughters must be gentle and calm, tranquil and dignified, and able to embroider a tasteful spray of flowers. When in their new home, whether washing clothes or cooking, they are wise not to give the father-in-law or mother-in-law any grounds for criticism, or to give the sisters-in-law any excuse for oppression, or to arouse the husband's anger.

"The world today is much more enlightened than when I was a girl. The life of a daughter is now much easier, compared to the life I led. But in fact there is still a big difference in how boys and girls are treated. I speak from experience. I'll only mention the fact that when a son grows up, he may go anywhere he likes, seducing women and sowing wild oats, and no one will say a word. But even before a daughter has set foot outside her family's gate or her laughter been heard beyond the living room, people are only too ready to gossip. The ancients said, 'In a daughter the first consideration is a good character and the second is a beautiful face'—what are you laughing at?"

When she saw that I was smiling as I listened she could not keep herself from smiling either. "Here I am talking seriously, and there you are laughing. Little one, of course you don't understand now and think it's funny. Someday when you grow up and have become an adult you'll understand and you'll say to yourself, 'Yes, what Grandmother said to me was true.' I'm old, and I've seen everything."

It was also during those tranquil spring and autumn afternoons that I learned about my father's and mother's lives. I learned that they had both attended schools instead of being taught by private tutors. The arrangements for their marriage, according to Grandmother, had been conducted half in the new way and half in the old.* They had liked each other at first sight and the contract was made later. Grandmother said that it had happened during the winter vacation one year when my father had come home for the New Year's holidays. It had snowed heavily, and there were unbroken sheets of snow on the ground and rooftops. On the third day of the new year, my father, wearing his new padded gown and a pair of winter shoes, and carrying an oilcloth umbrella, went to the home of his friend, a Western-style doctor, to offer him New Year's greetings. But as fate would have it, with no planning, he happened to see his friend's younger sister. As soon as he got home, he began praising her to Grandmother. "She isn't too tall nor too short, not too fat nor too thin, but exactly right. She has an oval face and her skin is fine and fair. She was wearing a red silk padded gown edged with narrow rolled black satin bands that set off her shining black hair."

Grandmother said, "As soon as I heard him talking that way, I knew what he was thinking about. I said, 'If she pleases you that much, it will not be difficult to make the arrangements. If you're bashful about speaking to your father, I'll speak for you. We can ask someone to act as matchmaker and bring her here to our home as your wife. Wouldn't that be the easiest way?' Can you guess what he did when he heard me talking that way?" She laughed. "He was so happy! He couldn't close his mouth for grinning, and his eyes crinkled into slits. For the rest of the day he couldn't say a word. He just sat there watching me and smiling foolishly."

Ten months after the engagement was made, my father brought my mother to her new home. The following year, she

---

*"Half in the new way and half in the old." In late-feudal China, most marriages were arranged by a family's male members, usually the father or the oldest brother and the couple might never have spoken to each other or even met before the wedding. "The new way" refers to courtship and young people being given a say in choosing their own partners. Baogu's parents chose each other but the negotiations were still carried on by the parents.

gave birth to me.

My grandmother also told me many other stories about my parents and my family.

"After they were married, since our resources were not great and the family needed money, your mother had to teach even while she was carrying you. Your father was still a year short of graduation, our second son was still learning his trade, and the other sons were still small and at school. Your poor mother had a hard time of it, coming into our family! She had to teach until the last month before you were born.

"When New Year's approached, that first year after your mother had joined our family, your father was still away at school and did not come home for winter vacation. I remember very clearly that it started about three weeks before the holiday. Your mother said nothing and made no fuss but became absorbed in cleaning their room, changing and washing the quilt covers and bed hangings, preparing the food your father liked to eat, and also trying to make herself beautiful. Every day she would stand and watch by the window for a long time. She waited and watched until the last night before the New Year. How could we know that he had been given so much work to do at school that even by the twenty-ninth he had not been able to leave? Your poor mother! All that day, from early in the morning till night fell, she ran to the window every few minutes to watch and watch, but no one came. When she could bear it no longer she came running to me, but before she could speak, her tears rolled down her face like pearls from a chain that has broken. I tried to comfort her. I said, 'The days are cold and the earth is frozen. The journey is difficult. Also, this is time when everyone wants to stay at home to celebrate the New Year. I'm afraid it isn't easy to hire carts, boats and sedan chairs. You mustn't feel unhappy. If he doesn't get here tonight, there is still the first day of the New Year—and I guarantee that he will be home by then, or by the second or third.

"When I saw that her tears were still flowing, I tried again to comfort her. I said, 'I don't blame you. A young husband and wife are like two blossoms on one stem—you certainly shouldn't be separated.' But even before I had finished saying this, she started crying all the more bitterly. When I saw how miserable she was, my heart melted and before I realized it, I was weeping too. Isn't it funny?" As Grandmother said this, she smiled, showing teeth that were still even and regular.

"Not only had I not comforted her but I had made myself sad as well.... Your father didn't come back after all. It was the summer of the following year before he was able to come home, and by then you were already six months old, plump and pretty. You were like one of those brightly-painted blossoms made of dough that the peddlers sell at New Year's.

"At last we heard him come through the main gate. We held you up high in our hands and offered you to him to hold. How were we to know that as soon as he saw you his face would turn as red as a pepper and that he'd drop his head and run through the door and not even look at you?

"But afterwards, he couldn't see you without taking you into his arms. He'd hug you tight and nibble your chubby little cheeks, but sometimes he'd bite you too hard and you'd cry and scream. Your mother quarrelled with him about this many times. Later, you'd hide your face against us whenever you saw him, as if he were a big tiger. Oh, young people, they can be so smart, and so stupid! Sometimes they don't know how to show their children how much they love them."

It was also on these tranquil afternoons that Grandmother sometimes liked to recall days of sweetness or sad days, the days when my father and mother were in their teens. She would tell me about their fleeting little joys and sorrows, and even about the sound of my crying when I was still in my cradle. My grandmother's gentle, vivid talk made it seem as if the days of my childhood were slipping away through the eye of the fine needle in her hand.

I was seven or eight years old before I learned that my grandfather and grandmother were not mine by birth but were really my great-uncle and great-aunt. I learned that my real grandfather had died young and that my real grandmother, who was then still young, had not been able to bear her widowhood and had remarried a year or two after his death.

Her remarriage, in the old-fashioned, feudalistic society of that time, was looked upon as a great scandal. It damaged the honor and dignity of our scholarly family. From that time on our family cut off all contacts with her and she was never mentioned again. In the years that followed, I would sometimes ask about her, but my great-uncle and my father would frown and cut me off, saying, "Don't ask so many questions. She's in heaven with your grandfather."

Once when I was eleven or twelve, I was helping my grandmother to tidy her chest when we unexpectedly came across a faded waist-length photograph, about four inches long, of a woman. The face seemed familiar, so I asked, "Grandmother, who is she? It seems to me that I've seen her somewhere."

Grandmother turned away and said casually, "Oh, that is your real grandmother, taken when she was young. It must have been at the bottom of the box and we forgot to burn it."

When I heard that it was my real grandmother, I picked it up and looked at it for a long time. She had a small, square face and delicate eyes and nose, and she was wearing a brocade satin coat with a fur-lined color. She wore her hair in the swallow tail style, coiled and looped into two chignons behind her ears. Her features and demeanor reminded me of my father and my second uncle. "Grandmother," I said, "my real grandmother was very beautiful."

"Of what use is beauty without character? Her beauty disgraced her."

I put down the photograph and said nothing more, and I never saw it again.

But my mother's heart was not as hard. I learned that when I was a little over a year old, my real grandmother who was by then old, asked to see me. She did not dare come to our home herself, but asked someone to bring a message secretly. My mother and great-aunt, whom I was raised to call Grandmother, discussed the matter for most of one evening and came to a decision. Without telling my great-uncle or my father, they decided on a day when Mother could steal out and carry me to the appointed place to meet my real grandmother. I do not know why it was but they told me that when I saw her I was not afraid of her, and I did not act as if she were a stranger when she came slowly to my side. She stroked my hair gently and I opened my mouth and gurgled. Perhaps this made my poor real grandmother feel even more unhappy, because she looked at me for a long time and did not say a word. My mother, who did not dare stay too long on the street, kept me there for only a little while before carrying me back home.

When my real grandmother remarried, my father was only five years old, my first uncle was three, and my second uncle was two. The three little brothers, still so young when their father died, lost their mother as well when she left them and had no one to look after or care for them. My great-uncle was about thirty at the time, and my great-aunt had just given birth to their first son. They went to my father's grandmother, who had wept for many days and nights, knelt down before her and vowed, "No matter what happens, we will bring up and care for these three orphans left by our elder brother." When my great-grandmother heard these words, she felt comforted, and little by little her sorrow eased.

My grandfather worked with words, but my grandmother worked with her hands. From that time on, a heavy burden fell onto her shoulders. She not only had to serve her old mother-in-law and obey and comfort her husband, but also to look after five children—she later gave birth to a second son, my youngest uncle. There were the old and the young to feed and house. Our family circumstances also worsened as time went on. Keeping the family fed, clothed, and housed was not easy, especially because my grandfather had been brought up to do nothing but study and be a gentleman. It was said that when he was fifteen or sixteen he had had an ambition to go to another province to learn to be a doctor of Western medicine so he could hang out his shingle and help to cure people's illnesses.

But it was also said that my great-grandmother could not bear to part from her young son or allow him to leave home and go far away. Grandfather himself was too young at that time to be sure of what he wanted. He could not withstand his mother's tears, or the circumstances that surrounded him, so that not only did he not go away, but he never even dared mention it again. He would often go to what was then the only medicine shop that sold Western drugs in the city to buy and bring home materials for making medicines, which became his hobby, and medical books, which he studied alone. This was how he spent most of the best years of his youth. But the result was that he could never attain a high position, and was not willing to accept a low one. Never in his whole life did he engage in work outside the home, nor did he earn money to support the family. This was perhaps why he always remained reluctant to allow the five boys to become students or learn a trade, no matter what the family's financial difficulties.

Although my grandfather had never taken a regular medical course and he realized he knew much less than my mother's brother, who was a qualified doctor, he nevertheless set up a little pharmacy for himself. It was a little space partitioned off by a few thin boards from the big room where he and my youngest uncle slept and was crammed with big bottles and little jars. We in the family, as well as neighbors and acquaintances who lived nearby, would come to Grandfather to have him treat little aches, pains and minor injuries. Grandfather was always delighted when people came to him for treatment. Patiently and carefully, he would wash a wound, apply a healing ointment and bandage it. Then he would lead his patients back to the living room and invite them to drink a cup of tea with him. If anyone tried to leave a little red paper parcel with money in it on the table, Grandfather would run after him and make him take it back. "What's this?" he would say. "It was nothing. We're all neighbors. We must all take care of each other. There will be times when I will need to seek help from you." Once the patient had gone, Grandfather would tell the family, "It was too small a thing even to be mentioned. I'd be ashamed to take their money!"

Because he did not hang out a shingle the way most doctors did, few people knew about him. No strangers or people who lived far away came to him, and more money went out of the house than came into it. The tiny inheritance left by his ancestors was gradually eaten away.

I can still remember how Mother would come home from teaching after school was over in the afternoons, and how, after dinner, she would sit with Grandmother beside the little oil lamp and hem garments for others. Every evening they would work to add to the family income until the watchman sounded midnight. I also remember that whenever we had to give money to relatives or friends, for the New Year or other celebrations, or for a wedding or funeral, Grandmother and Grandfather would open the chests in their room and take out a garment or ornament not being used. They would wrap it carefully in paper, making as small a parcel as possible so Grandfather could tuck it under his arm. Then he would wait until our neighbors were out and go to the pawn shop. The money he got from pawning took care of these extra expenses. The pile of pawn tickets grew higher each year; I never saw it get smaller.

But even in these circumstances I never heard Grandmother or Mother say one word of reproach. Sometimes when Mother was on her way to bed, I heard her say in a low voice to Grandmother, "It has been a long time since we have eaten any meat and I have felt uncomfortable these last few evenings when I've gone to bed. I've felt my stomach growling." The next morning Grandmother would come back from the market with a long, thin strip of pork in the basket along with the green vegetables, red peppers, pickles and tofu leavings. The fat part would be rendered for lard and the lean meat mixed with eggs and steamed with seasonings or sautéed with red peppers and preserved soybeans, and served for Mother, my youngest uncle and me.

What kind of childhood had Grandmother had? What kind of a life had she led as a young girl in her parents' home? Even now I am not sure. I know only a little. She too came from a middle-class family, so she could not only design and embroider patterns of leaves and buds, but also read a little. The marriage arrangements made for her and my grandfather were not like those made for my father and mother, who saw and liked each other first, but were made by her father and my great-grandfather. In a way, their marriage was a matter of chance. My grandmother had grown up near the Xiang River in Hunan Province, almost one thousand li from our home. When she was in her teens, her father came to Wuhu on business. One day he met my great-grandfather at a wine feast. They sat together and talked, then they met and talked again and again, until they became friends and realized they had a common interest. Several months later, they agreed that their children should marry.

About six months later, as the day of the wedding drew near, my grandfather's family made preparations to welcome the bride to her new home. Her family, I was told, rented a big boat, and arranged for suitable people to bring us the trousseau, the dowry, and their daughter. In those days, travel was slow, and the voyage down the river took more than a month. Grandmother was only seventeen or eighteen years old. What thoughts were in her mind? Even now I cannot keep myself from wondering. For a young woman from a traditional home who had never, even for a day, been out of the women's quarters, to leave home and sail to a faraway place as a bride to join a new family where she would sleep in the same bed with a young man she had never seen—did she feel frightened during that month on the river? Did she feel sad? Or did she feel happy and expectant? I never asked her these questions. Even if I had, I do not think she would have been willing to answer. And even if she had answered, she would probably not have said everything she felt.

I did learn, however, that something happened at her wedding that hurt her very much and that she would never discuss even with my mother.

It seems that, on the night of the wedding, when the wedding wine had made all the guests feel merry, everyone decided to carry out the custom of "disturbing the bridal chamber," teasing the bride and asking to see what she looked like. When her attendants threw back her red-embroidered head dress, everyone there applauded and said, "She deserves her reputation. She is indeed beautiful." But before the applause died away, one relative who was a bit drunk insisted on seeing the bride's feet. Her attendants, urged on by him and all the other guests, had no choice but to lift her embroidered red satin skirt a bit. How were they to know they would be revealing that Grandmother's feet were big, unbound and inelegant?

A couple of mean-spirited women relatives, unable to contain themselves, began to giggle.

The applause died away.

My poor grandmother! She blushed violently, all the way to the tips of her ears, and snatched her feet back under her skirt. Her eyes filled with tears and it was only with great effort that she kept herself from sobbing out loud.

People gossiped about it for a long time, discussed it saying, "What a shame! Such a beautiful woman, but with those big yellow fish feet." So Grandmother was nicknamed Half-Length Guanyin.*

But for many years afterwards, whenever Grandmother saw anyone she was ashamed and would draw her feet up under her legs.

I also heard that my great-grandmother was angered by this and that she treated my grandmother coldly. But Grandfather never said a word—perhaps that was why, though her whole life was painful and difficult, Grandmother never uttered a word of complaint against Grandfather.

My grandmother endured the long chain of years with great courage and strength of character. In her later life, everyone, in the family and outside alike, had nothing but praise for her. People would shake their heads admiringly and say, "She is a rare human being. Never, in all these years, have we seen her quarrel with the neighbors. Nor have we ever heard her and her husband raise their voices to each other. All year round she gets up early and goes to bed late. She doesn't know what idleness is. She raised not only her own two sons, but also her three nephews, and treats them so well that anyone who did not already know would not be able to distinguish the ones she bore from the ones

---

*Half-Length Guanyin—Bodhisattvas never bound their feet.

she reared. She has worked hard all her life, but even now she will not let herself rest. Still, we've never heard her complain."

Grandmother herself, however, sometimes talked a little about her marriage. I remember one winter evening when she and Mother were sitting and sewing hems by lamplight. "Ah," she sighed. She would always sigh first, and then look up from the water-pipe and gaze at Mother. "No one will ever realize how difficult it was when I joined my husband's family and became a daughter-in-law to Xiao Baogu's great-grandmother. She was so difficult. When I got married, the family had more money than we do now. There were a couple of servants, but my mother-in-law always treated me badly and gave me all the hardest, heaviest housework. She made me start doing the cooking three days after my wedding. And within two weeks—it was during the coldest weather—she told me one morning to wash the quilt covers and bed hangings. When I was at home as a daughter, I had never done work like that. For shame! I said nothing, but rolled up my sleeves, got the wooden tub, and went out to the well. But no matter how I tried to control myself, the longer I washed the more my heart ached. After all, I was young, and had led a protected life. As I scrubbed, I kept wiping away tears. By the time everything was washed, my hands were as red and swollen as radishes and my eyes were so puffy they looked like two purple grapes. I was afraid to let her see me—she might say I was trying to create a scene in front of my husband.

"Once when my husband was preparing to send Xiao Baogu's father away to school, my mother-in-law said he was her favorite grandson, and could not bear to see him go away. And so, the day before Xiao Baogu's father was to leave, the two of them, my mother-in-law and my husband, had a terrible quarrel. In any other matter my husband would compromise with her, but when it came to educating the children he would not give way one bit. And it was always the same—every time she quarrelled with him, she would vent her anger on me. This time, she refused to speak to me for a whole month, no matter how carefully I brought her pipes and poured her tea, no matter how often I tried to talk with her, and no matter how respectful I was. She pretended not to hear me. I might as well have been the wind whistling in the trees. When I think back to that month, it seems it was as difficult as climbing a mountain of sharp knives." Her gentle voice trembled slightly and she blew a grey smoke ring.

"Men, no matter how much they sympathize, cannot really

understand how hard a woman's life can be. My husband was thoughtful the first month or two. At night in bed he would try to comfort me, but as time went on he lost patience with me. When he saw me crying alone in our room, he became irritable and said, 'Is it really so terrible? My mother is old—she won't live many more years. When she scolds you, listen and ignore her. This is all inside the family, so why take what she says so seriously?' After that, whenever I felt like weeping I stifled my tears, no matter how difficult things were. I would clench my teeth in his presence and not even sigh."

Whenever Grandmother talked about the things that had hurt her she would sigh deeply, over and over. It seemed as if Mother too had her own problems, because Grandmother's sighs would make her sigh as well. And when I heard them, I felt touched by their sadness, and sighed along with them, but as soon as they heard me they would stop. They had tears in their eyes but would try to smile for my benefit.

For my grandfather, life seemed to pass slowly and uneventfully, without haste or bustle. He was always gentle and courteous and his leisurely footsteps whispered through the house. Every morning was just like every other morning for him. My grandmother's life was more hectic. By the time she shopped for food, washed, sewed and cooked and served two meals, the sun would have set. But then she and Mother would sit by the oil lamp, and sew late into the night.

Whenever Grandmother heard anyone criticize Grandfather because he had never worked, or if my uncles complained about him, she would sigh. "It's always easy to talk about what other people should do. If he'd been willing to lower himself and take an outside job, we would not have been so poor. But look at it from his point of view—his life has been difficult. He has always been frugal. He was determined that all of you would be educated. Do you think that was easy? You don't know how much of his life's blood he poured into trying to arrange your schooling, how many people he appealed to until he managed to get the tuition cut in half so you could be admitted."

When my uncles heard her talk that way they were silenced, and would change the subject.

From the time they were very young, my father and his two brothers called Grandfather Papa, but they called Grandmother Aunt, perhaps because my great-grandmother told them to. Though Grandfather seldom scolded them, all five boys were a bit frightened of him. Their fear melted like ice in the sunshine, though, when they were with Grandmother. What they could not say to him, they could always tell her. They told her all their problems, and when good things happened she was the first one they told. Whenever they had a little extra money, they would buy her a bit of her favorite water-pipe tobacco or something sweet, or would slip her a few coins.

Grandmother understood that Grandfather's lifelong unemployment was due to our reputation as a family of scholars. This reputation had already deteriorated by the time Grandfather became head of the family. But as long as it could be preserved and kept from crumbling entirely, it would have been very difficult for him to abandon the family tradition of scholarship. I also believe that he later regretted that his parents and grandparents had kept him back when he was young and that he had not been brave enough to insist on following his own path. He seldom let his regrets show, but sometimes, when he had drunk a little wine, he would grow depressed and withdrawn. At these moments, Grandmother would go over to him and begin chatting about everyday matters. Then, as if thinking out loud, she would say, "Time passes so quickly. Once the children are all grown up, we will have kept our promise. When that time comes, we'll still have a few years of peace and comfort ahead of us."

Grandfather would not reply, but her words would make him feel a little better. Eventually he would look up and his frown would disappear. He would look around and nod slightly, as if those years of peace and comfort had already arrived.

Chapter 4

M Y grandfather and grandmother made many sacrifices in carrying out their promise to raise the five boys to become independent adults. My first uncle, who did not like to study and ran away from school every few days, did not finish junior middle school and was sent out to learn a trade. My second uncle, who finished middle school but liked to paint his face and sing opera, joined a theater company, but his choice of profession was viewed as not having any future and as not proper or respectable. But my father and the other two brothers studied diligently and with determination, and graduated from both middle school and university.

When I was seven, my father stopped teaching school and joined a tea exporting firm in Nanjing for a position that paid a somewhat better salary than he had earned from teaching. He soon wrote to us and asked my mother and me to join him. The hope that Mother had been carrying in her heart during the eight years of her marriage was now to be realized—that Father, who had made unceasing efforts to earn a living during all the long years away from home, could now live with us, and that we could all be together. "Even if life is more difficult and we have only a thatched roof over our heads and only gruel to eat," Mother said, "I'll be satisfied and content." During the time we were preparing to leave, I remember that Mother's expression changed and her usual slightly pensive look disappeared.

When my grandparents were out of hearing, she cautioned me, "After we're gone, they'll feel very lonely. Try not to talk about the journey all the time—it might make them feel sad." Mother herself, however, could not hide her happiness. Whether she was talking with others or collecting and sorting out her clothes and possessions, the corners of her eyes and her lips turned upwards in a little smile. When she went up and down the stairs, her footsteps were light and quick as a breeze. And her eyes seemed to glow and sparkle more than they ever had in the past.

Grandmother always said that when my mother joined our

family her face had been as round as the full moon, and that her eyes always seemed to be holding back a smile. She was a sweet, gentle person, likeable and spirited. However, I always remembered my mother's face as thin and pointed, like an apricot seed. Even when she smiled, she never looked really happy. To me, she always looked a bit melancholy. Only her delicate, beautiful eyes were as Grandmother described, glowing with animation.

After Mother joined our family, she and Grandmother shared everything, the bitter and the sweet. They worked together day and night without stopping, and the feelings they shared became as intertwined as a hundred thousand threads. While they sewed together each evening by the light of the oil lamp, they would share all their thoughts and feelings in perfect sympathy with each other. In the days before we left, as Grandmother helped Mother pack, they both felt unwilling to part. Grandmother told Mother that she and Grandfather were both happy and sad about it. They were happy that Father had gotten a good job and would be able to set up his own home and establish his career, because from now on we could expect a prosperous, happy life. But they worried because Father was still young and Nanjing was a gay, extravagant place where people did not know each other and were not tightly bound together as they were in our small town. They feared that Father would forget the difficulties he had had in establishing himself and would become reckless once his work became easy and he had more money, because it is easy to become lazy and wasteful. Grandmother also feared that Mother, who would be managing a household for the first time, would not understand how to economize. So she told her about many ways to save on day-to-day expenses. She also told Mother that she should think ahead; when the days were bright and there were no problems, she should think of the possibility of dark days and problems that might arise. She said it was important to save at least a little money every month so that if difficulty arose, we would always have a way out. As she talked, Mother listened and nodded.

The night before we left, Grandmother cooked two especially good dishes that Mother and I both liked. She lit the living room and bedroom lamps, which had been filled with oil, trimmed, and turned up high in the carefully polished chimneys, so the house was full of light. After dinner, I followed Mother into her room, where she unlocked her small red, carved lacquered box and took out a parcel wrapped in a handkerchief. She unwrapped and counted out the shiny new silver dollars and ten- and twenty-cent pieces and placed them on the bed. She asked me to get the round yellow earthenware bank from its hiding place under the bed. Mother tapped it against the corner of the wooden bureau until it broke, poured out the copper coins she had managed to set aside, and counted them carefully. She added them to the other coins and divided all the money into two piles. She told me one pile was for our third-class open-cabin steamer tickets the next day and the rest of our trip. Mother asked me to wait until Grandmother could not see me and then go to her room and tuck the other money under her pillow. "So she can buy a couple of packets of especially good 'shredded leather' tobacco," she said.

Before long, Grandmother, having washed the cooking pot and bowls, came back upstairs carrying her water-pipe. She went over to Mother and said in a low, serious voice, "Daughter-in-law, I still have some important things to say to you. You must look after your health. That's the most important thing. It's not surprising that your health has suffered, because you have had to put up with so many difficulties while you've been living with us. But it isn't right for someone as young as you to get dizzy spells every few days and to have so much stomach trouble. Once you recover your health, we hope that a couple more children will come along. Wouldn't that be wonderful? After all, it's lonely, with only one child to keep you company."

Mother listened respectfully, but when Grandmother spoke of having more children she blushed like a young girl, hung her head, and giggled for a few moments. Then she looked up and said, "Grandmother, please don't worry. I'll do as you say. I'll be careful about money so we can set up our new home. We'll come back soon and bring both of you to stay with us for a while. It isn't far, only half a day by the steamboat, and I'll bring Xiao Baogu home often to see you."

"There's no hurry!" said Grandmother with a laugh. "First you must create a firm foundation for your new home there. When you're settled, we'll still be young enough to come. We might want to come too often." Grandmother blew on her paper spill, and puffed on her water-pipe for a while. "We'd have to buy round-trip tickets. It'd be too expensive, it's not worth it. There's no hurry. We'll be satisfied if you just write us and tell us you're happy."

It was very late before Grandmother and Mother went to sleep. They sat by the bed and talked for half the night about their plans for the future. Their happiness and excitement showed in their faces. When I was about to go to bed, Grandmother placed on the bureau beside the bed the new clothes I would wear for the journey, new shoes and stockings, a new silk kerchief, and new red yarn for my hair. "Tomorrow you will ride in a steamboat for the first time and go away with your mother. Remember to act happy. It's a happy occasion. None of us must cry."

The next morning Mother shook me awake before dawn. When I opened my eyes, the oil lamp on the table was shining brightly. I heard the steamer blowing its whistle in the distance, and I became impatient, afraid that we would miss the boat. The excitement drove away my sleepiness and I hurried to get out of bed, put on my clothes, and let Mother comb my hair and wash my face. Grandfather and Grandmother were downstairs boiling water for tea and noodles. They put two eggs into our bowls to poach. When everything was ready Mother and I sat down at the square table in the living room with the two bowls, decorated with red flowers and filled with noodles, in front of us. The lighted lamp sent up waves of warm air. Our baggage was waiting for us on the living room floor. We would start for the jetty when we finished breakfast. Grandmother, with her water-pipe, and Grandfather, with a big bowl of tea, sat facing each other beside the latticed window and said nothing. Silently, they watched Mother and me as we tried to eat.

It seems inevitable that there will be sadness when it comes time to part. The happiness and excitement that had been on Grandmother's and Mother's faces had vanished. Mother lifted her bowl, picked up a few noodles with her chopsticks, and put them down again. Even I—who for the past few days had done nothing but think about taking the steamboat down the Yangtze River and moving to a new home in Nanjing, where I could ride in a gay horse-drawn carriage—now, seeing Mother not eating and my grandparents so quiet made me lose my appetite too. At Grandfather's and Grandmother's urgings, I finally forced down the eggs. After I put down my bowl, Grandfather and Mother took the baggage down the stairs one piece at a time. I went to the window and stood next to Grandmother. It was when I saw Grandfather open the main gate and go out to call the rickshaws that I realized that we were really leaving and that the parting was upon us. I suddenly felt I did not want to go. I looked up at Grandmother. In the grey morning light, a cloud seemed to have settled over her face. Was it that I did not want to leave my old grandparents or that I could not bear to leave this old second-story apartment? I could not tell. I hid my face against Grandmother's breast. She put one arm around me and patted me on the back with the other. "Good girl, remember, when Grandfather and Grandmother are not with you, you must do as your father and mother say. We'll come to see you soon."

Grandmother's voice was so sad that she could not comfort me and made me sad too. Even children can feel sorrow—this I know. I hid my face in her arms to hide the tears that had gathered in my eyes.

Our new home would perhaps be more comfortable than this old house, and Nanjing would probably be a more interesting, gay and colorful place to grow up in. At that moment, however, none of those things mattered to me. I was young and had known nothing else, and this ancient courtyard apartment had been my home. It was where I had been born and where I had grown up. My grandfather and grandmother often said, "Our hearts are full of love." It seemed that these words made up for anything that might have been lacking in my life. If the food I ate as a child was simple and the clothes I wore were plain, it did not matter, but if my grandparents had not been there to love me, how cold and sad my life would have been. It would have been like grass trying to grow without water or sunshine. Although I did not realize all these things then, I knew that I was attached to both of them, and especially to Grandmother. From my birth till now I had been her companion. As I stood there with her I hoped that Grandfather would not be able to find a rickshaw and that Mother and I would not be able to leave. Then the baggage could be brought upstairs again and we could stay.

But just as this thought came to me, I saw Grandfather hurry the rickshaw men through the main gate and towards the stairs, where the chest and the big basket covered with string netting were waiting. Mother was calling, telling me to hurry downstairs because it was getting late. How difficult it would be to go down those ten or twelve steps. I had no choice. Still, at the top of the stairs I seized the railing with both hands and could not start down. When Grandfather could wait no longer, he came up and part-pulled, part-carried me down the stairs. Then I lost all that was left of my self-control. I reached out my arms towards Grandmother, who was coming down behind us, and started crying out, "I want my grandmother, I want my grandmother!"

We struggled to the gate with Mother pulling me by the hand

and not knowing what else to do. The three rickshaw men watched me, shaking their heads and smiling. Grandfather, still carrying me, labored on, his head covered with sweat. He took his handkerchief from his belt and mopped his forehead. As he turned, he saw Grandmother. She was leaning against the inside of the gate and wiping away floods of tears with the corner of her coat. Grandfather was feeling very sad himself, and suddenly it seemed to him that all his difficulties with me were Grandmother's fault. So he let all his anger pour out over her. He reproached her, "No wonder the little one is making such a fuss. You should get out of the way and hide, if you go on standing there looking so unhappy, she'll be even less willing to go with her mother. Listen, the steamboat has already blown three times. If we wait any longer, they'll miss their boat."

Grandmother heard what he said but did not reply. Still wiping her eyes on her coat, she turned and went back into the house.

The third-class cabin was crowded with people, but Grandfather found an empty spot for us near the door and laid our bedroll against the wall. Mother and I sat down on it. Grandfather said, "There is fresh air here and you can also watch the scenery. It's better than being in a bunk." He told us to be careful during the journey, and he also asked the steward to watch over us. When the gong sounded and the steamboat's engines started, Grandfather and the others who were seeing people off all hurried to leave the ship. They jumped into the little boats that were crowded around it. Then, with a row and a twist, the little boats slowly zigzagged and moved away. The steamer turned in the middle of the river and we heard the waves raised by the breeze beat against the hull as, with great dignity, we started to move down the river.

Soon the tea boy brought a big white metal pot of boiling water and a little porcelain tea pot with only half a spout. Mother opened the basket and took out a box of good-quality jasmine tea. It had been a farewell gift from a relative. She took out a few leaves and put them into the water. She also took out a little packet of bean curd cured in soy paste and a packet of sesame candy and gave them to me. While I drank the tea and ate, Mother pointed out the scenery on the banks. It was about the end of April. The winter cold was just leaving and the spring warmth was just beginning to return. The grass, flowers, and trees were all smiling and growing in the spring wind. Groups of birds came and went busily on the river bank. Though it was still early morning, the air was soft and warm. The sky in the distance was a light blue, like the blue of the thin silk-lined jacket my mother was wearing. A few white-walled houses with black-tiled roofs nestled under big trees. The Yangtze River seemed endless. Its water was a muddy yellow-brown, and the earth on the riverbank was brownish-red, like the cured bean curd I was eating. Blooming rape plants filled field after field with yellow. The long, slender branches of the weeping willows on the banks were just beginning to turn green, and twisted their waists lightly as they met the wind.

"Look how beautiful it is." Mother's cheek was warm against my ear. "You didn't want to come, but just wait. Soon you'll see your father, and then how happy we'll be."

My distress had by now melted away, but my eyes were still sore and swollen. I turned to Mother and saw that her face was as white as the tiny waves that broke against the side of the ship. Never before had I seen her look so tranquil. She waited for me to finish my tea and then, in a soft, gentle voice, began to tell me stories.

"Long, long ago, there was a family with three brothers. The eldest brother was a woodcutter, the second brother was a fisherman, and the third brother was a manure-carrier. One day ..."

I rested my head against my mother's knees. My eyelids grew heavier and heavier, until finally I could no longer lift them. Mother's voice, the sound of the engines, and the lapping of the river against the ship all blended together and gradually became so soft that I could no longer hear them. The three brothers in the story, and the first part of my own childhood, floated away behind me on the Yangtze River and would never again catch up with me.

Ahead of me, far down the river, a big city, a new home, and a long stream of new experiences were waiting for me and my mother.

Chapter 5

OUR new home was a small house outside Nanjing. It had a row of rooms in front and another row in back, with an unpaved courtyard between them. Father had rented the front row, which had three small rooms with a living room in the middle. The living room door opened to the south and wooden windows in each of the rooms gave them an open and spacious feeling. The wooden partitions and walls were clean, and bright with new paint and whitewash. We could still smell the paint and lime when we arrived. At one side of the courtyard was the kitchen, which we shared with the family in the back row of rooms. Two of the brick walls facing the courtyard were covered with gay morning-glory vines. In the corner near our side of the wall grew a small, slender pomegranate tree. The other side had several beds with cockscombs about a foot high. None of the other plants had yet awakened from the sleep of winter, but they were showing some green intentions.

Most of the furniture had yet to be bought when Mother and I arrived. There were only a big rope-strung bed, a little bamboo bed for me, and the necessary tables and chairs, but no rack for our clothes, or a stand for the wash basin, or any decorative objects on the long wall table in the bedroom. Mother said there was no hurry and that we would add them gradually. She liked our new home. She was glad that it was not far from the city but that at the same time the noise of the carts, horses, and city traffic could not be heard. There were few people living around us and we had the same quiet as in a country village. The space in front of the gate was surrounded by a low bamboo fence covered with creeping, twining squash and green bean vines. Though the fence was low and flimsy, Mother said we were safer with it than without it, both during the day when the doors and windows were open and at night when they were closed.

Not far from the front gate was a pond with blue-green water. Tiny waves rippled constantly across its glistening surface. A long earthen embankment, bordered by two rows of irregularly-spaced willow trees, which were just beginning to show their fresh yellow and new green, separated the pond into two parts. The willow branches floating in the breeze and reflected on the water vied with one another for the most delicate green. The embankment stopped at the foot of a high, majestic hill. All the leaves of the trees on the hillside shone green in the early spring sunshine. Father said that the water that flowed down the hill was clear and fresh and drinkable. Many fish and shrimps lived in it. The families who lived near the pond went there to soak their rice, wash their vegetables and clothes, and to catch fish and shrimps. When the soldiers stationed atop the hill fired a gun every day at noon, the artisans who worked nearby would put aside their work and go home for lunch.

Mother seemed to be filled with happiness by our new surroundings. I could not remember ever seeing her as excited and joyful as she was when she first walked through that flimsy little bamboo gate. As soon as we arrived, she rolled up her sleeves and with a light heart set to work putting our new home in order and making many plans with Father for our future. Father's income at this time was still small, and every month he sent part of it to Grandfather and Grandmother at home. After he and Mother bought some furniture and other little things that were needed around the house, there was not much money left.

Nevertheless, it was as Mother had said on the boat, "When we see Father, how happy we will be." That first year in Nanjing was the happiest of my childhood. Although Mother was not entirely free of her stomach distress, she seldom complained of being dizzy and her spirits were much better. Whatever she did she did happily: helping Father to leave for his office in the morning, getting me off to school, fixing lunch and dinner, often making Father's and my favorite dishes, watering the newly-planted flowers by the bamboo fence, or going to the lake and squatting on the stones to wash clothes. And as she worked, she would croon softly to herself. Every afternoon when I was on my way home from school I would see her standing by the gate waiting for me and my feet would fly faster all by themselves. My little puppy would wag his tail and jump up on me to greet me. As twilight approached, we would listen for Father's footsteps when he reached the entrance to our lane. My puppy was always first, and I was the second one to run out to meet him. No matter what Mother was doing, she would stop immediately and hurry after us. As soon as we reached the gate and she saw him, she would always ask the same questions, "How are you? Are you tired?" She was half-joyful and half-anxious, as if greeting someone she had not seen but had missed for a long time.

Neither Father nor Mother were yet thirty. It was the first time since their marriage that they had set up their own home. It was as if they were reliving the first days of their married life, their relationship was very sweet and harmonious. They would talk over everything they did. Their voices, as they talked and laughed before and after dinner, filled the whole house. Our rooms were not as big or long and spacious as those in my grandparents' home, so the oil lamp glowed much brighter and our shadows did not shake and tremble on the partitions. After dinner, Father would sit in his armchair and read his books or the newspaper. Mother would help me review my lessons and would sometimes stand behind me and bend over to support my hand as I wrote big ideographs with the brush. When I started yawning and couldn't stop, she would tell me I was sleepy and take me off to bed. After I climbed onto my bed, she would cover me with a quilt, turn off the oil lamp, and walk out of the room, leaving the door open a crack. The gentle, pleasant sound of their voices, and the light from the lamp on the other side of the partition came through the crack. I never had the feeling of suspense that I had sometimes had at night when I went to bed in my grandparents' home. I would close my eyes peacefully, and soon I would be dreaming.

Father liked everything that was lively and gay. He enjoyed going to Beijing opera, wearing good clothes, and visiting famous places. Nanjing had many renowned sights. Every Sunday if the weather was clear and bright, Father, carefully groomed and wearing clean clothes, would hire a horse carriage to take us into the city to see the hills and streams and to visit places of historical interest. Sometimes when famous actors were in town he would take us to the Beijing opera. These were pleasures that Mother and I never had the opportunity to enjoy when we lived in our old home.

The Beijing operas were lively and brilliant. It was not only the actors on the stage who wore clothes of rich bright colors and burning splendor that dazzled the eyes, the jewelry and hair ornaments of the women in the audience also shone and glittered. The sounds of fiddles, cymbals, gongs, and drums, the singing of the performers and the loud applause and shouts of "Good, good!" that came from the audience filled our ears. It was as exciting as when we used to celebrate the New Year in our old home, setting off firecrackers and viewing the dragon lanterns. On nights when we came back from the opera, I would lie in bed and think of the splendor of the theatre and how the actors looked, and I would be filled with admiration and wonder. I would toss and turn all night, too excited to sleep. For several days after we had been to an opera, Father would amuse himself whenever he had nothing to do by beating out the music rhythms on the table with his fingers and singing arias. Sometimes he would teach me to sing, while Mother sat nearby watching us and smiling.

Mother liked quiet and wanted to live a simple life. She did not have many clothes and only a few good ones to wear when going out, but because she was always careful and seldom wore them, whenever she put them on she looked elegant and attractive. We would all be happy and contented as we walked hand-in-hand through the gate. When we reached the street and climbed into the open, horse-drawn carriage, I always sat facing backwards in the seat behind the driver. Father and Mother would sit shoulder to shoulder, talking and laughing, opposite me. The carriage would speed along the wide streets. The driver's leather whip would keep swishing above my head. The sound of the horses' hooves would echo. It was as if we were flying above the clouds.

Mother was familiar with many places in the city because she had attended middle school there. She liked to climb Zijinshan (the Purple Hills) and enjoy the view, and go to Yuhua Tai (Rain and Flower Terrace) to collect its famous bright-colored pebbles. She would bring them home and place them in a bowl of water on the long table and look at them for days. She also liked to go to the Confucian temple to explore the antique stalls. In summer and autumn, she liked to visit Xuanwu Lake to ride in the rowboats, look at the lotus leaves and flowers, and pick red water chestnuts. She would buy a big package of lotus roots and seedpots and water chestnuts. The water chestnuts and their whisker-like roots washed clean, chopped, and fried with green and red peppers and salted black beans, were delicious with our rice. We would be hungry and the food would taste especially good when we got home after spending most of the day on the water and in the sunshine.

When she was not busy with household chores, Mother liked to read stories. There were many paper-covered, string-bound books in the house. When our neighbors learned that Mother could read, they would arrive after lunch with their sewing and, sitting in a circle in our living room, do their mending while they listened to her read. Even the old woman who sold flavored beans and cooked water chestnuts would sit near our gate and listen for a while if she happened to walk by. The women liked the ancient tales that had been told from generation to generation. These legends and stories were all long, sad, and beautiful, and if a story could not be finished in one afternoon it would be continued the next time they met. Even though the characters and events were hundreds or thousands of years old, they were still moving and true to life. When Mother reached the sad parts, she would be the first to show her emotion. Her voice would be filled with feeling and her reading would become even more moving. Her listeners would all be so intent on the story that they would stop sewing while they shook their heads, sighed, and shed tears over the people in the books. During happy passages, they would all laugh out loud. I remember the tears that so often filled my own eyes. Though I knew they were only stories and was afraid that everyone in the living room would laugh at me if I wept, I still could not hold back my tears. I would jump up and take my puppy to the edge of the pond and run along the embankment until I felt better and could return to the living room to listen.

On nights when Father had business meetings and worked late, Mother would not go to sleep until he came home. She would sit in the living room or bedroom, turn up the oil lamp, and read while she waited for him. Sometimes Aunt Fang, who lived in the back row of rooms and whose husband, a railroad inspector, often worked at night, would cross the courtyard with her sewing and come to keep Mother company. Mrs. Chen, our new cook and maid, would also come in after she had cleared up in the kitchen. They would sew together and chat until they heard Father's footsteps. Then they would snatch up their sewing and go home.

Mother got along well with the neighbors. Whenever we had candy or some fine tea, Mother would always share with them when the neighbors called. The neighbors also liked Mother, and when they had good things to eat they would invite Mother and me. Because Aunt Fang lived just behind us, we knew her better than the others.

Aunt Fang was two years older than Mother, and very thin. She usually wore a light-blue cotton jacket. Her voice was gentle. She told Mother everything. Her husband, Inspector Fang, was about the same age and also very thin, but he was not as gentle as she was. His expression was disagreeable and he seldom greeted the neighbors. The neighbors all liked Aunt Fang but none of them liked him. When he was angry, he would beat Aunt Fang in silence and not allow her to weep out loud. Whenever their son, Xiao Shunzi (Little Ease), saw his father beating his mother he would quickly bolt the door leading to the front courtyard to keep outsiders from seeing. But he would also jump up and down and weep so loudly that all the neighbors could hear. We in the front house could hear it most clearly. Mother would get very restless and pace around the house and courtyard until the sound of weeping stopped. But even then she could not calm down, and for days she would feel depressed and would lose her appetite. For several days afterwards, Aunt Fang could not bring herself to look at people, and her eyes would be red and swollen.

When Aunt Fang arrived to keep Mother company in the evenings, she would have a smile on her face, but after she had been sewing for a while her smile would disappear and her eyebrows would knit together in a frown. Mother and Mrs. Chen would try to console her. They would tell her that once Xiao Shunzi grew up, he would stand up for her. When Aunt Fang heard their comforting words her eyes would fill with tears. She would shake her head and sigh deeply. "That devil ..." Whenever she spoke of her husband she called him a devil. "He treats me as if I'm not human. Not a week goes by that he doesn't find the slightest excuse to beat me or kick me. Even if one day that devil were to bring me a mountain of gold to wear, I swear he could not make me forgive him. I will not hide it—this warm heart of mine has turned to iron and is as cold as ice." Another evening, I heard Aunt Fang whisper into Mother's ear, "Little sister, I'm going to tell you something you may laugh at. At night, when that devil tries to embrace me, I feel nothing. My heart remains cold as ice and like iron." Although I did not entirely understand the meaning of her words at the time, they made a deep impression on me.

But when Aunt Fang and Mrs. Chen chatted together, they always praised Father, saying men like him were rare and that he treated Mother well and was devoted to his family.

During our second year in Nanjing, Father was promoted and his monthly income increased. The business and social engagements that kept him out in the evenings grew more frequent, so Aunt Fang and Mrs. Chen kept Mother company more often, too.

Some evenings, when Father did not come home for dinner and Aunt Fang and Mrs. Chen did not visit, only Mother and I would be sitting cross from each other under the oil lamp. While I studied, Mother would riffle through a book with her long, slender fingers. The house would be still and we would feel lonely. The gleaming oil lamp stood in the middle of the square table between Mother and me. As the lamp burned down, the house became even quieter. My vision would blur and the black ideographs would start to look like ants, crawling one by one at first and then collecting in a clump that would not move. When I was almost asleep, Mother would bend over me. I would turn to look at her, and in the slowly dying light of the lamp I seemed to see in her face a hint of the old pensiveness that I had not seen for a long time. I wondered when it had returned. Mother would put down her book and urge me to go to bed, but I did not want to leave her and go to bed alone. When I could no longer resist her urgings, I would climb into her bed. Mother would set the lamp on the little tea table and sit by my side reading her book and waiting until Father came back, when she would wake me and put me in my own little bamboo bed.

The next morning the smile would be back on Mother's face, covering the faint traces of melancholy.

When Father came home late he would often complain that ever since his promotion he had not only more work to do, but also more outside social engagements which were meaningless but could not be refused. During our third year in Nanjing, Father was promoted to assistant manager of a branch office and he became even busier. Sometimes he had to go to banquets and was away even on Sundays and holidays. The exciting, happy days, when my puppy and I used to run to meet him, became fewer and fewer. I no longer heard my parents' happy voices at dinner time or drifting into my room along with the lamp light as I fell asleep. Then Mother began having stomach trouble again. Sometimes when I came home from school, I could smell medicinal herbs, and the little earthen pot in which they were brewed was often on the stove. But Mother's spirits were still good most of the time. She had not yet reached the point where she could not stay up, she was not willing to lie in bed in daytime like a sick person.

From her worried expression and from the conversations she and Grandmother had during Grandmother's two visits to us, I understood dimly that Mother's illness was related to Father's being out so often and also to the fact that I was a girl and that there were no sons. However, our circumstances were much better than before. Father's monthly income was larger and we did not need to be so careful about spending money. From time to time Father would give us money to buy more clothes and jewelry. He would also bring Grandfather and Grandmother to visit us, and talk with Mother about moving to a larger house. But nothing it seemed, could bring back the tranquil and harmonious atmosphere of the past. There seemed to be a thin layer of mist over our home. And though it was thin, it could not be dispersed.

However, the relationship between Father and Mother did not seem to have changed much. Earlier, when Mother had been spirited and gay, I knew she loved Father, and now that she was anxious I knew that she loved him even more. Then where had this thin layer of mist come from? I could feel it but could not see it. When we first moved to Nanjing, Father and Mother occasionally had differences of opinion. Father had a quick temper and became impatient easily, but he would also calm down quickly as well. Mother's disposition was calm and sensitive, and she could not bear harsh words, especially from him. When they flared up, however, it would last only a moment, and then they would forgive each other and be as happy as before. Every time they made up, it was like sunshine after rain, we would all feel at peace with one another. Now that Mother was ill and had only medicines to keep her company most of the time, it seemed that Father was kinder than ever to her. Their little disputes no longer took place, but the happy feeling of sunshine after rain was no more either.

I noticed that Father had become more particular about his clothes whenever he went out for a social engagement. He would always put on a clean, stylish long gown and short jacket and would seem animated when he left. When he came home late he would often bring back fruit or candy for us, but Mother always seemed indifferent to it. I also noticed that Mother no longer talked with Father about our plans for the future as she had in the beginning. These plans had been both large and small—to buy more household furnishings, to replace and repair the bamboo fence, to plant chrysanthemums for the autumn, to buy some chicks that would lay eggs when they were grown, and, when we had more money, to go on pleasure trips to Shanghai and West Lake in Hangzhou. They also used to talk about having more children—how I had hoped that I would have a little brother!—

but now I never heard them mention it. Instead, Mother often talked about treating me more like a son, saying she hoped I would be a good, talented student so that when I grew up I would be like my aunt, who was a school headmistress and could support herself and not be dependent on others. Although Grandmother had always told me I had been born into a family that wanted daughters, now Mother seemed to feel an anxiety about me that would not let her rest. When Father had received his first promotion, Mother had suggested that they should each, he from his salary and she from savings in our living expenses, buy me a six-dollar savings bond each month. These would mount up gradually and then middle school and college expenses would not be a worry. Father agreed, and each month when he brought his salary home, he would also bring the two savings bonds from the bank. Mother would put them in the little silver jewel box she kept in the back of the clothes press.

One evening, after waiting up late for Father, I fell asleep in Mother's bed. I slept there all night, because Father did not come home. He had not told her that he would be out and she waited for him until daybreak. I was awakened by his footsteps. The oil lamp had gone out and the grey morning light was just starting to come in through the cracks of the window shutters. The room was still dark and grey. I saw Mother, still dressed, propped against the foot of the bed with a thin quilt wrapped around her. Father, carrying a big package and with a wide smile on his face, went over to her. She looked quietly at him but did not say a word. Father, still smiling, held out the package to her, but she did not take it. Her lips, which had lost their color, quivered slightly. She turned her pale face away. When I saw her like that, I felt frightened and my heart ached. I jumped out of bed, ran barefoot to Mother, threw my arms around her waist, and began to cry. Father held the package out to me but I would not take it.

His smile disappeared when he saw us weeping in each other's arms. He sat down on the edge of the bed and slowly explained to her that his colleagues had forced him to drink wine and play mahjongg, that he had not been able to get away, that it had been an impulsive decision, and that because he had to make a living, things like that could not be helped. He talked a long time, but Mother said nothing. After a while the sun came up. Father took a handful of change from his pocket and gave it to me, telling me to go out and buy something to eat because Mother was tired

and should rest.

After that, there were few nights when Father failed to come home.

Another evening, Aunt Fang was sewing and chatting with Mother. At first they talked about everyday things, about Xiao Shunzi and me, but gradually their conversation turned to the bitterness women had to bear. Aunt Fang said a word or two in praise of Father but then lowered her voice and said, "Little sister, has your husband ever hinted to you that he is thinking of bringing a second wife into your home because he wants a son?"

She kept her voice low so I, half-asleep in Mother's bed, would not hear. But I did, and her words beat into my ears and drove away my sleepiness. I held my breath and lifted my head to listen. Mother did not answer immediately. After a long time she gave a great sigh and said, "I have heard no such hints yet."

I let out my breath in relief, but Aunt Fang's question, and the words she often said, "My warm heart has become iron, and as cold as ice," stayed with me.

Chapter 6

THAT spring, Mother began getting sick every few days, and as her illness worsened her spirits fell. Father became very anxious, and asked every eminent Chinese and Western physician in the region to examine her. But no matter how much Chinese or Western medicine she took, it seemed to make no difference. During this time, Mother still hoped she would recover, though she sometimes got impatient with the doctors when she saw no improvement. As soon as she felt a little better, however, she would be filled with hope again. I never really knew what her illness was. She said her stomach hurt, and both the Chinese and Western doctors agreed with her that she had a stomach disorder. But no one could say anything more with certainty.

About this time there came a ripple in our quiet lives. My mother's only two living relatives, first her mother and then her brother's widow, came from other provinces to visit us. My mother often longed for them, especially her sister-in-law, whom she had not seen for almost ten years. Their visits brought us great happiness and gave Mother much relief from the loneliness caused by her illness. Their visits also had an enormous effect on my later life, but this was not foreseen by anyone at the time.

I called Mother's sister-in-law "Aunt." She was several years older than my mother and their relationship was much closer than the usual one between sisters-in-law. They had been schoolmates and friends before becoming members of the same family by marriage. When Mother entered the school, my aunt was graduating from upper middle school and also teaching there. Mother was a student in one of her classes. Mother's older brother, my uncle, was at that time an intern at a medical school hospital in Nanjing. He would come home on Sundays and holidays to visit my mother, who introduced him to her schoolmate. It was said that they were attracted to each other from the start. Because the school forbade friendships between men and women students—even letters were censored—Mother inevitably became their go-between and secretly carried letters for them. This heightened the closeness between my mother and her friend, who married my uncle soon after she graduated. As it happens in many families, my aunt did not get along with her mother-in-law. However, my mother, unlike most sisters-in-law, always stood up for her and helped her in every way, openly and in private. So the affection they shared became even deeper.

Unfortunately, my uncle died a few years later and my aunt was left a widow while still young. This was a sad story. My uncle was the only physician of Western medicine in Wuhu. He had a good reputation and had cured many people, but when it came to his own illness, his medical knowledge not only did not save him but was a hindrance. It was said that when he became ill his over-confidence in his own ability made him unwilling to ask the advice of other doctors. He made his own diagnosis and treated himself. When his illness worsened, other doctors were consulted, but it was too late. My uncle died in the prime of his life, when he could have accomplished a great deal and built a large practice. It was a sad and difficult time after his death because, except for what remained in his office, there was nothing his old mother, widow, and daughter not yet six could use to make a living.

My aunt, as was expected of widows in the society of that time, never married again. And because of other events, which outraged her, and which I shall soon describe, she took her little daughter, my cousin Biying (Azure Flower), and moved to the distant province of Hubei, where she made her way on her own. She never returned to Wuhu. News about her, whether from her letters or by word of mouth through others, came slowly. We learned that at first she did private tutoring in Hankou and that later she opened a girls' school there. Opened a girls' school! This news immediately spread through our community. When people spoke of her, they would often raise their thumbs in praise and say, "She's wonderful. She has nothing to be ashamed of. She's a heroine." Or, "That wasn't easy. A woman needs more character and ability to raise a family single-handedly than a man does." Or, "If this were in ancient times, they'd build a memorial arch in honor of such a chaste widow."

Although I was too young to understand these words, I did realize that my aunt, who had left our region when I was only six months old, was regarded not as an ordinary person like us but as a hero, like those written about in books. From my earliest childhood I had felt a deep admiration for her that I could not express. However, no one seemed to think about her difficulties or to wonder how she had managed on her own to establish a new home in a strange city, how many disappointments she must have had, and how many times her courage must almost have failed her. Of these things no one ever said a word.

It was only later that I slowly came to discover why everyone praised my aunt so highly. Certainly her own merits—her young and faithful widowhood and her ability to establish herself so far away from home and succeed in a profession were part of it. But another important reason was their condemnation of my maternal grandmother. My poor grandmother! Comparing her worth with that of my aunt was like comparing a goose feather with Mount Tai, the holy mountain. The more they glorified my aunt, the lower my mother's mother sunk and how much the more so because the two were mother-in-law and daughter-in-law. Whenever people spoke of one, they would naturally think of the other.

I have already told of how my father's mother had been widowed young and violated the chastity of widowhood by remarrying, and how she was therefore disgraced and considered beneath mention by everyone. My maternal grandmother was middle-aged when her husband died. She then worked hard and suffered much to raise her children. But in her later years, after my aunt's husband, her son, died, and after both he and my aunt, and my parents had given her grandchildren, she was unable to keep to her widowhood. This was seen as all the worse because of her own young daughter-in-law, who had held so firmly to her own widowhood. It was an extraordinary set of circumstances —but because of this one misstep, my grandmother was judged and condemned and could never be pardoned.

When she remarried, my aunt was so angry that she moved away and never spoke to her again.

Although my maternal grandmother went on living near Wuhu and was separated from us by only a small river, she and my paternal grandparents did not see each other more than once or twice a year. Mother used to take me across the wooden bridge to see her but we never stayed overnight at her home. Although both my maternal and paternal grandmothers were about the same age, a little over fifty, my mother's mother looked much younger and stronger. She had almost no grey hair and her face was still unlined. When she smiled, her teeth were even, clean, and white. Her back was still straight, her chest was high, and she showed not the slightest hint of a dowager's hump. What was even more remarkable was that although she had endured much misfortune, especially after she remarried, she always looked cheerful and pleasant. However, this outlook, along with her youthful appearance, brought her only more scorn and criticism. I heard relatives say, "She's heartless, worthless and unrepentant —that's the only reason she's kept her looks! If any decent woman had behaved the way she had, she'd be full of remorse, not wearing smiles!"

Was my maternal grandmother really as stupid and heartless as my relatives and other people said? I seldom saw her and could not say for certain. But when I grew up, I learned that she was both courageous and stubborn, a person who would defy public opinion and be responsible for her own life. Her cheerfulness was in part the way she was born and in part the result of her experiences. The more blows and disdain she received from others, the less willing she was to give in and hang her head. Nevertheless, she must have felt pain; my mother knew this and I also know it now.

My father always seemed to resent widows who remarried, probably because he had suffered so much from his own mother's remarriage. But because Mother in her illness longed to see her mother, he was willing for her sake to invite my maternal grandmother to visit us. Although Mother never said so, she probably felt in her heart that her mother's remarriage had been a mistake, and never spoke of her in public. Because she knew that my aunt would be unwilling to see her mother-in-law, Mother arranged their visits carefully, so they would not meet.

My mother's mother came to visit us at the end of spring. She intended to stay until the end of June and return home at the beginning of July, when my aunt's vacation would start and she would begin travelling to see us. However, my grandmother left before the end of the month. Mother tried but could not persuade her to stay longer. During her entire visit, Father was always cool towards her and never treated her cordially. He barely spoke to her and never called her "Mother." Whenever they met, he would mutter something indistinct and consider it a greeting. His dislike was even more obvious at mealtimes when, sitting at the table with the bowls of rice and food between them, he would keep his face expressionless, not looking up from his own bowl and chopsticks, and eating in silence. Grandmother would also look uncomfortable and would eat her meal in silence. This made

Mother very uncomfortable. From time to time, she would pick up a choice bit of food and place it in my grandmother's bowl, or in Father's bowl, or mine. Or she would smile and make a trivial comment, hoping to ease the tension. Father, however, showed no interest in responding to her. And Grandmother, who ordinarily spoke easily with other people, seemed intimidated by Father's presence. When I saw Father acting so distant, I scarcely dared to move, and hoped that Mother would not say anything to anger him. For if he were to become angry and slam down his bowl and chopsticks and leave the table, that would make Grandmother even more uncomfortable. Fortunately, that never happened.

Grandmother's uneasiness and constraint would disappear as soon as he left the house, but her spirits were low. I would hear Mother plead with Father when Grandmother was out of hearing, "Take pity on her. Her husband is already over sixty. From what she says, his health has grown worse these last two years and their life is difficult. Ever since we moved away, she hasn't had any close relatives near her. Since we have invited her here, what would it cost you to treat her kindly?"

Father's only reply was a grunt, at the back of his throat. Mother tried again, coaxing him. "I'm not finding fault with you. You don't know how forbidding you look when you frown. I don't want you to treat her in any special way. It would be enough if you only looked at her with a little more kindness."

Father muttered a few words to the effect that Grandmother still had the same old faults, that she had not changed, and that she was still a busybody and a gossip.

"You're prejudiced," Mother argued with him. She kept her voice very low, for fear that Grandmother, who was in the next room, would hear. "When has she said a word about you, or spread a single tale?"

"I am not prejudiced." Father too kept his voice low. "Do you think I don't know what she's up to? I'm not blind! After all the trouble she has brought upon herself, she still can't mind her own business! It's disgusting!"

"It might be a good thing if you looked at your own behavior. Anyone who has done nothing wrong would never suspect that others were talking about him behind his back."

"All right, all right," said Father. Seeing that Mother was upset, he quickly changed the subject. He struck the table lightly, smiled, and said, "You see, it's as I said—as soon as she came here things began to go wrong. All right, all right. I'll be a little more careful. Enough, now."

But in spite of his promises, his behavior did not change.

Grandmother could not endure Father's hostility, and about two weeks after she arrived she told Mother that she thought she should go home earlier than she had planned. Mother tried to persuade her to stay and urged her to disregard Father. "You understand his temperament. He is one of those described by the saying, 'Even the tiger who does not eat men was born looking fierce.'"

"No, no. I'm not complaining about him." Grandmother sighed as if she had many regrets. "How could I complain about him? All I want is for you two young people to be happy."

"Then stay a little longer. I know there's no important reason you must go home now. It wasn't easy for you to get here, so now that you are here you should stay."

Because of this, Grandmother stayed a little longer, but not as long as she had planned. During her visit she seemed worried about Mother's illness and about Mother's relationship with Father. I often heard her urging Mother to look after her health and to accumulate some money of her own. She would say, "Men's hearts are changeable. They blow hot and cold. You share their misfortunes in the bad times, but when things get better they do not necessarily share their good luck with you. If something were to happen, you'd be in a better position if you had some money set aside." Mother looked heart-stricken as she listened to these words.

On the day Grandmother left, no one went to see her off at the boat. Mother had not slept well the night before, probably because she felt unhappy, and was dizzy when she woke up. She could only stand with me at the gate of the bamboo fence and watch Grandmother ride off alone in a rickshaw with her bundle of clothes.

Although Mother was unhappy, it seemed as if a load had been lifted from her shoulders once Grandmother left. Father did not ask any questions when he came home that evening, and Mother never again mentioned her.

It was almost July, and my aunt would arrive before long, so we all got busy preparing for her. Two weeks ahead of time, Father and Mother began preparing my room for her. They whitewashed the walls and took everything out. They put my bed behind Mother's bed and moved all the best furniture in the house into the room that had been mine. The door curtain, the bed covers, and the hangings were changed and washed so they looked like new, and a cool straw mat was placed on the bed. Father and Mother spent much time discussing what my aunt might like to eat and what they would take her to see.

Father also worried that my aunt, because she was a highly educated person, would be shocked by the popular local ballads and folk songs the blind beggars went around singing on summer nights. But Mother told him not to worry, because my aunt was a local person and had heard those songs since her childhood. All that was necessary was that we invite no beggars into the house to sing for us. A few days before my aunt arrived, Mother suddenly remembered something. She and Mrs. Chen hid away all the pins and needles in the house. Mother said this was because once, when my cousin Biying was three years old and no one was keeping an eye on her, she took a needle from the sewing basket and almost swallowed it. From that time on my aunt could not bear even to look at a needle. My parents kept busy preparing until the day my aunt arrived. Father took a day's leave from work and went to the pier to meet the boat. The weather was very hot. He got up early, ate his breakfast, and then put on a long white linen gown and a straw hat. He took along a big paper fan with sandalwood slats and started for the gate. But when he reached the fence, he thought of something and came back. Half-smiling and half-serious, he went over to Mother and cautioned her, "I have one more important thing to say. If we should happen to have one of our little quarrels, let's keep it from your sister-in-law."

Mother smiled and waved her hand. "Go, go. Don't waste any more time. You'll be late meeting the boat."

Father smiled and went out the gate. Mother and I, she with a palm-leaf fan in her hand and I with my puppy at my feet, sat on two little bamboo chairs outside the gate and waited. We waited until about noon, when we saw the rickshaws coming towards us from the other end of the embankment.

My mother and my aunt had not met for many years and were very much moved to see each other again. They stood at the fence and smiled and wept and could not speak for a long time. Father stood beside them and laughed. Patting Mother on the shoulder, he said, "Now, now, you haven't seen each other for so long—you should be happy, not sad. Your sister-in-law has had a long journey and is suffering from the heat. Why don't you take her into the house right away to rest, drink a cup of tea, and cool off? Don't stand out here in the sun getting hot and sweaty."

At this, Mother wiped away her tears, seized my aunt's hand, and led her into the house.

Chapter 7

MY aunt was a little over forty. Although I had imagined that she would be like a heroine out of a book, I realized once we met that except for her Hubei accent, she was not all that different from the rest of us. She was half an inch shorter than Mother and was on the plump side. She wore her hair combed straight back and coiled in a tight chignon. She used neither rouge nor powder. Her suit, a coat and skirt of grey cotton, was dowdy —Mother said that after my uncle died my aunt wore only grey and black. Her clothes, jewelry, and hair style were too old for her and added years to her appearance. Her voice was soft and gentle, and her attitude towards other people was calm and composed. She was an amiable, approachable person and was much esteemed, not only for her character and respectability but also for her success as a school headmistress.

With my aunt, Father was a different person than he had been with my grandmother. He turned into a thoughtful, indulgent host. As custom dictated, he often served her tea and hot water, always ushered her to the seat of honor at meals, and always put the choicest bits of food in her bowl. He always smiled at her and addressed her as "Sister," and would think of things to say that would demonstrate his respect and concern. He also became even more solicitous and sympathetic towards Mother, and seldom stayed out late in the evenings.

Mother also behaved differently. When her mother had been with us, Mother's shoulders were bowed and she looked despondent. But once my aunt arrived, she seemed to act like someone who had been vindicated. There was a hint of pride on her face and she stood up straighter. Her spirits, of course, were much improved. The two sisters-in-law, who had been separated for so long and were now reunited, seemed to have so much to say to each other that their talk would never end. They did not want to go out in the afternoons but would sit at the table in our bright, clean little living room with a pot of good tea between them, and would talk in low voices about everything. Besides catching upon all that had happened to them since they had been apart, they often talked about their relatives and old friends, but I never heard them mention my mother's mother. Ten years was a long time, and my aunt had forgotten who some people were. Some of their older acquaintances had died. People she had known as children were now grownups, and she probably would not have recognized them, and some were married with children of their own. As the two of them talked, their hearts were filled with emotion.

According to Father, my aunt was a person who had seen the world, knew how to conduct herself in her speech and behavior, and did not often show her feelings—happiness, anger, or sorrow —in the presence of others. But when she was with Mother and me, she was very emotional. She laughed easily and also wept, especially when she and Mother talked about my uncle. Though he had died many years earlier, my aunt still remembered every detail of his voice, his smile, his facial expressions, and the things he used to say. Mother and my aunt would recall how kind and patient he had been with the sick who came to him, how he pitied the old and poor, how he cared for his family, both old and young, and how affectionate he had been towards my mother. They spoke of one incident, when he learned that the family where my father was teaching tried to marry their daughter to him as a second wife. They knew that he was already married, but they wished to make him their heir. My aunt described how my uncle had rushed to the telegraph office in the middle of the night and wired Father to stop the negotiations. She also recalled the birth of her daughter, Biying. It had been a difficult birth and my uncle stayed by her side without sleeping for three days and two nights. She told us that while she was confined to bed, he had nursed her very patiently. Whenever she spoke of how he had gently picked her up out of the bed and put her down again, my aunt would stretch out her two short round, arms as he had, and start crying.

But when she and Mother recalled their teens and years together in middle school, they would laugh so hard that they could not stop. Their laughter about those days added life and interest to the hot, sleepy July afternoons.

"Little sister, do you remember ..." My aunt would begin, in her strong Hubei accent. "... That summer vacation not long after you were engaged, when my husband invited your new fiancé to spend part of the vacation with us? You stayed in your room the whole time and refused to come out. One morning, while I was combing your fiancé's hair—his pigtail had not yet been cut—I heard Biying crying in the courtyard. I called you seven or eight times before you came out of your room. I waited until you came near and then pulled you over behind your future husband, and pressed the comb into your hand, then I went to Biying. Your face flushed as red as the rising sun!"

"How could I not remember?" Mother leaned her head on her arm, and laughed. Her hair, which was fastened loosely behind her collar, swayed as her shoulders shook with laughter. "Big sister, have you forgotten how, when you graduated, my brother sent you a letter and a gold brooch? I waited until we were alone and gave them to you. You were so excited that you snatched them from me, stuffed them into your breast pocket, and ran away. You didn't even say thank you! I ran after you, calling you, but you didn't hear me."

My aunt replied, "After I graduated and went back home, he wrote to me every day, sometimes I even got two letters in one day. When my mother and sister-in-law saw the postman coming they would shake their heads and say, 'I don't understand how they can have so much to say. They'll be married in a few months. Can't they wait until then? Why waste it all in letters?' My aunt often teased me, saying that girls these days had become too forward. 'They aren't even married, but they're already writing letters to each other!'"

My mother and aunt talked and laughed as if they had forgotten all the years that had passed and had gone back to being girls together.

Another subject my aunt never tired of talking about, nor did Mother and I tire of hearing about, was my cousin. Whenever my aunt mentioned Biying, her eyes would shine and her face would beam. But her next words would always be, "It isn't just because I'm her mother that I'm boasting about her."

Once she told Mother, "Not to brag, but if you ever heard her play the piano, you'd be surprised how much you loved her.

"Poor Biying, I feel so sorry for her! Her father died when she was so young, and then she travelled all over with me. Fortunately she grew up early. For many years now she and I have depended on each other for everything. She's my right hand. How could I do without her? At my age I no longer have as much energy as I used to. Biying helps me with my work at school when I can't finish it. She reminds me of the things I forget. Besides studying, she also teaches. Sometimes, when I see her working so hard, I love her so much that I can hardly bear it. I was feeling somewhat anxious when I was leaving to come here. Little sister, guess what she said to me."

Mother shook her head, saying that she could not.

"She said, 'Mother, don't worry. Miss Li and I will keep an eye on the school. You haven't seen my aunt for so many years. Stay with her as long as you like, and enjoy yourself. You have worked so hard for so many years, you should take this opportunity to rest. You mustn't worry about the school. I'm all grown up now.' Just think of that! She's only fifteen, but she calls herself a grownup." My aunt was so moved by her own words that tears came to her eyes.

Mother nodded her head in praise. Then she turned to me and said she hoped I would be as capable and thoughtful as Biying when I grew up.

Mother glanced at my aunt, hesitated, and then said, "If Biying's own grandmother could hear what you've just said, she'd be so happy. Big sister, she is old now, and longs for her sons and daughters more than she did in the past. When she was here, she often told me that if she could see Biying just once, she would be able to die in peace."

"That can never happen! Never!"

As soon as my aunt heard the words, "Biying's own grandmother," her smile disappeared. "My child will never again see That Person." She always referred to my maternal grandmother as "That Person" because of her remarriage. "Just think about how That Person has behaved. Biying's father's coffin had been carried out of the house less than six months earlier. His bones were not yet cold in the ground. I was a young daughter-in-law, but I maintained chastity after my husband's death. But she was an old mother-in-law, remarried. Her disgrace has shamed all of us. I knelt before her and begged her." Aunt's voice was shaking and her face was white. I had never seen her so angry.

Mother hung her head and looked at her hands.

My aunt went on, "I begged her, 'Mother, you must not think of marrying again! No matter what the difficulties, we three generations should stay together. As long as my daughter and I have food, you won't starve; if the day ever comes that we lack even rice to eat, I will take Biying out onto the streets to beg and will bring home what I get. I will support you, no matter what happens. For the sake of the dead, we must maintain the honor of the Lu family.' But after I had said all I could say, That Person's heart of stone was still unmoved. She did not consider respectability important. She married that old man, her husband's accountant in the pharmacy. We were the laughingstocks of the whole neighborhood. I was so ashamed I couldn't face anyone. How would Biying have been able to hold up her head when she grew older? The two of us could do nothing but move away from our native town. And now she has the audacity to say that she wants to see her granddaughter?"

Mother's eyes were red and she hesitated a long time before she spoke. "It can't be changed now." She took out her handkerchief and wiped her eyes.

"She did it herself and she must take the consequences. No one else is to blame."

Mother did not answer and remained silent for a long time.

Then my aunt said more gently, "Little sister, we have always been closer than real sisters. Listen to me. Even if I were to forgive her and overlook what she did, public opinion and society would still be against her. Besides, I can't just think of myself, I also have Biying and the school to consider. If I were to re-establish a relationship with That Person, would people still be willing to send their daughters to my school? After I've endured so much and worked so hard to bring up Biying? I can't not be concerned about her future." My aunt's eyes were also red. She took out her handkerchief and wiped away her tears. "I have my sorrows, little sister. If you really want to understand my feelings and sympathize with me, I beg you, never mention That Person to me again."

Mother nodded, but she could not speak because of the pain she was feeling. For the rest of my aunt's visit they never again mentioned my grandmother.

My aunt's parents and all her ancestors were buried in Nanjing. She paid her respects by visiting their graves and also had her father's and mother's restored. She and Mother rode in a horse carriage to look at the scenery and to visit historic sites and their old middle school. When the autumn term was about to begin my aunt began preparing to return home. Mother knew that she had to get ready for school and did not pressure her to stay longer.

One day, my aunt spoke of Mother's weakness, caused by her illness, and said she should not work too hard. She offered to take me back with her to Hubei Province to study for a semester, and said she would send me home for Spring Festival. This would spare Mother some of her day-to-day responsibilities and give me a chance to study with my cousin. Mother liked the idea but felt hesitant. When Father came home that night, she talked it over with him. Father made up his mind on the spot, saying, "Naturally, we'd be uneasy if it were anyone else, but with her aunt, what is there to worry about? Who could be more suitable? Besides, she'll be gone only a few months and will be home again at the end of the year. The doctors maintain that your illness is partly due to worry, because you've had been weighed down by too many responsibilities. With Xiao Baogu gone, you will have much less to worry about. Nothing could be better."

So it was decided that I would leave with my aunt.

When I heard my aunt and Father talking, I felt like a big burden to my sick mother, and though I did not want to leave her I was willing to do so if it would make her life easier. On the morning we left, Father accompanied us to the steamer. Mother stood at the gate and watched us get into the rickshaws. She seemed calm, so I felt at peace. As the rickshaw carrying Father and me reached the end of the lane, I craned my head to look back. Mother was still standing at the gate with one hand on the bamboo fence. She was gazing after us, and when she saw me looking back her lips began to tremble. She wheeled around and walked through the gate as if she could not bear to watch me a moment longer. At that instant, our rickshaws turned the corner.

I do not know why, but the picture of Mother as she looked at me that moment seems to have been burned into my memory. Even now, many years later, I cannot forget it—in fact, it is clearer now than it was then.

Looking back, I realize how naive I was. I know now that the reason Mother was willing to let me leave was not so she would have fewer worries, but because she thought I could learn much from my aunt and Biying. Perhaps she realized that her chances for recovery were slight and decided to take advantage of the opportunity to make sure that there would be someone else to look after me.

Although I had been reluctant to leave home, my homesickness gradually disappeared once I reached the school and met Biying. She was just the age I most admired. She did not resemble my aunt. Her eyebrows and eyes were delicate and she wore a long thick braid. It was tied with red yarn at the tip, and swung from side to side against her narrow, sloping shoulders. She played the piano very well. When she was with girls her own age, she would talk and laugh and be very boisterous, but when she was in the classroom teaching handicrafts to the little ones, she would act almost as serious and dignified as my aunt. Biying immediately became my idol, and the other forty or fifty girls all became my new friends.

The school was on Sanming Lane in the French concession in Hankou. It was a three-story, red-brick building and looked half Chinese and half Western in style. My aunt's living quarters took up half of the third floor; the other half and the two lower floors were classrooms. Except for a big green sign with white characters, " Xiude (Cultivate Virtue) Girls' School," which hung at the corner of the lane, no one would have known there was a school there. It had none of the brilliance and glory the people at home had imagined. My aunt was busy every day and had little time to spend with Biying and me. In the afternoons after school was out and the pupils had left, she would go out and tutor in private homes. She often taught so late that we had lit the lamps before she came back. Biying and I would sit at the third-floor window and watch the activity in the street while we waited for her to return. The whole building would be empty. My cousin would act like a big sister and tell me about the world. It was from her that I learned that it was against the law for Chinese people to enter the gates of concession parks, which were full of trees and flowers. So when school was out, the lane was the only place where my schoolmates and I could play. Biying also told me that most of the people who could afford to hire private tutors were spoiled and arrogant matrons and daughters from wealthy families who were bored and idle and thought it would be fashionable to be able to read a little. But most of them had no understanding of the difficulties faced by people like my aunt, who had to earn their own livings. When my aunt finished giving them their lessons, they often asked her to write letters, work out accounts, and do other tasks without pay. Sometimes they would ask my aunt to intervene in family discussions and to try to make peace. In this way they ate up all her evenings.

Every Sunday, however, no matter how much work remained to be done, my aunt would put everything aside and spend the day with Biying and me. Our meals were better and more varied on Sundays. My aunt would pick up her bowl and chopsticks and say with a smile, "My poor big daughter and my poor small daughter, we've worked all week. Today we can finally have some good food. All three of us must eat well and enjoy ourselves today."

Before long, I got used to living at my aunt's. I was too busy to think of home except when I wrote to my parents on Saturday afternoons or received letters or parcels from them. In class, I "sang" my lessons in a loud voice and with a Hubei accent like the other girls. My feet played among countless other feet and ran up and down the three flights of narrow stairs as we laughed and talked. Out in the lane, we would kick shuttlecocks made of chicken feathers twelve feet in the air. After school was out, groups of us would play games and run around. When the teachers were not around, we would sing a local ballad from Macheng County. It was about a magistrate's daughter who loved a district court messenger who had been sent away by her father. She sang of love and longing, which we did not understand:

> "The sun fills the sky with rosy light, oh,
> Longing for my lover, oh,
> Longing for my lover my body is numb
> Daily I think and daily I long, oh,
> I watch and watch and do not see him, oh,
> Has my lover met a demon?"

Another song we liked even better was a popular one the children in other primary schools used to sing. It described scenes in the concession parks and we did not fully understand its words, either:

> "Walk, walk, walk
> Walk to the entrance of the foreigners' street.
> Saw a countryman, a Chinese brother
> Walk into the park.
> The foreign 'redheads" saw him,
> Took him to the police station.
> Beaten with sticks
> Fined many dollars
> He was told to get out and go away."

Those months passed like the water in the Yangtze River, flowing on without stopping. Before I knew it, it was Spring Festival and time for vacation.

------

*"Redheads." Indian police employed by the British concession and named for the red turbans they wore.

Chapter 8

I F I had known that this was the last year I would ever spend with my mother, the last year that I would have a loving family waiting eagerly for me, if I had known that after I left Mother would miss me and weep every time she saw a child my age, I would have rushed home without waiting for anyone to come for me. But I did not know—I was too young and inexperienced to be wise. I wanted only to stay in Hankou for New Year's because I had many friends there to have fun with, and all the Lantern Festival lanterns to see. Biying and my classmates all urged me to stay. So when Father sent my second uncle to fetch me in January, I refused to go home. My uncle went back alone on the boat. Ten days later Grandfather came to get me, but I still refused to go home and he too went back alone. Finally, Father sent a long telegram to my aunt telling her that he himself would ask for leave and come to get me. My aunt then hastened to arrange for me to leave. Fortunately, a young teacher she knew was leaving for Nanjing for winter vacation, and my aunt asked her to take me with her.

How contradictory our feelings can be! I had been so unwilling to go home, but strangely enough, as soon as I boarded the steamboat I hated not being able to leap through our front gate in one bound. The Yangtze River is low in winter, so the trip took three days and four nights. We reached Nanjing in the middle of the fourth night. The city was buried a foot deep in snow and tiny snowflakes were still drifting down. Except for the movement of the porters, the rickshaw pullers, and passengers under the dim lamps along the river bank, the whole city, quiet and calm, seemed to be sound asleep in the snowy night.

The teacher and I squeezed into one rickshaw and rode off in the sharp cold night wind of mid-winter. I felt as if there were countless fine needles pricking my ears, the tip of my nose, my fingers, and my toes, and I was numb and ached from the cold. Fortunately, our house was close to the wharf, and before long we arrived. As we neared the gate, even before I got out of the rickshaw, I began shouting, "Mother, I'm back! Hurry up and open the gate! Open the gate!"

"Xiao Baogu is back! I'm coming, don't be impatient! Mother is coming to open the gate." Her voice rang out immediately from the house. "Father, listen! Our little girl's voice sounds completely different! She has a Hubei accent!"

A shaft of lamp light shone through the crack of the window shutters and the gate groaned open. Mother appeared carrying a blue-shaded oil lamp in one hand and fastening the shoulder button of her gown with the other. She came to meet me with warm greetings on her lips. Father, his padded gown thrown around him, was just behind her. They both seized my cold, numb hands and enfolded them in warmth.

I cannot describe how happy Father and Mother were to see me. They could not stop thanking the teacher who had brought me back. After we had drunk tea and were preparing for bed, the teacher asked me to sleep in her room to keep her company, perhaps because the house was unfamiliar. But Mother shook her head gently and put me in bed between Father and her. When we were all settled, she told him, "We can each hold one of our daughter's hands."

That night I was so excited that it took me a long time to fall asleep. Besides I did not want to turn my back on either my father or my mother. So the only way I could sleep was on my back, which I was not used to. I kept opening and closing my eyes. Soon I heard Father's snoring on my right, Mother's short, quick breathing on my left, and the sound of the snow beating on the roof tiles and against the windows. As the wind blew through the cracks I could also hear the rustling of the few remaining pages of the old calendar that hung by the window. The night wind kept howling outside, and it seemed as if the trees on the hill were sighing. There seemed to be no peace anywhere. But I could not hear the clear flowing sound of the mountain streams as they flowed over the stones; they must have been frozen. As I lay between my father and mother on that cold and frozen night, how warm I felt!

Like the other winter nights on the old calendar, the page marked with that night would soon be torn off. But that night can never be torn from my heart. Later on in my life, whenever I heard the howling of the night wind of winter it would remind me of that night. Though I did not realize it that night, Mother's life, like that calendar that had only a few pages, had only a few days left. But I could see that she was much thinner than when I had left six months earlier, and her palms were so hot that they seared mine.

Mother was very happy when I first came home. She took me by the hand and we went to visit all the neighbors. Perhaps because I wanted to show that I was now a polite, civilized student, I would make a deep bow whenever I met anyone. All the neighbors laughed and said, "She has really changed. She really acts like someone who has seen the world and learned a great deal. Look how well she understands etiquette. She bows as soon as she sees us."

"You have no idea how thoughtful she is," said Mother, smiling. "This morning when she awoke, she got out of bed and dressed very quietly, afraid that she would wake us."

As in past years, we celebrated that New Year with great merry-making. The living room and kitchen were full of all kinds of good cooking smells. Mother and Mrs. Chen would give me the first taste of each dish as soon as it was finished. In the evenings, just before I went to bed, I would turn up the oil lamp and carefully take out my new red padded coat and trousers, the embroidered satin shoes and the new kerchief that I would wear on New Year's Day and look at them over and over. I could not get to sleep immediately after going to bed. From all around the pond and the mountainside came the sound of firecrackers mingled with the beating of drums and gongs. I was so happy that my heart would race, and I wished that New Year's Eve had already come.

On the last night of the old year a pair of red candles with the "double happiness" characters on them burned brightly on the long table against the living room wall. Narcissus, winter plum blossoms, and other potted flowers stood on the tea tables on either side. Mother had wrapped inch-wide strips of gold-splashed red paper around the flower stems. A fire burned brightly in the charcoal brazier on the floor so the room would be warm enough that the flowers could give forth their delicate fragrance. Everything inside the house looked bright and new—the table cloth, the cushion covers on the chairs, the door curtains, the bowls and plates, the bone chopsticks, and the candy boxes. Outside, spring couplets from poems had been painted on red-and-gold paper and pasted on the kitchen doors and the gate. Everything was so bright it was dazzling. For New Year's Eve dinner, we had air-dried chicken, salted duck, fish, cured meats, and an abundance of fresh vegetables and fruit of all kinds to make up for what had been lacking in the old year and in the hope that the coming year would be prosperous. All words with unfortunate meanings had to be changed. Some foods were given new names suggesting fortune and prosperity; for instance, red pepper was called "number one scholar," red chicken eggs were called "silver eggs," and sliced celery was called "inch gold candy." People were careful to use only auspicious and positive words in the hope that the coming year would bring wealth and comfort for all. After dinner, I put on my new clothes, Father and Mother gave me my New Year's gifts of money wrapped in red paper along with many congratulations and good wishes. Finally, we sat down near the brazier, watched the flames of the red candles, and waited eagerly to see the old year out and the new year in. The warm, calm light of the red candles called up many beautiful, pleasant daydreams for me. It was a long wait until midnight, when the New Year came, but then the deafening sounds of the firecrackers, drums, and gongs filled the sky. I suddenly became a year older.* How happy I felt, how very different, and how important!

Only a few days after the new year began came the Lantern Festival. Colorful lanterns made of paper and silk, in various shapes, were on display; some performers walked on stilts and some danced inside dragon boats. Others danced the lion dance, for luck and prosperity. So many companies of performers came and went one after another throughout the first two weeks of the new year that I could not see them all. Ancient Nanjing, sleepy most of the year, had awakened and turned into a lively, gay, interesting city. After we had eaten the traditional sweetened balls of rice flour on the first full moon of the new year the holiday mood gradually died away and life returned to its usual pattern. The things we had brought out for the end of the year were all wrapped up and put away to be used again the following year.

Between the time I returned home and the middle of February, Mother forced herself to get up and be active every day because she wanted Father and me to be happy. But after the holidays were over, she could not keep going any longer. She had a fever

---

*"I suddenly became a year older." The custom of adding a year to one's age at New Year's is now rare, except in rural areas. During the period described here, children were said to be one year old when they were born. They would be given another year at Spring Festival and still another on their real birthday. So a three-year-old could actually be one.

that lasted the whole spring and she almost stopped eating. She was so weak that she spent every day in bed and talked very little. By summer she was even worse. Father called in both Chinese and Western doctors but they shook their heads and said there was little hope of saving her. Grandmother hurried to us from Wuhu to prepare for her death. The house became unusually quiet. Grandmother, Father, and Mrs. Chen all spoke in murmurs and whispers and tiptoed around the house. Even my puppy, who always slept in the corner with his head on his paws, only wagged his tail listlessly when we went by. The silence would be broken only by the sound of Mother's moans when she was awake.

Father and I could not believe that she was actually dying. He kept bringing doctors in to see and treat her, trying to find a cure, hoping he could save her. This hope was only a slight comfort in the midst of a situation where no hope was possible. Mother was already beyond human help. Then, early one August morning, Mother closed her eyes and never woke again.

The coming of death, like the withering of flowers and the fall of the leaves in autumn, is part of nature. Death would not matter so much were it not that the person who is dying is sad to leave loved ones behind, and that the ones left behind cherish and mourn those who are gone. These are the reasons for our grief.

Mother died peacefully, but in the final seconds before she left us it seemed that she could not let go entirely. Two crystal tears, as bright as pearls, ran down her pale, thin face. Grandmother, sobbing, tried to gently press down Mother's eyelids,* and said, "Dear daughter, close your eyes and go in peace. Don't worry about Baogu—I promise you that we'll bring her up. Go now in peace …"

"No, no! You cannot go! Wait a while, please wait …" I suddenly heard the sound of harsh weeping that rose above all the other sobbing and knew it was Father.

I think Mother heard Father weeping. Her lips quivered once and her eyes closed. Peace filled her face. No sound from the world of the living would ever disturb her again.

After that came the black-lacquered coffin, the monotonous, heavy thuds from the living room as the workmen nailed down

---

*" … press down Mother's eyelids." It was believed that dying with one's eyes open was a sign that the person was not at peace. This is why the grandmother tried to reassure Baogu's mother.

the lid, the mournful music played continuously by the hired funeral musicians under their mat lean-to near the gate as guests came to pay their respects, and the large waist-length photograph of Mother hanging high on the white curtain behind the coffin. She seemed to be watching the two white candles on the table, and she looked as if she were about to smile. In my white mourning garments and coarse hemp shoes, I knelt by the coffin and bowed my head to the ground in response to the kowtows of the mourners who had come to honor her. The sounds of grief rose and fell in the house. Every morning when I woke up, I thought Mother was still asleep in her room, and it was only when I turned over and saw my mourning garments and hemp shoes that I remembered that she was not in bed, but in that cold, black coffin. Those thick, black boards separated her from us forever.

The following month, her body was taken back to Wuhu, where she would sleep eternally with Father's ancestors under some ancient pines on a hill of reddish-brown earth.

From then on it was only in my memory and in my dreams that I could see my mother, see her beautiful, lovable, serene yet pensive face, and see those two crystal tears like drops of the morning dew on the petals of a white waterlily. Even today, they still glisten faintly before my eyes.

Chapter 9

THE sun rose every morning from behind the hill as it always had. The pond was the same turquoise blue and the waves rippled as gently as they always had. The willows on the embankment swayed gently in the breeze as they had always swayed. The water ran down the mountainside as it had always run. The magpies sat in the treetops and sang as they had always sung. The slender pomegranate tree in our courtyard had put forth fiery blossoms that did not bear fruit, as it always had. Nothing had changed except my destiny. People said that since I had lost Mother my destiny had become a luckless one.

Our neighbors no longer waved and called gaily to me when they saw me walking by. They would all look silently at me in my white mourning clothes, and I could see the compassion on their faces.

Aunt Fang would wait until she thought I was out of earshot and then sigh and whisper with Mrs. Chen. "That poor little girl —she's so young to have lost her mother! I wonder if she realizes how our hearts ache for her."

"She doesn't realize it yet, but her father is bound to marry again. Stepmothers never feel the same as real mothers do. Also, the coming of a stepmother will mean that her father will change. When that day comes, it'll be difficult for her."

After Mother's burial in Wuhu, her mother drew me aside as we were about to leave. Though in tears herself, she tried to comfort me and tell me what to do. "My poor child, your mother is gone and things will never be the same. I live too far away to take care of you. Remember to behave yourself always and be careful that your stepmother doesn't take advantage of you. When you get back to Nanjing, you must gather together your mother's fur coats and clothes, her jewelry and ornaments. If you fail to take them now, you'll never see them once your father remarries."

I heard her words and thought I understood them, but actually I did not. I felt sad and vaguely anxious. Grandmother's talk about Mother's jewelry and fur coats did not make me anxious, but her talk of Father remarrying did. My father's mother, however, never mentioned these things. After the funeral she came to live with us and take care of us for a while. Father treated me better and with more affection than when Mother was alive. Every morning on his way to the office, he would take me with him in the rickshaw and would go out of his way to take me to school first. In the afternoons he would pick me up. When he got home, he would not go out again. Instead, he would often sit alone in the living room with his head in his hands and think sad thoughts. Sometimes Grandmother would urge him, "Go for a walk and get some fresh air. Find some friends to talk with. You'll ruin your health, staying at home mourning."

Father would shake his head and sigh. "I feel so much remorse about Xiao Baogu's mother. She stood by me during all the hard years, but then, when life got easier, she never even had a chance to enjoy it, and left me behind."

"You mustn't reproach yourself. It was her own destiny that she had to die young and leave all of us behind." Tears came to Grandmother's eyes and her voice was full of sadness. "All you must do is see that Baogu is brought up properly, and you will have carried out your duty."

"I have no plans to marry again. I will live this way all my life. This will do."

"Let what comes come. You have many years ahead of you. Time changes everything." Grandmother drew slowly on her water-pipe. "Men need wives and homes. You should have someone to care for you. This is only natural. Also, Baogu is still so young.... When the time comes, things will look very different."

Father shook his head but said nothing. Grandmother silently smoked her pipe, and the anxiety I had been feeling seemed to fade away.

Grandmother, Father and I lived together very comfortably and the memory of Mother gradually faded. But there were mornings when I got up and suddenly realized my great loss. I would wander around the house and courtyard in confusion and then go back to bed, run my hands through my hair, and cry. When they asked me why I cried, I could not give a reason. But after I had cried for a while, I would be all right again.

As time went on, we spoke of Mother less and less. One afternoon, Father came home and saw that the two pots of orchids on the tea table had bloomed. At first he was pleased, but when he looked at them more closely and saw that one was completely white, he became very upset. He took the plant out to the backyard and ordered us never to bring it into the house again. That evening he talked with Grandmother for a long time. He said that one of the prescriptions given to Mother had called for white orchids to be taken with the medicine and that he had looked everywhere for one but had not been able to find one. "Now, when she's already dead, it blooms! Look at it, with its white heart! What use is it now? Seeing it only makes me feel worse!"

"You know that Dr. Li is a charlatan," said Grandmother. She was trying to console him, but her voice too was angry. "Every single one of his prescriptions included one or two strange ingredients that we couldn't find. The day before she died, he was assuring us he could cure her. Even if we could have found white orchid, it wouldn't have done any good."

"I know he was a cheat, but I would always have regretted it if we hadn't kept on trying to the very end."

After that life went on quietly. At the end of the year, we moved to a two-story house near the city wall. The rooms were larger and it was livelier there than in our former house. The back gate faced the city wall across the road. There was a large public cemetery at the foot of the wall. In the spring a constant stream of people came to see peach blossoms in the orchards half a li away and to burn paper money on the graves according to custom. After school, I liked to climb onto the wall to fly my kite. From the battlements, I could see Mrs. Chen washing clothes by our back gate. Sometimes I played at the cemetery with other children. When I came home I often found the living room full of guests whose talk and laughter pervaded the house and drowned out the memory of my mother's voice, image, and smile.

Several times I heard guests joke that they were eager to drink a cup of wedding wine soon and would like to be matchmakers for Father. I also saw photographs of unfamiliar women on Father's desk, and more photographs arrived constantly. The women in them all looked to be between seventeen and twenty-one. Some were standing and some were sitting, but in front of each were pots of flowers. Although they did not look alike, they all had one thing in common—their expression. They all had their lips pursed and seemed to be smiling, without smiling, and their eyes seemed to be looking without seeing. They all looked uncomfortable and shy. Although the photographs held no interest for me, Father and Grandmother would study and compare and discuss each one. Sometimes they would go to the market or theatre at an appointed time to meet the girl and her mother. The old anxiety, which I had almost forgotten, overtook me again.

Grandmother often told me that the sooner Father brought home a new wife, the sooner there would be someone to look after us. I could not understand why we should have a stranger move in when we were living so happily. However, Grandmother's wish soon came true. Father picked out a new wife from among the women in the photographs. I heard them say that she was a little over twenty and that she came from Wuhu, had had a few years of schooling, and could read and write. An auspicious day was chosen for the wedding and everyone in the house immediately got very busy, buying golden and silver ornaments and jewelry, silk and satin as betrothal presents. Tailors were brought in to make wedding clothes. I heard Grandmother say that Father had chosen her partly because their divinations were favorable and auspices matched and partly because she was a little older than the others and would take better care of me. Grandmother said that once the wedding took place she would be able to go back to Wuhu with a peaceful heart.

Father's new bride moved into our home a short time later. The house was even more festive that day than on New Year's. Red candles burned brightly in the living room. A red wedding hanging with huge "double happiness" characters hung high on the wall facing the door, and the room was festooned with red silk lanterns. Relatives and friends drank wine and crowded around tables laden with food. The living room rang with uproarious talk, laughter, jokes, congratulations, and the popping of firecrackers. The fragrance of the food was overpowered by the smell of cigarettes and the reek of firecrackers, which lingered in the house and drifted outside.

Our gate was crowded with neighbors who had come to see the excitement. A band of musicians, wearing red and green silk garments, squeezed through the crowd blowing trumpets and beating gongs. Behind them came the bride's red-embroidered sedan chair.

A few minutes later, Father, wearing a long, dark-blue robe and a short black jacket, both of satin brocade, and his bride, dressed in a scarlet coat and skirt, also of satin brocade, and with a red silk scarf on her head, knelt before the portraits of our ancestors and bowed their heads to the floor. I felt very confused and strange. Because everyone else was smiling, I too wanted to smile. I was disappointed that Father was so happy, but then I remembered that Grandmother had advised me that morning when I got up that the wedding was a happy occasion and that I must appear happy and gay. I wanted obey her, but my feelings would not follow my will. I had not thought about Mother for a long time, but that day I could not put her out of my mind. I waited until Father and the bride had completed the wedding rituals of worshipping heaven, earth, the gods, and the ancestors, and then bowing, first to Grandmother, then to each other, and finally to the guests. Then the crowd followed them to their bridal chamber. I started creeping up the stairs towards my room. After a few steps I stopped, held onto the wooden rail, and looked back to see if anyone was following me. There was no one. No one was paying any attention to me. Not even Grandmother or Mrs. Chen had noticed that I was gone. Only my puppy came with me. He followed at my heels, sat down by my bed, and wagged his tail at me. Laughter kept rising from the bridal chamber. For the first time since Mother had died, I felt neglected. And the loneliness I felt that day has, unfortunately, never left me.

I cannot remember now exactly how the changes came about because they happened one by one, but I know that from that day on my life started to change until it was completely different.

Father and his new wife seemed to care for each other a great deal. She was as pretty as the matchmaker had said, with big eyes and fair skin. Although her nose was rather flat, her eyes made up for it. Her movements were rather languid and her voice was soft and polite. She was especially polite with me.

Grandmother and Father both asked me to call her "Mother." I thought I could learn to like her and tried many times to get close to her, but each time her cool politeness pushed me away. Gradually Father stopped taking me to school and bringing me home in the afternoons. Every day when he came home he would spend hours with her in their room. As long as Grandmother was with us I could sit and talk with her in the living room or upstairs in our room, but once she went back to Wuhu I would wander around upstairs and downstairs and from the back gate to the front gate alone, feeling lost. Nor did Mrs. Chen talk as much as she had in the past, when she used to come into the living room with her sewing and, sit with us. Now she always stayed in the kitchen and did not come out unless called. Even my puppy was less lively and no longer jumped around. Once my father's new wife had shown her dislike by pushing him aside a few times, he avoided her by hiding under the tables and chairs. The only time he showed his old liveliness was when he saw me.

Though Father seldom asked me how I was, I could tell from his voice and expression that he felt compassion and concern for me. I thought that he probably still loved me in his heart, even though he was not as affectionate as he used to be. Twice when he came home from work and saw me sitting alone in the living room, he said, "Why aren't you out playing? Why are you sitting here alone thinking?" Hearing him ask me this made me unhappy. I thought, "Why are you asking me this? Don't you know why already?"

"What's wrong?" He felt my forehead. "Are you feeling ill?"

I shook my head.

Father took out a silver coin. "Go outside and play. Here, take this and buy something to eat. Children should always be happy and cheerful—that's what makes people like you. Go on—don't sit here moping." Then he lifted the curtain and went into their room.

I remained in the living room holding the coin for a while. I hoped that he would come out again, or that I could perhaps go in and sit next to him the way I used to. That would have made me happy even if he had not spoken to me. I stood there looking at the door but the curtain did not move. And in my heart I knew that Father would stay in there until dinner time. I turned and ran upstairs.

Though my stepmother was always very polite to me, whenever she talked about me with others she would wave both hands quickly as if waving away some misfortune or disaster. With a faint smile, she would say, "I'm always polite and formal with her. I don't want to discipline her—I leave everything in her father's hands. If she turns out well, all right, and if she turns out badly, that's all right too. I won't be to blame."

I realized that she not only did not care for me, but actively disliked me and considered me a nuisance. Like most children I could not analyse things, but I was very sensitive to other people's attitudes towards me. Sometimes children's perceptions are more acute than adults'. I realized she did not like me within days of her moving into the house. So when I later heard her talking with others, and saw her expression when she waved her hands and spoke of me, it only confirmed this realization. She disliked not only me but everyone, except perhaps Father, who had had anything to do with Mother. Mrs. Chen was soon discharged.

Usually my stepmother had little to say to me. In the mornings when I started for school, I would go out to the courtyard and call to her from outside her window, "Stepmother, I'm off to school."

"Oh, you're off."

In the afternoon when I got back I would call, "Stepmother, I'm home again."

"Oh, you're back," would come her cool, distant voice from behind the window.

On the surface she seemed to be treating me the way she said she was—she never interfered with me, never said a harsh word to me, and never criticized me, no matter what I did. It was always Father who talked to me. At such times she would stand quietly to one side as if it were no concern of hers. Gradually, however, I noticed that, whenever I said or did anything wrong during the day, Father would learn about it as soon as he returned in the evening—and also that these deeds and words that were being passed on indirectly seemed to get magnified many times, as though under a microscope, by the time they reached Father's ears. I also noticed that the concern and compassion Father used to show me had disappeared. Now when he saw me, his expression was often distant, as if he was angry with me. And when he looked at me that way, it made me uneasy and I would stop enjoying myself, even if I had been playing happily.

One time, when two women tailors were at the house making summer and autumn clothes for my stepmother, she was kind enough to have them also make me two sets of flowered-cotton long underwear. When they were finished I tried them on. They were so long and wide that they made me look like a balloon lantern, so I asked the tailors to make them smaller. My stepmother heard me. As usual, she said nothing at first, but just looked at me disapprovingly. Then she waved her hands in her negative gesture and said, "If you have them made smaller and they don't fit, it's no concern of mine, or of the tailor's. It'll be your own fault." That night, when we were halfway through dinner, Father suddenly seemed to remember something. "Baogu, you're still young," he said. "You must learn simplicity, and not try to be fashionable. Fashion is for adults. Why should you want to look pretty at your age? What does it matter if we have your clothes made a bit too big for you? After all, you're still growing. Do you think I can afford to have new clothes made for you every year?"

I was just about to eat a mouthful of food when Father said this. It upset me. I wanted to explain, but did not know what to say. Besides, since my stepmother was sitting there looking indifferent but also a bit self-righteous, I felt even more upset by the injustice. Tears filled my eyes in spite of myself.

"Now what's the matter?" Father frowned. He slammed his chopsticks down on the table and said in a loud voice, "Now I understand why no one dares to say anything to you. All I was trying to do was give you some good advice, and look at you! What's next? What do you want us to do—make a little shrine and feed you and bow down to you like a little ancestor?"

"It's all right. Come on, eat your food. Don't get so angry with her," my stepmother told Father. She put a tasty morsel of food in Father's rice bowl. "Eat it while it's hot. Cold food isn't good for you and will give you indigestion."

"She really is naughty," Father muttered, picking up his chopsticks. But I had lost my appetite. I put down my bowl and chopsticks and fled upstairs. Halfway up, I heard Father say, "The older she gets the stranger and more difficult she becomes. I never realized it before, but now I see that her personality has become quite disagreeable."

Sometimes my sense of injustice was so great that I wanted to answer Father back, but I never did. I do not know whether it was out of fear or because of how I had been brought up, always being told, "When those older than you speak, they must be heeded, right or wrong, and with no answering back." Although I had never acted too submissive with Mother, I couldn't answer Father back no matter how much I wanted to. I always swallowed my words. But at such moments, I felt very depressed and hated even being alive. I would ask myself, "Why is she always against me? Why does she dislike me so much and why is everyone else starting to dislike me? Why has fate done this to me?" I thought and thought but could not understand it. And when, at such times, I heard Father and his wife talking and laughing together downstairs, I would feel even more as if I had no one on earth to depend on.

Whichever way my thoughts turned, they always returned to the word "strange." I remembered the stories of demons and strange creatures that Grandmother used to tell me on summer nights as we sat on the porch in our old home, cooling off under the moonlight. I remembered them all. But now I was no longer afraid of them. Instead, I felt that, compared to people, those demons and strange creatures were probably kinder and more reasonable, more generous and more capable than most humans. I wished I could become friends with them, and that they would come and help me. I also wished that Mother would appear one night in a dream, so those two cold-hearted people downstairs would not dare oppress or mistreat me again. As I thought about these things, I began to feel happier. I forgot my troubles and immersed myself in an imaginary world.

Chapter 10

I was turning into a strange and troublesome little girl whom no one liked.

Instead of getting better, my faults seemed to grow worse each day. Now, when I look back, I think that Father's anger with me was not totally unjustified. But how could he not be aware that I felt insecure and unhappy? I often thought about how I could be better and more likeable, so he would not be angry with and distant towards me. I wished I could be happy and gay like other children. But I felt disliked, rejected, like a victim of fate, and these feelings were like a dark grey curtain, separating me from all the happiness and joy I should have had as a child. Whenever Father scolded me, his wife would stand beside him, anxious that his anger might damage his health—as if he were the only one with feelings. She would take his arm and try to calm him, saying, "Why let yourself get angry with her again? Your health is too important. Come into our room and rest a bit. You know her too well to get so annoyed with her so often." She would almost hiss the words "she" and "her."

However, if Father listened to her and did not lose his temper and treated me more kindly, her face would cloud over. If I was around when she was chatting with others, she would go out of her way to say things that seemed to be aimed at me. "Since girls always marry and become part of another family, teaching them to read and write a little is enough. Giving them any more education would be like making a gift to people outside the family, a waste. What good is that? One daughter in this family is enough. We could not afford the dowry if we had another daughter. I want a son. If I had a girl, I'd certainly give her to another family to raise. I wouldn't keep her.

"Girls shouldn't expect much from their own families in the way of food and clothes. They should wait until they've grown up and married and living in their mother-in-law's home to wear good clothes. That is really good fortune. It is as the proverb says, 'A girl without property can still hope to marry well, but a woman who marries badly will never have anything.' When I was still at home, I never asked for anything, but now that I am here I have fine clothes and jewelry to wear." And she waved her hands so that the gold and jade on her fingers and wrists glittered.

I have never been able to understand why she used to say such things when I was around. Perhaps she wanted to remind me that I was one of those "worthless girls" she spoke of. But how strange, because had she not once been a girl like me? Perhaps she thought I was like her and would demand my mother's jewels and ornaments, all of which she was now wearing. Perhaps she thought I was like her and only interested in Mother's little silver jewelry box, which also held the savings bonds Mother had bought to pay for my schooling. Stepmother, you were wrong. How could all the wealth in the world compare with a kind heart? If Father and you had said one loving word or shown any concern for me, it would have meant much more to me than all those useless ornaments. How could I be hurt by things or by not having things? What hurt me most were those cold days when no one loved me.

Even if I really was what they called me, a strange and difficult girl, I was barely nine years old. How could I stand up to her, a grownup? My stepmother felt no affection for me; I did not resent her. Affection cannot be forced into existence just because people are related. But she treated me like an opponent. I was openly rejected, baited, pushed around and ridiculed—even now, the memory of those days makes my heart freeze.

When I was at my most despairing, I would feel hatred. I hated everything, hated Father, and hated myself. But once I felt calmer, my rage would turn into self-criticism and remorse, and these were harder to bear than my rage. I wished I could run to Father and beg his forgiveness, because no matter how badly he treated me, I was helpless and had no place else to go. So I still turned to him, and even, once or twice, to my stepmother when she treated me a little better because she and Father had had a quarrel.

Once it was about his age. Though Father was only thirty, my stepmother liked to tease him about his age. "A man of your age, still leaving things around!" She would say. Or, "At your advanced age, your memory can't possibly be as good as mine."

At first, Father just laughed when he heard her talk that way, but later it annoyed him. One time, he snapped, "At my advanced age! When the matchmaker talked over our marriage, I didn't try to hide my age." Word followed word, and they ended up not speaking to each other for three days. When they had to say something, I would carry the message. Not only did Father show me more affection during those three days, even my stepmother treated me differently. When I came home from school she would call me into her room and ask me to sit down. She said that if Father really was going to go on acting like that, she would move away and live by herself. With tears in her eyes, she told me she would take me with her if I wished, and that we would leave Father to live in peace and comfort all alone. Though I did not say I would leave Father and go to live with her, and did not sympathize with her side of their quarrel, I forgot all her coldness to me when I saw her weeping and treating me more kindly. I treated her with affection and hoped that Father would not go on as he was—but, then, as soon as she and Father made up, they both turned against me again.

It was as if I were a tiny blade of grass by the roadside, unnoticed, unimportant, and at the mercy of the wind and rain. Perhaps I was even less fortunate than that blade of grass, because I was not wanted in my own home. To Father, I was nothing but a problem, a difficulty that had to be dealt with sooner or later. One day shortly before New Year's Father asked me gently whether I would like to go to a girls' boarding school in the northern section of Nanjing. "At New Year's, you'll be a year older. You're no longer a little girl—before you know it, you'll be all grown-up. It will do you no good to go on this way. For the past six months, your new mother and I have done everything we can for you. I think it would be good for you to have a change and to live somewhere else for a while. Boarding school will improve your behavior, which will be good for you."

I made no reply, but hung my head and picked at the corner of my jacket. He said coaxingly, "The school isn't that far away. You can come home every month for a visit. Won't that be almost like living here? What do you think? I'll find out about the regulations and when the school begins. Your new mother says she'll have some clothes made for you and will help you get ready to go there."

I did not need any time to think. I knew that Father had already decided and that I had to obey. I even felt glad because the school was the same one my mother had attended when she was in her teens. When my aunt visited us, they had taken me to see it. Mother had laughed and said that when I was older she would send me there, because she wanted me to go to the same school where she had lived, played and studied. My only fear was that Father would change his plans, because he had begun changing mind easily since his remarriage. My fear was justified. A few days after New Year's, he summoned me and said, "If you were not such a bother, it'd be all right to let you attend day school nearby. After all, for you, going to school is only a stopgap. All you need is to be able to read and write a little—no one expects you to become a real scholar who could earn money and support us like·a son. But right now, what you need most is to learn how to behave. I have made inquiries, but none of the schools here are strict enough. Also, they cost too much and won't take you as a boarder until you are sixteen. I think we should send you to your grandmother. Your new mother says that there is a foreign convent near there, with the strictest regulations. It's famous for its discipline, and it also takes little girls, ten or younger, as boarders. This is exactly what I've been looking for. I've written a special-delivery letter to your grandfather, asking him to come and take you there.

"Then, too, during monthly holidays, you can go to your grandparents', and for summer and winter vacations you can come home. How does that sound?" He sounded very matter-of-fact. "Why are you frowning and looking so unhappy? When your elders talk with you, it goes without saying that you must listen cheerfully. What's wrong? You'll not lack food or clothes. We're willing to spend money on your education. So what do you have to complain about? You're no longer a baby. You're old enough to understand that all of this is for your own good. Now go and think it over. If I've forgotten anything, ask your new mother to buy it for you." And he waved his hand to dismiss me.

While Father and I had been talking, my stepmother had remained seated near the brazier, poking at the charcoal with the fire tongs but not saying a word.

During the next few days, she came to my room several times and looked through my boxes. She told me I did not have enough clothes and said she would have a tailor make me two sets of underwear and two suits, one lined and one unlined. She also bought me several kerchiefs and pairs of socks, and had a sewing woman make six pairs of grey cloth shoes for me. When she came upstairs, she would never sit down. She would just stand there for a while and then go back downstairs.

My feelings kept changing. I was happy to go back to my

grandparents' but the idea of being sent to a foreign convent so I would learn to behave frightened and upset me. However, there was no way to avoid my fate, because Father had made up his mind. If I protested, it would only displease and anger him.

My stepmother was quick to prepare everything I would need. Grandfather arrived as soon as Lantern Festival had ended. He stayed only two days. On the third morning, as light snow was falling, he and I began our journey back to Wuhu. Father and his wife were still in bed when we were ready to leave. I went to their room. My heart was sad and aching. When Father heard my footsteps, he pulled back the bed curtain, wrapped himself in his robe, and sat up to talk with me. My stepmother kept her face turned to the wall. Father asked me if it was snowing, and whether my clothes were warm enough. Then he gestured for me to come closer and, taking my hand in his, he patted me on the head. He told me to obey the teachers and nuns, to strive to be good so I would become gentler and better-behaved, and to write often so he and my stepmother would not worry. I nodded as he spoke. "Good. Now go with Grandfather like a good girl, and I'll come and bring you home next summer."

As I reached the door, I remembered something I should have done. I hurried back to the bed. My eyes were blurred with tears. I tried to wipe them away with my hand. I said, "Stepmother, I'm going now ..."

She turned over and, raising her head slightly as if just waking up, said, "Oh, you're going. Have you had your breakfast? Have safe journey."

As Grandfather and I rode to the jetty in the rickshaw, I could not control my sadness and loneliness. Tears kept running down my cheeks, and the wind was cold in my nostrils. The fine snow blew in under the rickshaw hood and melted into my warm tears, turning them into cold pearls of water that dripped onto my coat and knees. I kept wiping my eyes, I used up two of my small handkerchiefs before we were even halfway to the jetty. Grandfather took out his big handkerchief and gave it to me. He warmed my left hand by holding it in his right and tried to get me to talk, but my throat was so swollen with grief and tears that I could not speak. I felt I could not bear to leave Father and wanted to turn back and see him again. Even though my warm home had become as cold as ice since he had married again, I still felt as if I was losing something I would miss.

Even now, I feel sad when I think back to that parting. This departure was so different from the first time I left home, to go to my aunt's. Then, Mother was at home to think about me and I could go back to that in security. This time however, I left my home for good. Though I later returned twice, it was only as a guest—an unwelcome guest.

From that day on my father's home was no longer mine.

Chapter 11

FATHER sent me to the Convent for the Cultivation of Holiness, where I spent the next four years. It was located atop Fengjia Hill, on the site of the old ancestral temple of the Feng family, about three miles outside Wuhu. The rest of my childhood and my early teens were a succession of mornings and evenings of sermons and prayers and days of lessons. It was at this school that I finished primary school.

When I look back now, those years seem to have gone by quickly, but when I was living there the days felt endless. We were almost completely cut off from the outside world. The school was so far from the city that a round trip took half a day, and the school rules were very strict. Except for Sundays, or when our parents came to see us once a month, or during church festivals when the nuns and teachers took us all down the mountain to the big church on Haojia Hill to religious services, we were isolated. The only outsiders we used to see were the peasants, who brought vegetables every morning, and the postman, who brought us our mail. Few others ever climbed the dirt path that led from the foot of the hill to the convent gate.

The school covered about a dozen acres and was surrounded on all sides by trees. It had only about seventy people there—four American [Episcopalian] nuns, five Chinese teachers, Deacon Tian and his family, about fifty students and some men and women gardeners, servants, and cooks. Most of the students came from families so poor that they could not support them, or were orphans cared for by the nuns. Another group, children of Chinese who had become converts, received half of their support from the church. The rest were from upper-middle-class families from around Wuhu. Their parents were anxious for their daughters to get some education, but did not want to send them to any of the other new girls' schools because their regulations were not strict enough. So they were sent to the convent to learn good conduct and how to read and write a little. The oldest among us were seventeen or eighteen, though there were two widows in their mid-twenties who were preparing to become nuns, and the youngest were seven.

Each of the younger students had a "big sister," an older girl appointed by Sister Aihua (Love China), the assistant headmistress, to keep an eye on us—to make sure that we were clean and neat, that we got up on time in the morning and went to bed on time at night, that we said our prayers, and that we did everything we were supposed to. We slept in wooden bunks like the upper and lower berths on a steamer. The big girls slept on top and the little girls slept underneath. Each bed had its own mosquito net of white homespun cotton stencilled with blue flowers. The beds faced each other in two long rows. Windows filled the rooms with fresh air and sunshine.

The school had three groups of buildings. On the west side of the hill, the dormitories for the students and for the Chinese teachers, the classrooms, and the dining hall formed a square compound of black-tiled, white-walled, Chinese-style buildings surrounding a courtyard. On the east side of the hill near the fruit orchard stood a two-story Western-style building with verandas upstairs and downstairs. It was the nuns' residence. A red brick chapel, where the nuns meditated and prayed, stood next to the residence. A few dozen yards down the hill from the chapel was a three-room, one-story, tile-roofed Chinese house where Deacon Tian lived with his wife and their two children. A gravel path ran from the nuns' house to the main gate, fifty yards down the hill. The path was lined with saplings about three feet high. To the right of the gate was the small wooden gatehouse where the gatekeeper, an old lady lived. We called her Grandmother Li.

I arrived at the convent in late February. The weather was still quite cold, and when Grandmother took me there we were both wearing thick padded clothes. The trees and shrubs on the hill were all bare and looked inky and dark in the distance. Only the grass in the school courtyards promised that spring would soon come.

Early every morning when it was barely light, Grandmother Li would come up the path carrying a lantern and ringing a bell until she reached the dormitories. She would hang the lantern in the doorway between our dormitory and the washroom and then would go on, still ringing the bell, until she came to the women teachers' bedroom. That bell marked the beginning of our day.

My big sister, Xing Shuangfeng (Double Phoenix Xing), slept in the bunk above me. She always got up before the bell and would put on her uniform and finish washing and combing her hair before coming to wake me up. My eyes barely open, I would wrap myself in my padded coat, and before I could put on both shoes she would pull me towards the washroom. The washroom had five long wooden washstands around which we all crowded to wash our faces and comb our hair by the light of the lantern. No one talked much. I washed in the warm water Shuangfeng had already used. She would stand behind me with a wooden comb and a hairbrush saturated with cold resin out of wood shavings and would brush back the short hairs from my forehead with one or two strokes, for she did not have time to comb it out. Then she would grab my hair, bind it tightly at the roots with black yarn and braid it into a queue that stuck out high on top of my head like a chicken's tail. The resin trickled down my temples and made me shiver, but I dared not say anything because all the big sisters were short-tempered in the mornings. After braiding my hair, Shuangfeng would tell me to run and put on my blue cotton uniform. Then she would pull me out into the corridor outside the dormitory rooms, where we would stand in line until the matron, Miss Shi, and the four women teachers came to lead us to the two classrooms that were opened into one big room for morning prayers.

The four nuns, wearing their long, full, blue cotton habits and starched white wimples, and holding their small gilt-edged Bibles, would sit on the platform with Deacon Tian waiting for us. We would tiptoe to our seats, the young ones in front and the older ones in the back. When we were all in our places, Sister Superior Lihua (Help China) would signal us to kneel for silent prayer. Then Deacon Tian would stand and read us a few Gospel verses in Chinese. Then Sister Qihua (Awaken China) would play the organ and we would all stand up and sing a hymn. The music and singing seemed to drive away what remained of our sleepiness. Morning prayer did not last as long as evening prayer because there was no sermon. After morning prayer was over, we all had to stand and wait until the nuns and Deacon Tian had left before we could leave. By this time, it would be full daylight.

In the dining room, the steaming-hot rice porridge would be waiting in two big wooden tubs. Eight or nine of us would hurry to each of the five square tables, where we would wait until Miss Shi had read the breakfast prayer and the teachers had all sat down at their table. Then we could sit down and start eating. At breakfast we always had porridge along with four little plates of salted vegetables and a dish of coarse salt. We were all so cold and hungry that early in the morning that the food tasted good. The porridge was always boiled until it was thick and filling, but we never had enough salted vegetables and would eat them all before finishing our first bowl of porridge. We would use the salt to flavor the porridge and would eat two or three bowlfuls. After breakfast, first our hands and feet and then our entire bodies would warm up. Then we would hurry back to make our beds and to sweep and clean the two big dormitory rooms, the washroom, and the latrine before Sister Aihua and Miss Shi arrived for morning inspection. After morning inspection, we had a few minutes of free time before the bell rang at eight forty-five for our first class.

We had our most important classes—the daily Bible lesson, English, and arithmetic—in the mornings. Chinese, history, handicrafts, music, world geography, and other subjects were taught every other afternoon. But Bible study was the most important subject. If our marks there were bad, we would not be promoted.

Deacon Tian taught all the Bible classes. I heard that he was also teaching the nuns Chinese. He was the one who took care of all the convent's dealings with the outside world, and all letters in Chinese, whether sent or received, passed through his hands. All our letters had to be read by him before they could be mailed or handed over to us.

Deacon Tian was over thirty and was from Hefei. He was short, thin, mild-mannered, and quiet. He never scolded us but he did have one eccentricity. Like a literature professor correcting essays, he would often write his own opinions at the end of students' letters from home, especially if they contained advice or reproof from parents to their daughters. We younger students did not mind this much, but it annoyed the older ones. They would not dare say so out loud, but grumbled about him behind his back. In my third year, when I experienced a disaster that I will shortly describe, Father wrote me a two-page letter full of advice and warnings that I should obey the rules and listen to the nuns and the teachers. "If you are not diligent in doing so this semester," he wrote, "I will wash my hands of you." Apparently Deacon Tian thought very highly of this letter, because at the end of it he wrote, in two rows of big red characters: "You should read this letter over and over and until you learn it by heart. Very important. Very important." And next to each character he drew big and little circles, as if he thought I would not pay enough attention.

We had one other male teacher at the convent. He was Mr. Shu, who taught Chinese and history. My classmates said that before the end of the Qing Dynasty he had passed the first of the imperial examinations and that his scholarship had been very good. He did not live at the school, but came up the hill every other day to teach.

Though Mrs. Tian lived on the convent grounds, she never came into the school except on Sunday mornings, when she would bring her little daughter for the morning service. She always sat on the back bench with Grandmother Li. She never said much, but she was very amiable. When the flat peaches, apricots, pears, loquats, cherries, and mulberries were ripe, the nuns would send us out to the orchard to pick fruit. When we passed Mrs. Tian's door she would always come out and greet us with a smile. On hot days she would often bring us a pot of cold tea. Mrs. Tian looked much older than her husband and her feet were bound. The older students said she was illiterate and that although she brought a Bible and hymn book to the Sunday services, she was as uneducated as Grandmother Li and could not read a word. All they could do was hold their books, follow us, murmur, and try to look correct. Because he wanted to live on the hill, Deacon Tian had brought her to the convent from the countryside a few years earlier. Both their son and daughter were lively and loveable. They were Sister Aihua's godchildren and their names were derived from hers. The boy was named Aiguang (Love Light). He was nine and was the only boy at the school. The girl, Xiao Aide (Little Love Virtue), was only three and was still at home with her mother.

Sister Aihua was the biggest and strongest of the nuns. She had a quick temper. Because she was the assistant superior and in charge of everything to do with the lives of the students, she had more contact with us than the other nuns. She also taught arithmetic. Every morning, when the second-period arithmetic class began, we all felt apprehensive, especially those of us who were not as good as the rest. I was the youngest in our class; Shuangfeng was the oldest. She was better than all the rest of us in Chinese, calligraphy, and handicrafts but very bad at arithmetic. Unfortunately, it was Sister Aihua's practice to write problems on the blackboard and to make us go up and solve them. Whenever she called on Shuangfeng, my big sister would turn pale. With her head drooping and her feet dragging, she would edge up to the platform. Even after the rest of us had finished and gone back to our seats, Shuangfeng would still be standing at the blackboard. Hesitantly, she would write down a number, then erase it and write down another one. Sister Aihua would stand there beside her, watching and waiting. We too would watch and wait, not making a sound. Eventually Sister Aihua would get impatient. First she would clap her hands several times. Then she would start pacing back and forth. Finally she would pick up the chalk and begin helping Shuangfeng to solve the problem. By this time, however, Shuangfeng was so flustered that she could not answer the easiest question. We were all upset, but could do nothing to help her. Sister Aihua would question and question; then, suddenly, she would lose her temper. Her face would turn red and she would grab Shuangfeng's braid and shake her, pushing her against the blackboard. In her English-accented Chinese, she would bark, "What's wrong with you? Your brain seems to be asleep! Is it dead?" Shuangfeng would wrap her arms around her head and run back to her seat. The rest of us, not daring to look at them, would keep our eyes glued to our books and pretend to be studying, but actually we could not concentrate at all. We could only hope that the bell would ring soon and that Sister Aihua would not call on any of the rest of us. We would restrain ourselves until the class ended and Sister Aihua, her textbook and our exercise books under her arm, left the classroom. Then we would all crowd around Shuangfeng. She would rub the red bruise on her forehead and blame herself, saying, "Whenever she calls on me I get so confused. I don't know why but as soon as I'm up at the blackboard it's as if I've been bewitched—I can't even add two and two."

Shuangfeng was one of the best big sisters. Though she was impatient and hurried in the mornings, the rest of the time she treated me very gently. When Grandmother was about to leave after bringing me to the convent, she had clasped her hands together and bowed and begged Shuangfeng to watch over me. Shuangfeng had studied the Chinese classics at home with a tutor, but because she had started school late, she had no foundation in English or arithmetic. So, she was still in the third year of elementary school even though she was sixteen or seventeen. She had to spend more time on her studies than most of us, and was not like the other big sisters who spent all their time making friends and teasing each other about their "special friends."

Almost every older girl had a special friend. They would go around in pairs with their arms around each other, and not even think about the little sisters they were supposed to be watching. Sometimes they would even make us wait on them. Shuangfeng never did that, but was always very responsible towards me. On Saturday afternoons, we were supposed to wash our clothes, even our own sheets, because the school believed we should learn to bear hardships and austerity. Shuangfeng would unobtrusively take the big heavy pieces from my tub and wash them herself, and would have me help her get water, wash the small things —handkerchiefs, socks, and underwear—and put them out in the sun. Though she had been baptized a Christian and the church was paying half of her expenses, she was not like the other converts, who were prejudiced against those of us who had not joined the church and told us we were unenlightened believers in "Buddhist superstition." Shuangfeng was so agreeable that she got along with everyone.

The mornings were so boring that most of us had to use all our self-discipline to get through them. Our third-period English teacher was Miss Shi. My friends said she had graduated from a Shanghai school famous for its English. Because she was the only teacher who could carry on an English conversation with the nuns, they held her in high esteem. Miss Shi was the oldest and tallest of the women teachers. She had a big, square, flat face and a few pockmarks around her mouth and nose. Though she looked strong, she had some health problems and was often ill. Her mother often brought her five-year-old grandson, Miss Shi's nephew, and stayed for ten days or two weeks. She would say she had come for a visit, but all the students said it was really to take care of Miss Shi. On some days, Miss Shi could not get out of bed to teach. She would have her mother bring our lessons to the classroom. Mrs. Shi would sit on a chair near the door and, if she heard one of the nuns coming, she would run to the stairs and call for her daughter to come down. Miss Shi would come into the classroom all out of breath, and her face would be as yellow as the leaves in autumn. She would make each of us in turn stand up and recite our English lesson, but would punish those who did not know it by making them stand up for a long time. When she was feeling better, she had a lot of energy, and she expended it all on us. We were all a little afraid of her. It was said that even her mother and her little nephew were afraid of her. Her nephew often had blue marks the size of fingertips on his face, and my schoolmates said his aunt pinched him when she was angry. They also said that Miss Shi's frequent absences from class were kept hidden from the nuns.

The afternoon classes were more interesting than the morning ones. The teachers who taught us handicrafts, and calisthenics were all young and friendly, and were recent graduates of middle school. Sister Qihua, the music teacher, was young and patient. She had been in China for only three years and had trouble speaking Chinese, but she had a big voice and when she taught the whole school she would play the organ and sing herself to lead us. Her white wimple, with its starched pleats, would sway from side to side in time with the music she was playing on the organ. Without realizing it, all of us surrounding her would begin swaying too, following her movements. Our voices would gradually become louder until they filled the classroom. Sister Qihua was very kind and liked to eat Chinese food, so every term, the teachers and students would write to Sister Superior Lihua inviting Sister Qihua to our dining room to eat with us.

When the afternoon classes were over, groups of students would take turns scrubbing the floors and washing the blackboards and desks under Sister Aihua's supervision. Others would clean up the exercise court and some would clean the nuns' chapel. Only students who had been baptized worked in the chapel. Before going in, they had to cover their heads with a soft piece of light blue cloth and change to soft light blue cloth shoes. When they finished working, the nuns always gave them a few pieces of candy as a reward.

Those of us who had no chores assigned to them would all go to the dispensary to see Sister Huihua (Benevolent China). She nursed us and gave us medicine when we were ill. We younger students had to give her all the fruit, candy, and snacks our families brought us. The food was kept in a cupboard and she would dole it out to us every day at this time. Sister Huihua had the gentlest disposition of all four nuns. She never raised her voice to us. It was cold on the hill and there was heat only once a week, when we had baths and the bathrooms were heated. We often had chilblains on our hands and feet. Sister Huihua would wash, dress, and bandage the younger students' chilblains herself. While she worked, she would say soothingly, "Ah, no cry, no cry." She would take out a big white handkerchief and wipe away our tears. Her manner was always kind and her words were more comforting than any candy or fruit. None of us were afraid of her. It seemed easy to cry in her presence, and we little ones often did.

By the time we finished our chores, it would be late afternoon, and time for dinner. If the weather was good, we and the teachers would all go outside after dinner and walk around the exercise court as dusk fell and the light faded. The birds would flit around the trees as if looking for the nests where they would spend the night. The rose-colored clouds on the horizon would deepen to crimson and then dim to purple. In the cool, clear evening air, the bell for evening prayers would sound far away.

The lamps on the walls of the two big classrooms would be lit and there would be candles burning on the platform. All of us, nuns, teachers, and students, would gather to sing hymns and listen to a sermon. The nuns and Deacon Tian took turns teaching us about Christianity. They often told us about miracles and other strange events. The deep darkness that covered the hill made us feel even more isolated and alone than we already were, and we showed more reverence than we did at morning prayers. Sister Superior Lihua and Deacon Tian would preach to us, saying, "The true God is most kind. Satan is vicious and wicked and constantly tries to tempt us. If any of you have told lies or said unkind things, now is the time you should kneel down and confess to the one true God and repent. If our hearts are reverent and sincere, God will forgive us our sins. Although Satan's strength is great, God's strength is greater. It is boundless. When the world comes to an end and the day of judgement arrives, those who have committed grave sins will not escape. They will be cast into hell to suffer torment. But those who are without sin will go up to Heaven and sit by the side of our Heavenly Father."

When I heard these things, I could not keep feeling empty and frightened because the very ideas of heaven and hell seemed incomprehensible and overwhelming. I dared not let my mind wander, but tried with my whole heart to pray, repent, and hope that Satan would not harm me. My only hope was that my sins would be forgiven and that I would not go to hell. But then the tranquil music and singing of the hymns would bring peace to my heart.

After evening prayers we had to prepare our lessons. In the long nights of winter and early spring, this period was short. The bell that signalled bed time rang at eight-thirty and the dormitory lamps were put out at nine, but we would not have quieted down completely and would still be running back and forth. However, soon the long, dark corridor would suddenly be illuminated by lantern light and we would hear footsteps coming nearer. All sounds in the sleeping rooms would stop immediately. The footsteps were those of Miss Shi, Grandmother Li, and one of the nuns, coming for night inspection. All the nuns except for Sister Superior Lihua, took turns coming each night. The nuns were most concerned about us younger students, who slept in the lower beds, and always had Grandmother Li shine her lantern on each of us in turn to make sure our quilts were tucked in around us and that our heads and faces were outside the bedding so we would not smother. Miss Shi took a special interest in the older students who slept in the upper beds. She would check to see if any of them had violated the rules and crept into their best friends' beds or if, before monthly or term examinations, they had hidden candles under their pillows or at the foot of the bed so they could study more. After the sound of footsteps and the flickering light of the lantern disappeared, muffled laughter and whispers would erupt again. The older students would squeeze into bed with their friends, and others who felt cold would take their quilts and sleep with others. Soon the laughter and whispering would die away. The only sounds would be the wind, the noise of the branches chattering in the darkness and the rattling of the windows. But these would quickly fade out of hearing as we all fell asleep.

Chapter 12

THE days in the Convent for the Cultivation of Holiness passed in a monotonous routine. Except for the changes in the seasons, when the flowers bloomed and the leaves fell, the fruit trees grew heavy in the winds and mists, the stars and the moon circled, the snow changed to rain, the birds flew away and then returned, everything seemed to remain the same.

Because I heard about them from morning to night in our classes, I became familiar with all the foreign names and places —St. Paul, St. John, Jerusalem, Sea of Galilee, Bethlehem—that had been unfamiliar and difficult to pronounce. Each week at Sunday School, the nuns would give us little brightly colored picture-cards printed with simple, easily-memorized stories from the Gospels. These cards stimulated our imaginations.

Of all our lessons, I liked history and Chinese literature best. Mr. Shu, who taught both subjects, was about sixty. He had seen much during his lifetime, and he was also disturbed by much. In our classes he would often sigh and tell us stories that were not in the textbooks. One day when we were studying the lesson about the Opium Wars, he closed the book, shook his head, gave a long deep sigh and said, "The world today is in disarray. You young people, do you realize how corrupt and inept the Qing Dynasty was ..." Then he began telling us how the British had begun illegally importing opium into our country, which caused more harm and suffering than any natural disaster and how, ever since the first Opium War, China had suffered insults and oppression from the foreign powers, and how our great national heritage had been destroyed. Then he went on to tell us what he had seen with his own eyes—how the soldiers of eight nations had invaded, captured, looted, and burned Beijing and killed many of its people during the Yi He Tuan movement (the Boxers)* in 1900.

---

*"Yi He Tuan movement." An anti-imperialist struggle waged by peasants and handicraftsmen in northern China in 1900.

"The sky above the city was red with flames and black with smoke. The foreign soldiers killed everyone and everything they saw—even women and children could not escape. I'm not sure you young people can even imagine what a calamity it was!"

As he talked, his voice became softer and softer, partly because he was so moved and partly because he was afraid other teachers would hear him. His voice became even sadder, and all seven of us in the class lowered our eyes and listened in silence. My nose stung from the tears I was trying to hold back. I was afraid that if I let them flow my classmates would laugh at me. Whenever Mr. Shu spoke of these events, I always thought how wonderful it would be if one day I could help my country and my people as the heroes of our history had.

When Mr. Shu was in a good mood in our Chinese class, he would teach us ancient poems by Du Fu or Li Bai. When he read them, it was as if he was singing—their rhythms and melodies would circle and soar and circle back again, and his head would weave from side to side in a way we found very funny. But even when he saw that we could not stifle our laughter, he would never scold us. After he finished teaching, he would hurriedly take up his bundle of books, which were wrapped in a kerchief that had once been white but was now yellow, and go down the hill. It was said that he lived in the city and that because his salary was so small he always walked both ways and was always in a hurry. He always wore a long gown of grey homespun cotton. Although it had patches of all sizes all over the elbows and cuffs, it was always starched and clean. As he walked down the gravel path he always held himself erect, as if balancing all his ambitions and pride on his head. His eyes always seemed focused on the sky, never the ground. His back, his walk, and the way his head moved when he recited the poems gave us many contradictory feelings about him. I felt sorry for him because he was old, and we all felt kindly towards him.

Besides Shuangfeng, I had one other schoolmate who was close to me. Her name was Qiao Xiulian (Graceful Lotus), and she slept in the lower bunk opposite mine. She was a year older than I and one grade ahead of me. We always sat at the same desk in the evenings when we prepared our lessons. She liked to draw and read storybooks in secret. I could not draw, but liked to write little essays and stories. I often read storybooks with her. When we had free time after our classes, we would play together and talk about things that were important to us. We would take our pencils, paper, and books and steal away to the school garden in front, or to the empty area in back where the clothes were dried, and find a quiet corner where we would sit on a couple of stones, open the books, and read together. Sometimes we would climb trees and hunt for colored birds' eggs. Sometimes she would busy herself drawing birds and insects and I would be busy writing my story, "Qing Er's Misfortunes," which I could never finish. Her exercise book was soon filled with amusing drawings of insects, while mine often remained half blank. It seemed as if I had many stories in me that I wanted to write, but I could never get past the beginning. I was determined, however, to finish this one. Qing Er (Little Green) was a little orphan of six or seven who had no one to care for her and was disliked by everyone. One moonless night, she was walking along a dark, deserted country road, far from any village. She was cold and hungry. Then, in the distance, she saw a light shining from a house with a thatched roof. She ran to the house and knocked at the door. Inside, an old woman was sitting by an oil lamp mending clothes. When she saw Qing Er, she felt sorry for her, and made her come in and sit down. Then the old woman made her some hot tea and cooked her some food—but once I had gotten this far it was as if I had used up all my imagination, and I did not know how to go on. This was probably because my mind was too immature, my experience too limited, my universe still too small. In those days, children's books were pitifully scarce; in fact, there were almost none. Besides, the school forbade us to read anything but our textbooks. Xiulian had received a few copies of a children's magazine and some storybooks from her brother in Shanghai at New Year's. We treated them like treasures and read them over and over again.

Shuangfeng was like an elder sister to me and kept an eye on me but Xiulian was my friend and playmate and confidante. Like Shuangfeng, she had a half scholarship from the church. Her grades were good, but she was stubborn and obstinate and liked to argue, even with Sister Aihua or Miss Shi. If she thought her punishment was unfair, she would always dispute it. Because of this, she was often punished and sent to the Repentance Room to ponder her sins. Her marks for conduct were often the lowest possible. She had no parents. Her only relative was her father's younger brother and his wife. Except for this aunt, who sometimes took her home for a few days during the monthly holiday, almost no one came to visit her. In this respect, I was more fortunate than she was. Every Sunday, except when it was too windy or a heavy rain had made the roads too muddy, Grandfather would walk the ten or fifteen *li* from the city to see me. He never arrived empty-handed, but always brought me a big bundle, wrapped in a kerchief, containing special foods Grandmother had cooked for me. There might be a big bowl of green and red peppers cooked with beans and meat, or fresh shrimp simmered in soy paste. These dishes were big enough that I could share them at dinner with everyone else at the table. Sometimes there would also be a small package of peanuts, flavored beans, brittle candy or other treats. Every monthly holiday, Grandfather would come and take me home for two or three days. Grandmother would always cook special foods for me. She said it was to make up to me for the bad food I had to eat all month long at the school. For the first two years, I was like the other students who had homes and could not wait for the monthly holiday to arrive. But sometimes, when my schoolmates received parcels from their mothers, or their mothers brought clothes, shoes, and socks to them when the seasons changed, or when I saw their mothers' love and concern for them, I would feel I was missing something. However, compared to my schoolmates who had no homes, I was much better off.

Although all of us who had homes waited eagerly for each monthly holiday, there were also several big festivals each year that we looked forward to. These holy days added excitement to the thin, monotonous routine of our lives and brought gaiety, laughter, and songs to the quiet courtyards. The holiday atmosphere was especially strong at Easter and Christmas. I still remember my first Easter at the school. The weather was just turning warm. Sister Qihua started teaching us Easter hymns two weeks ahead of time. The melodies were delightfully melodious and "Hallelujah, hallelujah," echoed throughout the courtyards all day long. We were all excited. The big girls all washed and ironed their best blue cotton uniforms well ahead of time. They prepared their handkerchiefs, shoes, socks, and even the ribbons they used to tie their braids and stored them in their boxes until Easter morning. On the night before Easter, after inspection, we were all so excited that we could not sleep. We talked and laughed and chattered for half the night about what would happen the next morning when we went to the Easter service at the church on Haojia Hill. When morning came, we were all up even before Grandmother Li arrived with her bell. The older girls, laughing and talking, took turns combing each other's hair and paid great attention to their appearance. They combed more ice-cold resin than usual into our hair. That morning, we did not have morning prayers because we were going to the church, and breakfast was served half an hour earlier. Since it was a feast day, the cook had prepared a special treat, two big iron pots full of fried-dumplings stuffed with vegetables. On any other day, we would all have been pushing each other aside to fill our bowls, but that morning none of us seemed able to swallow our food. Because we were afraid Miss Shi would scold us, we all forced ourselves to pick up our bowls and chopsticks and pretend to eat, but then we would put them back again. The two big iron pots remained full.

When we left the dining room, we hoped that the bell would soon sound for us to line up and go down the mountain to the church. Impatient at having to wait, we all wandered restlessly around the verandah. Suddenly we saw Sister Aihua, Miss Shi, and Grandmother Li hurrying towards us. They all looked very serious. Sister Aihua clapped her hands and told us all to go back to our bedrooms and to line up according to height because they had something important to tell us. When we were all standing in line, they came in and scrutinized each of us from head to foot. They checked to see that we were neat and clean, that our tunics came below our knees, that our sleeves covered our wrist bones, and that our trouser cuffs were below our ankles. Miss Shi showed a particular interest in the older girls' faces. Like a Chinese physician examining his patients' faces to study their color, she searched for any trace of rouge or powder and to see that their hair was combed back straight and tight. Two fourth-year students, one whose hair was a little loose behind her ears and another who had a few bangs on her forehead, were ordered to pin their hair back with bobby pins. A fifth-year student who had put a dot of white toothpaste over two little pimples near the corner of her mouth had to go wash her face clean with soap and hot water.

"You must remember at all times," Miss Shi warned us, "that you are not students at an ordinary school. You are students of the Convent for the Cultivation of Holiness, and you must live up to its standards at all times, especially outside the gates. When we get to the church you must be even more dignified than usual. We are going to a boys' school. You are forbidden to look around. Although I will be in the front pew and you will be behind me, I will see your every movement. Don't think I like having to tell you these things—it's all for your own good." As she spoke she looked around at Sister Aihua, who nodded her approval. When she finished, they clapped their hands and Grandmother Li rang the assembly bell. But the excitement we had all felt during the previous weeks had melted away in the wake of that inspection and Miss Shi's speech. Without a word we went to the front lawn of the school and lined up.

The young women teachers smiled as they nodded and greeted us. Although their blue cotton tunics and black cotton skirts were as old-fashioned as our uniforms, they were carefully pressed and the teachers looked neater than usual. Their hair was smooth and shining. Without realizing it, we all kept following Miss Shi and Sister Aihua with our eyes. Soon afterwards the other nuns came out of their residence. They all looked happy. Although Miss Shi had kept her face impassive when speaking with us and the women teachers, she broke into a wide smile when she saw the nuns, and walked all the way across the courtyard to greet them. It was as if the nuns' faces were a kind of drug that could make people smile. Some of the women teachers winked at each other and a few of the older students pursed their lips knowingly as they watched Miss Shi. Then the whistle blew. With Sister Aihua, Sister Qihua, and Miss Shi in the lead, Sister Lihua, Sister Huihua and Deacon Tian bringing up the rear, and the four women teachers walking two to each side of us, our little regiment marched through the big iron gates and down the hill.

The laughter and tears of teenage girls are like the wind and rain in the summer—they come easily, and just as easily go. Miss Shi and Sister Aihua had just done their best to suppress our gaiety, but as we walked along, as we met the cool wind of early spring and walked on the thawing yellow soil, as we heard the birds singing to each other from the tops of branches where yellow and green buds were starting to appear, and saw the water buffalo working in the fields, and the ducks—some with their heads underwater and their round, fat rumps exposed—calling to each other near still-melting layers of ice, we could not restrain our laughter.

"Be good now! Keep your eyes lowered and look at the path. Don't be wild. Don't laugh," commanded Miss Shi as she patrolled back and forth. But out there in the middle of the huge, natural world, her words were ineffective. As soon as she turned away, our smiles would break out again.

There were three or four hundred people in the beautiful,

light-filled church on Haojia Hill. We sat to the left of the altar and waited quietly. Suddenly the organ sounded and everyone stood up. Pastor Qin, who was also headmaster of the boys' school on Haojia Hill, came through a small door to the right of the altar. Behind him came a choir of thirty or forty boys. Like the pastor, they were wearing white surplices and singing, and when they appeared, we all opened our mouths and sang as well. The sound of our voices was high and clear. The lamps and the candles on the altar shone on the gold incense burner. White smoke rose from it and wound around and around, merging with the people and the animals in the tall, narrow, stained-glass windows and adding to the brilliance that dazzled us. Pastor Qin began to pray and preach. His voice was high, clear, and rhythmic, like those of Buddhist monks reading their scriptures in their temples or Taoist priests singing of the Way. He preached for more than an hour. By the time he was half-finished, we little ones, sitting in the front row, could hardly keep our eyes open. When our heads fell forward, Sister Aihua or Miss Shi, who were sitting at each end of the row, would nudge the student next to her. That student would nudge her neighbor, and so on, all down the row. With all our strength, we would force our eyes open, but a few minutes later they would close again, until the organ sounded and we all roused ourselves and stood up to sing.

Our walk back was different from the walk down. Our excitement had disappeared. The big girls looked dejected and walked with their heads drooping and their eyes on the ground. We little ones were tired from all the walking and from not having gotten enough sleep the night before, and hungry because we had not eaten enough at breakfast. We wanted only to get back to school as quickly as possible. Our lines broke up when we reached the school garden. After lunch, everyone seemed lethargic. We little ones obeyed the nun in charge and took our noon nap, but all the older students seemed restless. Some sat on their beds, pulled their mosquito netting low, and whispered, as they would for many days, about what had happened at the church. Some leaned back on their beds and let their minds wander, others leafed through books, and some did a little mending. The convent seemed more peaceful than usual, but there was an agitation underneath that could not be quieted, as if our former peace had been destroyed.

During my first two years at the school I did not understand the older girls' restlessness. I was too young. But in my third year,

I began to grow up and to understand and interpret earlier events differently. All at once, it seemed, I got bigger and taller. I outgrew all my clothes, shoes, and socks within the space of a few months. When I looked into the mirror every morning to comb my hair, it seemed as if I was seeing myself for the first time, and without realizing it I began to pay attention to my appearance, whether I was clean and neat, and whether my face was beautiful or plain. My thoughts and moods were not as simple as they used to be, and I liked to muse. Sometimes on Sunday afternoons I would take a book and go to a corner of the garden where I could sit alone and read, but after only a few pages I would put it down. Sometimes, through the half-open chapel windows I heard the nuns' melodious voices singing hymns, I would wonder why they had made the long journey from the other side of the world to China. Did they have families, friends, and relatives in their own country? Did they miss them? Were they happy? Twice when Sister Qihua came to teach us hymns, her eyes were red, as if she had been weeping. All my schoolmates guessed that perhaps Sister Superior Lihua had rebuked her. All of us, teachers and students alike, were afraid of Sister Lihua. I would think about Sister Huihua, so young, so pretty, so kind and agreeable, why had she "put aside worldly things" to become a nun? I would think about how life was like ... I could never say what. Sometimes I would suddenly feel sad, but I never knew why.

If, as sometimes happened, an elder brother or young uncle of another student came to visit on a Sunday or holiday, all of us except the student being visited, who would be chaperoned by Deacon Tian, would all be driven from the garden and classrooms to the back courtyard or dormitories by Sister Aihua and Miss Shi. They would clap their hands as if we were chickens and ducks. In the past, we had always felt that being shooed away was funny and as we ran we would clap our hands and laugh. But now it was different—I found it embarrassing and humiliating. Now, when we went to the church at Haojia Hill on holidays, I would feel Miss Shi's eyes fix on my face and then turn away. Her words, "Be decorous and dignified. Don't look around—" had sunk deep into me and held a different meaning than they had in the past. I could not hold my head up in the church. If I looked up and happened to meet the eyes of a boy student, his bold, searching gaze would seem strange and yet familiar to me. My heart would begin to pound and face would turn red and I would not know why. So I would hastily lower my eyes, feeling I had

done something wrong or "committed a sin" and was afraid that someone had seen me.

Another thing that haunted me during this period, when I was about to go into the fifth year, was whether Father would let me go on to middle school once I finished the sixth year. I had no idea; Father never mentioned it in his letters. Graduation was still too far away and I dared not write to ask, because if he said no now it would be harder to ask again later. Since I had left home, Father had invited me to go back to visit only twice, during the winter and summer vacations of my first year. I went back for twenty days each time. After that, he never sent for me. His home was neither warm nor welcoming, and I did not want to go back. My emotional ties to Father and my home seemed to dissolve a little more each day.

I had many problems on my mind. I could not solve them and had no one to confide in. But then, in the middle of my fifth year, after the end-of-term examinations, I experienced an unexpected misfortune, one that seemed to drop on me from the sky. It was an experience that bound me with invisible locks and chains during my final one and a half years at the convent. These chains were heavier than real ones. I felt them and everyone else saw them. No one spoke of them and no one ever gave me a chance to explain. It was a load I had to carry silently, every day, from morning till night.

Chapter 13

EVEN now, I cannot believe that it actually happened. While I was living through it, I felt as if my world had collapsed and the school had been shaken to its foundations, but now, as I look back, I realize that it was really no larger than a sesame seed.

I still remember the day it started, when everyone, teachers and classmates alike, suddenly abandoned me. It was the day after the winter end-of-term examinations and we were all feeling let down. After dinner we all went into the garden for our usual stroll. Suddenly I saw that all the students were milling around in pairs and trios and whispering among themselves. But as soon as I came near, they would stop talking and move away, as if avoiding me. I saw Xiulian leaning against a big tree and talking with Shuangfeng some distance away, but before I could reach them they too moved away from me. I walked around in the garden all by myself. It seemed to me that there was excitement on their faces and triumph in their eyes, and that they were looking at me with contempt. At evening prayers that night, Deacon Tian and the four nuns looked unusually serious. The evening sermon was omitted and Sister Superior knelt and led all of us in silent prayer. It might have been a funeral, the atmosphere was that somber. I knew something was very wrong, but had no idea what. By bedtime I could not stand it any longer. I went to Xiulian and asked her what had happened, but she shook her head and said she did not know. Then I asked Shuangfeng, but she also shook her head. I went to my grandparents' the next day for winter vacation and did not think about it any more.

It was only after New Year's when my report card arrived at my grandparents' home that I was again overcome by the feeling that something was being kept from me. At home, however, there was no suppressed excitement or contempt, but rather an atmosphere of silent concern. I still remember Grandfather's deep, long sigh after he read the letter and report from the school. He folded the letter and put it in his pocket, but silently handed me the report card. I read it from top to bottom. Everything looked all right at first—as usual, my course marks were near the top. My only C's were in handicrafts and English, but they were still passing grades. However, when I reached the space for conduct, I saw that they had given me a D, the lowest mark. And in the space for teachers' remarks there was just one word, "Expelled."

Expelled! Sent away from school! Was it because my conduct mark was a D, lower than that of any of my studies? I looked over at Grandfather, who was sitting across the table from me. I did not have the slightest idea how to even begin to explain.

I took the report card and went into the bedroom. My heart grew heavier and heavier. What seemed most important to me was not that the school had expelled me, but to know what I had done to deserve so harsh a punishment.

I knew that my marks for conduct had never been as good as my grades for my classes. Like Xiulian, I often received a C. Also, like most girls, I liked to play and laugh and make noise and could not be as respectful and serious as Miss Shi wanted us to be. I knew I often misbehaved, getting sleepy during sermons and quarrelling with my schoolmates. A few times, I had not been able to recite my English lesson and when we were all kept standing as punishment, I had laughed out loud and all the class had laughed with me. But these were things we all did. Some students always managed to get away with mistakes and mischief, but I never did, and was always punished, and was always frank about owning up to what I had done. Sometimes I was sent to the Repentance Room. If I felt I was being punished unjustly, I would be reluctant to go to the nuns and admit I had been wrong. Even after all the other students who had been punished had left and I had to go on sitting alone in that dark little room. I would not come out until one of the nuns, hoping that the devil in my heart had been driven out, came to let me go. This was what came of a stubborn disposition. I was punished a little more than the others and my life was more difficult, and the nuns and teachers had to spend more effort on me—but these could not be enough justification to expell me. And besides, I had gradually become less mischievous during the past year.

No matter how much I thought, I could not come up with a reason. How miserable I was! Even Grandmother seemed to be treating me coldly. No one would say much to me, and I did not know what to say to them. If I really had done something wrong, or if my grandparents had talked with me about it, perhaps I could have opened up and talked with them. But their silent rebukes and unhappy expressions were much harder to bear than words. And even when I wanted to ask about it, I could not bring myself to. My heart felt like lead and I was very anxious. I did not know what might happen next.

One evening when it was almost time for school to begin again, Grandmother came into the room as I was going to bed. She had her water-pipe, and after smoking in silence for a while she told me that Grandfather had gone to people who belonged to the church and asked them to appeal to Sister Superior, and she had agreed to let me return to school. But Grandmother also told me I would no longer be able to come home each month. She warned me that I would have to be extremely careful not to make any mistakes, or I would disgrace the family.

"I don't understand. What have I done?"

"How can you ask?" Grandmother looked at me searchingly, as if surprised I would even ask. "Don't talk about it. You are still too young to realize how careful you must be when it comes to boys. Just consider it over and done with. For young women, there are only two words, 'character' and 'reputation,' that cannot survive even the smallest misstep. Everything else is secondary. You thought it was just in fun, but you're too old for such mischief. You must be more careful. You're thirteen now—next year you'll be fourteen. In a few years, before you realize it, you'll be given in marriage. Do you think you're still a child?"

Though Grandmother's tone was light, her words were serious. She was a gentle, flexible person, but when it came to sex and relationships between men and women, she was very traditional and unyielding. I understood this, but did not understand what she meant when she talked about being careful around boys. I immediately began to wonder, and then a suspicion arose—had one of the boy students perhaps written me a letter that had been discovered by the school? There had been trouble recently in the two upper primary mission schools in Wuhu after a boy student wrote a secret letter to a girl student, asking her if they could become friends. It had been discovered and they had both been expelled, but a student strike had resulted and the story had spread throughout the city. As I thought about that and about how the teachers and students had whispered, and how grave the nuns and Deacon Tian had been, it all seemed to fit. I wondered and guessed, but I could not ask any more questions. Even if I had, Grandmother would probably not have answered.

My grandparents seemed content that the school was willing

to take me back, but I was not. I felt that having been expelled and then re-admitted through an appeal was a humiliation. I went back the day school opened, but I went unwillingly. My apprehension was justified—though neither the nuns nor the teachers said anything to me, they looked at me coldly. My schoolmates all seemed surprised to see me and to be wondering, "Wasn't she expelled? Why is she back?" Only Shuangfeng and Xiulian seemed happy to see me, but during the first few days they also seemed afraid that the others would gossip about them, and dared not spend too much time with me. I kept myself aloof. I went to class and always had my books with me, but I could not concentrate. I was confused and did not know what to do.

When the first monthly holiday came, all the students who lived in and around Wuhu went home except for Han Jindi and me. She was in the fourth year of lower primary. Her family had a bad name. It was said that when Jindi was growing up, her mother had taken in many poor girls, turned them into prostitutes, and lived off them. When Jindi got a little older, her mother gave up that business and mended her ways. She became a convert to the foreign church and sent Jindi to the convent school. I also heard that when Jindi was accepted, it was with the understanding that for the sake of her own reputation, she would not return home as long as she was a student there and that the school would take responsibility for her. Her mother had agreed to this. My schoolmates all knew about Jindi's background and had little to do with her.

There were very few students left. After dinner I saw Xiulian alone in the dormitory folding her clothes. I thought this was my opportunity and went over to her. She let me sit down on the bed next to her and we exchanged a few idle remarks. I looked around to make sure we were alone and then, hesitantly and in a low voice, brought up the episode that had been haunting me and which I still did not understand. She listened quietly as she continued folding her clothes. Finally I said, "Xiulian, please tell me—do you know why they expelled me?"

She gave me one quick, surprised glance and then looked away again, but she stopped folding her clothes and sat still. "Baowen, don't you know?" she murmured. Baowen, "Precious Learning," was my school name. It came from my home name, Baogu, "Precious Girl." She hesitated, looked to see if anyone was coming, and then almost whispered, "I'll tell you, but you mustn't tell anyone I did. The day after the examinations were over, late in the afternoon, someone found a letter on the lawn. It was addressed to one of the boy students at the school on Haojia Hill and it started out, 'To my older brother.'* It gave his name, and said another letter would be sent after the examinations were over. It was signed 'Precious younger sister.' Everyone saw it and knew about it. It couldn't be ignored because someone gave it to Miss Shi and she gave it to Sister Superior."

When Xiulian told me this, I was thunderstruck. I felt as if I had been bludgeoned. I wanted to cry out, "I didn't write it! I didn't write that letter!" But I was too afraid that the nuns would not listen. I kept my voice low, but it trembled a little as I said, "Xiulian, I didn't write that letter. Really I didn't."

How could I have written a letter to one of those boys? I had never had a chance to meet any of them. Also, ever since I had started to mature, everyone at home and at school had begun guarding me as if against thieves. Grandmother had told me I was still too young to understand anything about sex and relationships with boys. I might not have known the meaning of the words but I already knew how serious they were. The Convent for the Cultivation of Holiness was famous for strict discipline. When Miss Shi talked about being "dignified and restrained," and when Grandmother talked about "character" and "reputation," were they not referring to this without quite saying so? Even if I had wanted to write to a boy, I would not have dared.

I could not imagine who would play such a trick on me. Who wanted to hurt me? How could I clear myself of this false charge? They had already convicted me. How could I make them believe that I was innocent? I thought and thought but could not decide what to do. In those days, I had no idea that the handwriting of the letter could be compared with mine, but even if I had, what use would it have been? The episode was already two months old, and who knew if the letter was still in existence? Those in authority at the school had decided, when the letter was discovered, not to investigate or question me, but had convicted me on the spot—and since then had remained silent. No one had said a word to me, so how could I dare be the first to break the silence

---

*"Older brother." The terms "brother" and "sister" were often used to indicate a boyfriend-girlfriend relationship. Even today, Chinese young people are likely to say they care for someone like a brother or sister. But while in America such a statement indicates a lack of romantic interest, in China it tends to mean just the opposite—that the feelings involved are more than "just friendly," that the young people are or could be in love.

and raise questions? Even if I found the courage and went to the nuns, would they listen to me? Perhaps they would accuse me of lying and punish me even more.

Xiulian and I discussed it quietly for half the evening, but could not think of a good plan of action. We were both too young to know what to do. This was something outside our experience and we dared not turn to anyone else for advice. Just before she went to bed, Xiulian knelt beside her bed and prayed for me. I knelt with her and we prayed for a long time. We both believed, truly and sincerely, that our prayers would be answered, just as they were in the stories of miracles that we heard about every day, and that whoever had really written the letter would come forward and confess. Then the truth would become clear. But the second day, the third day, and the fourth day passed, as did all the rest of the days I spent at the convent, and the miracle never happened. To my teachers and schoolmates, I always remained a person who had committed a crime. To me, it seemed as if I carried an indelible mark on my forehead.

To this day that unresolved episode haunts me, but as I said, it has become as small as a sesame seed. The letter might have been a practical joke written by a classmate who, seeing that the situation became so serious, dared not speak out. Or perhaps someone I had quarrelled with wanted to be malicious and make a fool of me. Neither of these possibilities would surprise me now. What does surprise me, and what I still do not understand, is the attitude of those in authority and in my family, and how they handled it. Even someone who has committed the most hateful crime should be tried before being convicted; the investigation should continue until the truth becomes clear. Even if no defense is permitted, the criminal should at least know what the crime was.

The weeks and months that followed were not easy for me. I was watched closely. On Sundays and holidays, when Grandfather came to see me, one of the nuns or Deacon Tian always had to be present. I was not allowed to see anyone from home alone. I was allowed to go home only every other month, and though the other students could leave as soon as one of their relatives came for them, I had to receive permission from Sister Superior Lihua in person. At the big festivals, when we all went to the church on Haojia Hill, I always had to sit in the back row with Miss Shi and one of the other teachers on either side of me. I felt as if they were noticing every time I blinked. When Mr. Shu held an essay-writing contest in the spring term on the topic, "The Building of Character," no sooner had he written the words on the blackboard than his eyes and those of six or seven of my classmates swivelled around of their own accord to look at me. Usually I received ninety or more on my essays, but this time my mark was low. The first five places were taken by other students and Shuangfeng got the class prize. I did not mind—but it was difficult for me to bear when Mr. Shu gave me back my essay. He sighed and said in a grave voice, "You usually write so well. Perhaps this time the subject restricted you too much. You should pay attention to the words 'building of character.' I beg you not to let yourself be led astray by your intelligence." Father also wrote me a long letter urging me to be a model of good behavior. He wrote, "Those who do not work hard in their youth regret it in vain when they are old." This was the letter in which he wrote that he would wash his hands of me the following semester if I was not diligent, and the one Deacon Tian advised me to read again and again and learn by heart because Father's advice was "very important."

In short, everyone looked at me as if the black mark on my forehead had suddenly made all of them pure, holy and perfect. Some, even Jindi, kept me at arm's length, while others seemed to offer me condescension and pity. Only Xiulian went back to treating me the same as she used to, after our confidential talk that night. At first, Sister Huihua seemed not to have changed either. But then, once when I was in bed with a fever, she came to take my temperature and give me medicine. She seemed as kind to me as she had always been, and my poor, wounded heart was touched. I could not keep from weeping. I wanted to reach out to her and tell her about how I had been wronged, but she just made me lie down and tucked the quilts around me. She patted me gently on the shoulder and said, "No cry, no cry. Sister Huihua understands. Sister Huihua does not like to hear talk of boy students and girl students." Then she picked up her basket of medicines and left. I could not understand why her gentleness and warmth had turned into such coldness and distance.

Once, when I was going home for the monthly holiday, I packed my clothes the evening before so I would be ready the next day at noon when Grandfather came for me. But before he arrived, Sister Superior went out for some business without leaving any word concerning me. As a result, Grandfather had to sit and wait in the gate house and I had to sit on the back lawn, with my little bundle of clothes and wait. All the other students who were going home left, but we had to wait until the sun was slanting down behind the roof tiles of the big classroom before Sister Superior's long, thin shadow appeared at the black front gates and I could leave. While we were waiting, several scholarship students walked by. I heard them asking each other, "Why is she still sitting there? Why hasn't she left? Didn't her grandfather come for her before lunch?"

"Don't you know she's not like the rest? There's a special rule for her—" Then they started whispering among themselves. I heard one girl laugh and say, "If it were me, I'd rather never go home than be put through such humiliation."

Although she scarcely said this out of kindness, it expressed my feelings. During that long afternoon of impatience and anxiety, the warmth I had felt during my two-month-long wait to visit home had chilled.

I was unhappy when I left the school and even more unhappy the next day when I returned. It seemed as if no one knew about the sorrow that weighed down my heart. The days passed as usual, everything seemed the same, and we lacked nothing, except perhaps, something I could not see or express at the time—that those in authority had no understanding of us teenagers, and that they were not practicing the Christ-like virtues of love, humility, and compassion that we heard so much about during the prayer services. I was not the only student in that school who needed that understanding; we all did. It was as if we were all bound by a circle, a very small, very tight circle. We could not make a single move without being punished. One student in the class just below mine—I do not know why she was so incautious—once said a word we were forbidden to say. The teachers and nuns found out and immediately, her parents were called to take her home to be disciplined. She returned a week later with dark bruises all around her mouth. Everyone praised her family, saying, "They're officials. Their strictness is admirable." Another girl, an orphan of about thirteen who received aid from the church, often failed to wake up at night when she needed to and would wet her bed. Sometimes she would get up in the morning and not eat her breakfast after morning prayers, but would run back to the dormitory and make her bed. However, when Sister Aihua and Miss Shi came on morning inspection, they would often pull back her quilts in front of us all without any sympathy for the shame she would feel. They would order her to carry her wet quilts and mattress to the back yard to dry. They would also scold her and tell her she was too lazy to leave her bed at night, and would punish her by making her do chores. But none of this made her change. Nor could the older girls' habit of making friends among themselves be changed, much less done away with. It seemed everyone was looking for understanding and love, but that it just took different forms.

The days passed as usual and gradually everyone seemed to realize that I had developed some strange behaviors. I seldom spoke to anyone, no matter what happened, but I wept often, and when I wept I would cry until my hands and feet were cold and numb and my lips turned white. The nuns, thinking I was sick, would send me to bed to sleep, but after sleeping for a few hours I would feel all right again. Bit by bit the nuns and the teachers became more lenient towards me. Even Sister Aihua, who was the most abrupt and impatient, showed me more kindness than she did the others. But even this could not heal me. I never felt happy or at peace, but after I wept I felt better.

One time, the other students got very upset because they said someone had been stealing things. I had lost a few handkerchiefs. Everyone gathered together for search. I suddenly grew afraid that someone might have secretly hidden the missing articles under my bed or in my box. I could not stop my face from flushing hot and red, as if I were the culprit. I hurried to the searcher and said, "I want to look under my bed and in my box first—then you can search." Sometime later, all the missing articles were found in a little back room where the firewood was kept. The thief turned out to be a widow, more than twenty years old, who had hoped to become a nun. She was expelled, and only then was I able to rid myself of the burden of feeling falsely accused.

The days passed, and I continued to conceal my unhappiness. The seasons followed one after the other, and the trees and shrubs that covered the hill grew taller each year. The girls grew older each year until they graduated, and left, and new girls came. Xiulian finished upper primary and was sent by her father's younger brother's wife to teach in a little school in a small county town. Shuangfeng was within six months of finishing upper primary and graduating when her parents gave her away in marriage. My last year at the school was very lonely; there had been seven in our class at first, but by graduation we were only five.

On graduation day, the two big classrooms were opened into

one. The walls had been newly whitewashed and decorated and the platform was decked with all kinds of fresh summer flowers. We and the lower primary graduates all wore short white coats and long skirts. The nuns wore their long blue cotton habits and the big white pleated wimples. Deacon Tian wore a short, black, gauze topcoat over his long white linen gown. The women teachers all wore white coats and skirts. Everyone sat dignified and erect on the platform, on either side of Sister Superior. Mrs. Tian was also dressed up in a coat and skirt of blue gauze and did not sit in the back row that day, but in front with students' parents and relatives. Grandmother Li, sweat beading her face, bustled back and forth. Everyone was smiling and happy. When the organ began to sound, Sister Qihua's white wimple began swaying from left to right in time with the music. All fifty of us students sang the graduation song together. Its clear, sweet melody floated out on the summer breeze and encircled us.

Thinking back on our childhood, oh
How foolish to play all day long
Everything to us was new and strange
And black from red we did not know

Whenever we sisters talked together, oh
Carrying our books under our arms
We thought of all the knowledge we'd have
And what distinguished women scholars we'd be

As I marched with the other graduates up to the platform to get my diploma, tied with pink ribbon, from Sister Superior, she and the other nuns, the teachers, and Deacon Tian all nodded to me and smiled. It was the first time in more than a year that anyone had shown me a sign of approval. Tears came to my eyes and my throat tightened. I heard the burst of applause as we left the platform and returned to our seats. My sight was so blurred that I could hardly see the smiling faces. Why was I weeping? Because that invisible weight still burdened my heart? Regret and longing for the years of innocence that had now come to an end? Or was I weeping out of anxiety about the problems—the unknown and undecided future—that now faced me? I did not know. My heart was full of too many conflicting emotions.

After a farewell party given by the teachers and our school-mates, I took my bundle of clothes, my luggage, and my diploma and walked down the mountain with my grandmother. The sun was halfway to the horizon. The early summer wind was cool. When we reached the bottom of the hill, Grandmother hired a rickshaw and we rode into the city. I never returned to Fengjia Hill.

BOOK II

I Am Pushed into the Ancient Well
Reserved for Unwanted Daughters

Chapter 14

How yellow the flowers atop Goat Mountain,
How hard to become a child bride.
Mother-in-law watches me clean rice by the well,
Sister-in-law looks on as I wash vegetables in the river.

I am taught by a stick of green bamboo,
And fed just hot or cold gruel.
Who pities me, unwashed and uncombed?
I feel my way down the dark passage.

ONCE I graduated and returned to my grandparents' home, I faced two serious problems that caused me great anxiety. The first was whether I would be allowed to continue my studies at a middle school and the second was whether Father and his wife were still considering the idea of marrying me off, something I had overheard them discussing six months earlier. I learned that Father was planning to move to Shanghai to start a business and that before he went he and my stepmother would visit us, partly to see friends and relatives and worship at our ancestors' graves and partly to decide on the matter that would affect my whole life—my marriage. I did not hold out much hope of going on to middle school. In the previous few years, Father had not been very successful in his business, and I doubted that he would have any money left over to pay for more schooling for me after they moved to Shanghai. Besides, he had never thought my education was important. If, however, the only obstacle was money, I thought I had found a way to manage. I could take the examinations for the Second Provincial Women's Normal School in Wuhu. I had heard that they would accept forty students in the first-year class. If I passed, and if my family would let me go there even though it was less strict than the convent, and if I lived at home, I would need no money except for small daily expenses because tuition would be free. Even if I lived at the school, the boarding fee was very low and everything else would be free. The examinations were different from the mission school's because they emphasized Chinese literature and history, while English, mathematics, and natural sciences were secondary. Many students would be taking them, but if I worked hard on literature and history—the other subjects would be easy—during the summer, I thought I might do well enough to be admitted. But the other problem—my marriage—was more difficult. I hoped that Father would at least let me finish upper middle school, so I could study and become independent, before they made any such plans for me.

This was probably the first time I had ever clearly faced my own intimate problems and concerns. I think it was the first time I realized clearly that because I was a woman my life could never be as free as if I had been born a man. The five or six years since Mother had died, though lonely and sad, were nevertheless just the beginning of my life. What road now lay ahead of me? Although I could not see it clearly, I already realized it would not be wide and level or easily walked. It would be uneven, winding, and beset with many obstacles. I also understood that there was nothing I could do about it and—bitterest of all—that I had no right to choose my own path. So my heart was full of anxiety and confusion.

During the previous year, my grandfather and grandmother had endured many misfortunes. Their greatest anxiety was for my third uncle. They had planned, and worked hard all their lives in the hope that he would graduate from college and establish himself in a career that would lesson the burdens on them and give them a chance to throw off their burden, straighten their shoulders, and enjoy their later years. But when that long-hoped-for day finally arrived, so did bad news. No sooner did he receive his college diploma than he began coughing up blood. The doctors said he had tuberculosis. He immediately returned to Wuhu by boat and was being treated in a hospital run by foreigners. But there was no sign of improvement yet, and no hope that he would recover in a few months.

That was not all. My first uncle, who had moved away from home and had been diligently working at his trade, had taken the small amount of capital he had squeezed out and saved over the years and set up a stall at the end of a busy street. It brought in enough for him and his wife to live on, and they were even able to send some money home every month to my grandparents. Then the unexpected happened. A few months earlier, the stall had been looted by some soldiers who had been dispersed in the warlord fighting.* Everything they had gained in those years of sweat and tears had been taken away, and my uncle seriously injured. He and my aunt were now stranded far from home with no money, and certainly could not send anything to help my grandparents.

And then our old "racetrack" apartment, where we had lived for so many years, was near the Christian church. A few years earlier, the church had proposed buying the land on which our house stood to build a large primary and middle school. But the landlord had been unwilling to sell and they had not come to an agreement. Recently, however, the church had asked the county magistrate to act as a broker. The landlord had no choice but to agree, and it had been decided that all the tenants must move out before the end of November. All the families in the house were looking for new places to live and preparing to move. This was an added layer of distress. And finally, my youngest uncle, who was just graduating from upper middle school, had to give up his plan to enter college, at least for the time being, because of my third uncle's illness. Nothing seemed to be going according to our wishes. It was as though everything had happened at once, and this made Grandfather and Grandmother, who never talked much anyway, even more silent.

If I had had ten thousand worries, instead of only two, I could not have added to those two old people's burdens by speaking of them. Nor would talking with them have made much difference, because it was my father who would make all the decisions about my life. I felt it would be better to wait until he and my stepmother arrived before bringing up my going to school—that it would be better to talk face-to-face than to write because there would be more chance for discussion. But how could I bring myself to say anything about a possible marriage, which frightened me so much? They would not consult me, and my grandparents were powerless. They could make decisions for me in other matters, but in this one, which would affect my whole life, they had to step aside for Father and could not speak, and even if they did speak he would not listen. I thought and thought and

---

*"Warlord fighting." Referring to the period of about 1918-1925, when rival military factions fought among themselves to gain control over different regions, especially Beijing, because it was the capital and received customs revenues.

realized that the only person who could make him change his mind, the only person I could turn to for help, was my stepmother, who had never shown me any affection. As I thought about this, I told myself that since I had not been home for more than three years and since they would soon be moving to Shanghai, and since I was sure they would not take me with them, they would see even less of me in the future. Perhaps my stepmother would take these things into account and temper her past dislike. If she was willing to help me, I knew Father would listen to her. Then perhaps he would postpone marrying me off, which would make it easier to resolve the question of my going on to school.

My doubts and disquiet did not last long. Father and Stepmother arrived. Remembering it still makes my heart ache. I had not seen him for three years, and was so excited and happy when we met that I put aside my problems and doubts for the time being. After all, I felt, we were still flesh and blood, even if our relationship had been neglected in the previous few years. He did not seem to show me much affection, but I thought that since I was his own daughter he could not dislike me as much as my stepmother did. I decided that now that I was grown, I would even get along with her and that if she showed me the slightest good will I would forget the past.

I never expected that that hope would be dashed as quickly as it was.

Father looked thinner and darker. He had tired wrinkles at the corners of his eyes, but his spirits were good. My stepmother seemed much paler and plumper. Her waistline had thickened. When she walked she shuffled a bit and her steps were not as light as they used to be. It was as if she had to use more strength to get around—a sign that she was about to get fat. Father looked happy and surprised when he saw me. Sitting in the living room he pointed at me and told Stepmother with a laugh, "Look, Baogu is so tall! I think she's even taller than you. In the turn of an eye she's grown up and become an adult right before our eyes!"

"It's as they say, 'A growing girl changes eighteen times.'"

Nothing had changed in my stepmother's attitude towards me. Her voice was still light and slow. Her large, cold eyes measured me sharply. "Not bad. I thought she'd turn out to be heavy-set. I never thought she'd grow up to be so delicately beautiful."

"I've often told you she would be—the older she gets, the more she resembles her mother," said Father without thinking.

My stepmother grunted deep in her throat but made no reply.

She was still eyeing me up and down until she had scrutinized my entire body as if hoping to find a flaw. I could feel the old hostility in her look and way of speaking to me. I remained seated on the square stool beside the open latticed window and she continued to inspect me, but I was uncomfortable and turned to look outside. A small fleecy cloud was floating over the black tiles of the house across the courtyard. A cold feeling of disappointment drifted and floated, like the white cloud, in my heart. I knew that my father's wife still disliked, despised, and was jealous of me.

My grandparents were naturally very happy to see my father and stepmother. Relatives and friends who had not been frequent visitors now hurried to call because Father had been away so long and would soon be leaving again. Among the callers were some old acquaintances who had an eye to the main chance. When they heard that Father was going to work in Shanghai, they took advantage of his visit to renew an acquaintanceship that they might be able to trade on someday if he became successful. So my grandparents' apartment, which had been so quiet because all the other families had already moved out, suddenly became very lively, with people coming and going all day long. Father and my stepmother often went out to see people and were seldom at home. When they were there, they talked with Grandfather and Grandmother about family affairs, but never brought up the question of what would happen to me.

A week went by, but I could not find an appropriate time to talk with Father. They would leave soon. I became more and more uneasy each day. I had thought that when Father came we would be able to talk face to face, but I had not expected that so much time would pass without his bringing up my future. My old fear of him had not decreased, even though I was now older. I still felt constrained when he was around, and not as natural and free as when I wrote to him.

If they did not bring up their plans for me, I would have to. There was not much time left. I had to find out, before they went away, what would happen to me.

One warm evening when Father was out having dinner with friends, I gathered up my courage and decided to try to find out what my stepmother would say. She and my grandmother were on the sun porch cooling themselves. There was no trace of a breeze, the stars were like thousands of tiny, flickering balls of fire, and the flowers and leaves were so still that it was as if they had been glued together. We were all dripping with perspiration because the house was like a stove. Carefully, I outlined my plan to take the school examinations, emphasizing that if I passed, the tuition would be free.

My stepmother just kept waving her big palm-leaf fan. She seemed as indifferent to me and my concerns as ever. She did not say yes and she would not say no. When I finished, she went on waving away the mosquitoes and did not speak for a long time.

Grandmother, sitting to one side and seeing that she was saying nothing, stepped in. "Girls today are different," she said, smiling. "They seem to have an affinity for books, and study morning and night. If boys liked books as much and studied as hard, they could probably all become ministers of state!"

"Hmm ..."

My stepmother pursed her lips, laughed a little and then, not answering me directly, began telling Grandmother that Father's business affairs had not been satisfactory in recent years, that their circumstances had become more and more difficult, and that they needed a good deal of money for the move to Shanghai, for the train and the boat fares, and to set up their new home. Then she said that Father had had great difficulty trying to borrow some capital from his relatives and friends. She counted out a long string of objections in detail, and then, as if to smile but not smiling, waved her hands back and forth and said, "I dare not bother him at such a time." Then she turned to me. "From the beginning I've never said a word about your affairs. I always let your father make the decisions. But now that you've brought your questions to me it would not do if I didn't answer. I'm afraid you're not going to like what I have to say. You are now grown up. You're no longer a child, but a young woman of fourteen or fifteen. It's time for us to be thinking about your marriage. What good would it be for you to continue studying? You can't eat books. If I were you, I'd stay at home with your grandmother and sew and learn how to manage a household—that will be much more useful to you later on."

"What I'm saying is for your own benefit in the future," she went on. "When I was your age, I had many younger brothers and sisters. I helped make all of their clothes, shoes, and socks. My father worked in the customs house and earned very little. If I had not helped, it would not have been enough. I was not free to be idle and think idle thoughts."

Her words fell like hail, beating down on me one by one. The tiny hope I had been cherishing, that I could go on to school, had been extinguished. She was giving me her opinion and I could not dispute it. Even if I had tried, to answer it would only have led to a quarrel. But I could not stay there with her. As soon as she stopped talking, I got up and went inside. I stomped off, my footsteps heavy on the wood floors, as if I could stamp away the anger I was holding back inside me.

I blew out the dimly-lit lamp in my bedroom with one breath. The room felt empty and somber. Without undressing, I crawled under the mosquito netting and lay on the straw summer mat. My heart felt as hot and stifling as the room. I fanned myself rapidly with my palm-leaf fan. Outside the netting, the mosquitoes buzzed like a band of musicians. Their continual whining made it feel even more stifling. Even the breeze from the fan was hot. The sweat on my body refused to dry. I tossed and turned but could not get to sleep.

"Perhaps," I thought, "what she just said is not really what Father thinks. Perhaps I still have a chance, if I talk with him. The final decision cannot be made until I get an answer from him." When I thought of this, I felt calmer and quieter. "But if I am to speak it must be soon—I must find an opportunity to talk alone with him in the next day or two. If I wait too long, she'll have talked with him first and made suggestions, and it'll be even more difficult.

"When I talk with him, I must be calm and determined. Studying is not like other things—it's important. Times have changed and many girls are now studying at universities. My own mother graduated from upper middle school, and she always said she wanted me to attend a university. Wanting to take the examinations for the Women's Normal School isn't asking for much. Father can't use lack of money as an excuse. The school won't cost much. All I'll need is a coat and skirt, or two, of coarse blue cotton, but I'd need those anyway, and a little pocket money. I'll be very careful. It is crucial that when I talk with him I present all of this in an orderly, logical, and forthright way, and leave nothing out. I mustn't let myself get confused. Education is proper and important. Why should I hesitate?"

This plan rekindled the hope that my stepmother's words had extinguished.

But if I had understood human nature a little better and not been so naive, I would not have taken my stepmother's words as expressing only her own ideas and would have realized that they also represented Father's. That they had been home for more than ten days without him saying a word to me about my future was not because he was too busy to think about it. There had to be another reason. But my dream of going back to school was too overpowering. I was afraid to think I might fail, and I did not know that what was to come would come even if I refused to think about it.

Chapter 15

IT was midnight before Grandmother came to bed that night. She heard me still fanning myself and knew that I was not asleep, so she came to my bedside and told me quietly that for the time being I should set aside my desire for more education. I knew she was trying to make me feel better, so I did not argue with her. The next day Father and my stepmother went to visit her family. When evening came, they still had not returned. I sat alone in the bedroom studying under the oil lamp. I had decided that I would not go to sleep until Father had returned and I had talked with him.

Grandmother called to me several times, telling me to come outside and to come cool off because it was too hot in the bedroom, there were too many mosquitoes, and that studying under the lamp would make me ill. After she realized that I did not intend to move, she brought her water-pipe into the bedroom and sat down on the chest near the window. She looked at me as if she wanted to talk, but then she would lower her head and smoke as if she were thinking. I knew that this meant she had something to say to me, so I waited quietly for her to speak. But after she had smoked four or five pipefuls, and sighed several times, she stood up and picked up the pipe as if she was about to leave. I then asked, "Grandmother, do you know when Father and his wife will be back tonight?"

"I'm afraid they'll be very late."

"Grandmother, after I left last night did my stepmother say anything to you? I was only telling her of my plans for the rest of the year. I didn't expect her to talk such nonsense! If I'd known that, I would have kept quiet. I'll talk with Father tonight when they get back."

Grandmother remained standing near the bedside table and looked at me for a while. Then she said, "I think you had better not bringing up the idea of studying. What misfortunes you've had to suffer! If your mother were still alive, you wouldn't be treated like this."

"Grandmother, what have you heard?" I turned and faced her. "Is it true? Have they already picked out a husband for me?"

Grandmother sat down again. "Marriage is no crime. When sons grow up, they should marry. When daughters grow up they should be given in marriage. Daughters must be given to other families. It's not right for them to stay home all their lives. But I think it was wrong of them to promise the Shao family that you could go to live with them now as a child bride, before you actually marry."

Go to live with the Shao family as a child bride!* It was as if I had suddenly been swept up in a whirlwind. I now understood my stepmother's talk of the night before ... they had been planning this for a long time. She had not been talking casually. She had had these plans for a long time and had only been waiting for the right moment to add enough pressure to bring them about. My future did not matter to them. They had decided it during the previous ten days. All the time I had been dreaming that they would let me take the school entrance examinations, they had been making a contract with the Shao family.

My head felt heavy. I rested it in my hands. Grandmother's voice continued to sound in my ears. "They didn't talk it over with Grandfather and me before they made the contract. Your father told us about it when he came home last night. It has been decided that the betrothal will take place in early August. They are consulting the geomancer to determine the most auspicious day. When Grandfather heard this he insisted they tell you, saying, 'You'll be leaving in a few days. Although by tradition a child's marriage is decided by the parents, you should tell her about your plans so she'll understand and so that when the time comes she will not make a fuss and refuse to go. It's one chance in a thousand, but her grandmother and I would not be able to force her to go.'

"I said, 'We have no say in the contract you've made for her. Naturally, such decisions must be made by you, her father and mother. After all, we're only her grandparents. But I think it would be a mistake to send her to live with the Shaos right away. Mrs. Shao has a reputation for being difficult and demanding. I

---

*"Child bride." The old Chinese custom in which young girls from poor families, usually ten or younger, were given over to the family of their future husband several years before the actual marriage. Although Chinese women were in general expected to serve their mothers-in-law, child brides were often little more than servants.

worry that being a child bride in her home will mean a hard life for Baogu. She would have so many young brothers-in-law to take care of.' Your father heard what I said but would not look at us or answer us."

"Your stepmother said, 'Shao Anlin's wife has made up her mind she wants Baogu. They sent someone six months ago to talk about an engagement. When we arrived here, they again sent someone to talk with us. We have seen Zhongyao, their son, and think he is quite suitable. Their social position is also acceptable. He and Baogu are the right age apart, and the geomancer says the times of their birth and their eight characters* match each other. Also, he is the eldest son and has also been adopted by his mother's mother, so when her estate is divided up he will get two shares.' She also said that the Shaos' young daughter had been at the convent with you for one semester, that you were friends, and that you have met everyone in the family. Your stepmother said that now that you're grown up, it would cause them too much concern if you were to remain unmarried and that once it's settled, we'll be relieved of one worry.

"Then your father said, 'She won't really be a child bride. It's because they like her that they want her to go to live with them. That way she'll have two homes, and they will treat her like a daughter.' The Shaos also said that your father will be far away and that we are old and should not be burdened with so many responsibilities. They said that having you move there now will make the relationship between our two families closer, and that it would be simpler and easier than moving and being married all at once. Your father said the family also has a second daughter-in-law, two years younger than you. She also comes and goes, living sometimes with them and sometimes with her own family. We can talk with the Shaos about Baogu's desire to study. They're enlightened people—all of their children are in school."

Grandmother gave another long sigh. "Fortunately they are still waiting for the geomancer to determine the most auspicious

*"Times of their birth and their eight characters." At this period, the go-between bringing the two families together would be asked by the young man's family to first obtain the girl's name and time of birth from her family. Then a fortuneteller would examine the two horoscopes to see whether the proposed marriage would be an appropriate one. The eight characters, in four pairs, indicating the year, month, day and hour of a person's birth, each pair consisting of one heavenly stem and one earthly branch, were formerly used for divination purposes.

day for the betrothal. There's still time for discussion. It seems to me that you must go and talk with your father yourself before they leave. Tomorrow morning would be best. You should say, 'I am not complaining because you've chosen a husband for me, but you must not send me to the Shaos as a child bride. Would you do this to me if my mother were still alive?'"

While she talked I said nothing. I kept my face buried in my hands. My feelings were so tangled that I did not know how to begin to make sense of them. I did not feel angry or sad—it was as if I had been walking along in the sunshine without any cares and had suddenly been pushed into a bottomless dark pit. I felt as if I were falling. I was full of fear and confusion, and could not keep my thoughts straight. I felt my life was over. Grandmother got up and left me alone. I felt I had reached bottom and that I now knew just what I was up against. A bitter sadness overwhelmed me. I felt I had no one to lean on, no one to help me.

How could they do this? Father, can it really be that you have forgotten all about my mother, and what you promised Grandfather and Grandmother after she was buried—that you would bring me up carefully to be a student and a responsible adult? Now, before I have even entered middle school, you have lost interest in me and want to send me to another home as a child bride.

A child bride—for thousands of years, families had been getting rid of their daughters by sending them off to live with their future in-laws' families years before the wedding took place. Father, do you want so badly to get rid of me? No. I will not go. Even if I die, I will not go.

I blew out the lamp and crawled onto my bed. I sat on the matting, drew my knees up and rested my aching head. I stayed this way for hours. Soon after the clock in the living room struck eleven, I heard someone tap at the front gate. I heard Grandmother go downstairs to open the gate, and then their footsteps coming up the stairs. I also heard Father and Grandfather talking on the sun porch. I wanted to run out and question Father, but my body refused to move. Grandmother had told me to wait until morning to speak to him because I was still too upset. I knew I ought to calm myself, but I could not. I did not know how late I sat up before I dozed off, and even then I did not fall asleep completely. All night long, our voices—Grandfather's, Father's, my stepmother's, Grandmother's and my own—rang in my ears.

When I opened my eyes the next morning, Grandmother was standing at my bedside. She lifted the curtain quietly and motioned to me. I realized that Father and my stepmother were already up. I threw on my clothes and got out the bed. Hurriedly, I washed and combed my hair and went to Father's room. My stepmother was standing at the basin about to wash her face. When I came in, she quickly wrung out the washcloth, picked up a covered cup of tea, and left the room. Father was sitting in a bamboo chair by the window drinking tea. After what seemed a long silence, I went over and stood before him with my head drooping.

Father broke the silence. "Oh," he said, looking as if nothing was the matter. "Grandmother has just told me that you have something you wish to say to me. What is it? You had better tell me."

During the night I had thought of many things to say, and I had been weighing them carefully before coming in to see him. I wanted not only to tell him that I did not want to become a child bride in any family but also to plead with him to postpone the engagement and let me take the examinations at the Women's Normal School so I could continue my studies. But now that I was with him, he seemed so nonchalant and so unconcerned about me that I started feeling upset and resentful again. Wave after wave of bitterness rose up in me, and I could not open my mouth.

"What is it? Out with it!"

"You ... you cannot—cannot!—send me off to be a child bride—"

"Who's been telling you that? No, no—there's been no talk of that. It's only that you're to visit back and forth ... All right, don't cry! We won't send you there and that's all there is to it!" The last few sentences came out in a rush, as if he wanted to end our conversation.

I wiped my eyes with my hand and sleeve—in my haste to see him, I had forgotten my handkerchief. Then I looked at him. It was the first time I had looked directly at him since I had entered the room. There was a smile hovering on his lips, but it was not a happy, natural one. It was the smile of some one who was not at peace with himself, someone who was embarrassed or ashamed.

"That's right—Grandmother did say that you wanted to go on with your studies. That's no problem. We can discuss it. Don't worry. You can go on living here ... Is there anything else? All right, then, it's settled."

He took out his watch, stood up, and called for my stepmother to take out his long gown for him. Then he said, "I have an appointment. I must leave immediately."

"What did she say?" I heard my stepmother ask in a low voice as I went into the livng room.

"She said she did not want to be a child bride."

"Oh, girls are all alike—as the saying goes, 'When the big red embroidered sedan chair comes for them they weep, but once in it they smile.' Shall we hold lunch for you?"

"No, I'm invited out."

I ran into my own room and shut the door. Father's footsteps hurried down the stairs.

Two days later, Father received a telegram from Shanghai. He and my stepmother left in great haste.

However, Father did back off from his promise to the Shao family and asked them to move slowly in selecting a suitable betrothal day. I was told that the Shaos agreed to let me take the school entrance examinations, but that the day of betrothal had already been decided and could not be changed. The beginning of August was only a few days away.

After my Father and stepmother left, Grandmother seldom talked with me about the betrothal because the die had already been cast and further talk would be useless. She and Grandfather began busying themselves with preparations. All the red-embroidered table hangings and chair-back covers, the silver candlesticks with the double happiness ideographs, the round tabletops, the best bowls and plates decorated with red flowers, the ebony chopsticks mounted with silver—all the things we used at New Year's were brought out. It was not strange that Grandfather and Grandmother should look at my betrothal to another family as a happy occasion. Everyone would. The night before the day set for the betrothal, when we were going to bed, Grandmother told me, "Mrs. Cheng has invited you to spend tomorrow visiting her. She said to go there early. Her courtyards are wide and airy and it will be cool there." She did not ask me, as she usually did, if I would like to go or not. She added, "You must stay there until late afternoon, until I come to fetch you."

I knew in my heart that Mrs. Cheng, who lived in a house across from the Bridge of Lions, had a special reason for inviting me, especially since her daughter was away on a visit. Why had she invited only me? It was, of course, because tomorrow was betrothal day and my grandparents were holding a banquet at our home. It would not be appropriate for me to be there, so Grandmother had arranged this invitation for me. I did not think this was strange, but I wondered whether I would behave like a proper guest the next day. On the other hand, for me to refuse to go, and to stay at home, would be even more improper. After telling me this, Grandmother took some red paper out of the drawer and began wrapping up tips for the servants who would bring the betrothal gifts from the Shaos' home. Then she went back into the living room and occupied herself there.

The next day, Grandfather and Grandmother got up earlier than usual. I could not sleep, but I did not want to get up. I lay on the bed with my eyes closed, pretending to be asleep. I heard Grandmother come in to look at me several times, but since I was so quiet, she went away again. When the living-room clock struck eight, she came in, lifted the mosquito netting and sat on the edge of the bed. She shook me lightly on the shoulder and asked gently, "Did you sleep well? Dear girl, it's getting late. You must get up. Comb your hair, wash your face, and change your clothes. The water and your breakfast are all ready. After you eat, I'll take you to Mrs. Cheng's." When I did not move or answer, she stood up and said, "All right. I'll let you get up by yourself. I'll be in the living room." Then she went out.

I wished I could go back to sleep, but it was no use. If only I could have pulled the sheets over my head and slept away the whole day and been left alone. But I could not. I did not know when the guests would start arriving, but if I was still there when they came it would be even worse. I had no choice but to turn over and sit up. It was a beautiful day. I put on my slippers and went over to the window. The shadows of the leaves quivering in the gentle breeze made circles on the bricks that framed the window and on the window sill. The shining green leaves of the locust tree, now taller than the window, flickered bright and then dark in the sunshine and shadows. The sun was high and the sky was blue. A scrap of white cloud floated in the distance. The sparrows hopped and chattered on the window sill and roof. It was an ideal midsummer day, the kind of day most loved by those of us who lived south of the Yangtze River. But everything—the gentle wind, the green leaves, the blue sky, the white clouds, the sunshine, and the sparrows—seemed to have conspired to tantalize me that day.

For many days I had been seeing the images of the people in

the Shao family in my mind's eye. I could not rid myself of them now either—they drifted before my eyes. I sat on the square stool and picked up my comb but put it down again. I went over to the washstand and put my hand into the copper basin. The water was already cold. I wrung out the washcloth and scrubbed my face a couple of times, as if I could scrub away the shadows that haunted me. I looked aimlessly around the room, then returned to the stool. Looking into the mirror, I combed my hair.

After a while, Grandmother brought in my second-best suit, a coat and skirt of white linen with blue stripes, newly pressed. She laid it on my bed, and next to it, she laid two little orchids whose petals were not yet fully opened.

Chapter 16

NATURALLY I could not eat my breakfast, and Grandmother did not urge me to. I drank only one small cup of tea. Then we went out the front gate. I walked at her side with my eyes downcast, looking at the cobblestones and feeling that everyone we passed was staring at me. Fortunately Mrs. Cheng's house was only about ten steps beyond the Bridge of Lions.

I do not know if my feelings that day were unusual. When we reached Mrs. Cheng's and she came to greet us, she looked happy. She seized my hand, smiled and looked me up and down and said, in a kinder, gentler voice than usual, that because her daughter had gone to visit relatives and there was no one to keep her company, she wanted me to do as I pleased and to treat her home as my own. Grandmother did not stay long. She would not sit down, but remained standing in the living room, said a few words, and then took her leave. Mrs. Cheng accompanied her to the gate, where I saw Grandmother tug gently at her sleeve and whisper to her. Mrs. Cheng nodded. When she came back inside, she took me into her daughter's bedroom. After hunting around in the desk and drawers for quite a while, she discovered a couple of old storybooks and gave them to me. She sat and smoked her water-pipe twice, but when I continued to remain silent, she got up and went out, dropping the curtain in the doorway and half-closing the doors.

At first I sat in formal dignity near the bed. If I heard footsteps in the living room and thought someone might be coming, I would quickly pick up one of the books and pretend to be reading, but Mrs. Cheng, who was understanding, left me alone all day except for bringing me tea and coming in at lunch time. This was what I wished. I took off my skirt and walked back and forth. I sat for a while and stood for a while. I went to the little wooden window behind the bed. It was open, and I could see dense masses of yellow and white honeysuckle growing at the foot of the mud wall and smell their fragrance coming up in waves and floating into the room on the breeze. Sometimes I lay back on the rattan chaise longue, unable to decide whether to sit or stand. My heart ached, but that was not all. My feelings were mixed, and I did not know why. The whole time, I could not get one thought out of my mind—whether the betrothal presents from his family had arrived or not. Also, I could not rid myself of the images of the people in the Shao family. They kept passing in front of my eyes.

Zhongyao was always at their center. This was his betrothal day, too. What was he feeling? Was he willing, or unwilling? His image was indistinct. I wanted to see him clearly in my mind's eye, but I could not. I had seen him from a distance a few times when we had gone to the church on Haojia Hill for one of the big festivals. He had been part of the choir and had been sitting on one of the long benches to the right of the altar, exactly opposite our seats. My clearest memory of him was from the previous Christmas, when his school had put on a play and we all marched over to see it. He was one of the shepherds and had on a white sheepskin coat turned inside out. We took more notice of him than of the others because he was Rolan's older brother. His forehead bulged slightly. His face was long and his complexion dark. I could not remember what his eyes, nose, or other features were like. If I had known that he and I were to be engaged, I would have stolen a much closer look at him.

But I now realized why Rolan, who was at the play that night with her mother and grandmother, had come over to chat with me. Her mother and grandmother had stood near her and stared at me so much that I was embarrassed. Grandmother had told me that his family had sent a go-between to discuss an engagement more than six months ago. Mrs. Shao seemed to know how to dress and make herself up. She was tall and strongly-built. Her glossy, black hair was plucked back from her temples, as married women wore it, as neatly as if it had been shaved. Her eyes tilted upwards a bit at the corners. She was wearing a fashionable coat and skirt of thin light-grey wool and looked very youthful.

Rolan looked like her mother. She had spent one semester at the convent in the fall of my first year in upper primary school, but had not come back after winter vacation, perhaps because she could not stand boarding school life. She was probably more than ten at the time, and I still remember that she was always chattering, like a sparrow. While she was at the school a little slave-girl,* about twelve or thirteen years old and with thin sparse hair, would bring things up to her every Sunday. The food was always well-prepared and abundant—several big bowls of cooked fresh meat, salted meat, and fish. Rolan often said that she had five brothers, that she was the only daughter, and that her mother loved her best. She also said her grandmother, her mother's mother, loved her oldest brother best and had adopted him and given him her own family's name. She said that her family owned a drygoods store and a general store too.

Why could I not stop thinking about his family? Why not think about my studies? Today, however, my dream of studying seemed as distant as a kite that had slipped its string and flown far away. I could not pull it back, no matter how hard I tried. But my obsessive thoughts about his family were like my shadow, which I could not drive away, no matter what.

Was I dreaming? How wonderful it would be if this were all a dream—but Grandmother's words about how difficult Mrs. Shao was rang in my ears. I did not know where Grandmother had heard this talk. But as I thought more about Mrs. Shao's appearance, it seemed to me that, although she was attractive and fashionable, there was also an air of cleverness and sharpness about her. Perhaps that was what had led Grandmother to make that comment about how difficult my life could be in the Shaos', household. I could not stop thinking. Although the Shaos had agreed that, for the time being, I would not go to live with them, what if they should insist? Father was now far away and my grandparents could not take the responsibility of refusing them. And I, it goes without saying, could not make trouble for my family. If that should happen, there would be no way out. My father and stepmother had been so hardhearted! Our family was not that poor; it was not as if we had nothing to eat. Also, I was almost grown up, so why should I be made to bear the humiliation of being given away as a child bride instead of being properly married?

I thought further. Ever since I could remember, I had heard countless stories about how sad it was to be a child bride. My own mother had read us such stories when we were living in Nanjing, during those afternoons and evenings when Aunt Fang and our housekeeper and the neighbor women used to come and sew. My

---

* "Slave-girl." Young girls were often sold as domestic slaves by parents who were too poor to care for them.

memories were like scenes from a scroll that had been rolled up a long time ago. I could still hear Mother's sighs. Neither she nor I could ever have imagined that my fate would be like those unfortunate heroines' in the books and that I would be cast into a deep pit and forgotten.

I suddenly realized that the house was completely quiet. I could no longer hear the women servants washing in the courtyard or the children playing and laughing in the lane behind the back window. Why was it so quiet? Had Mrs. Cheng gone to our home to the betrothal party? I was about to go to the door to look out when I heard the sound of footsteps running into the courtyard and an outburst of laughter.

"Good, good! Very impressive!"

"Could you see how many loads there were?"

"There were four."

"How much gold jewelry was there?"

"There were too many people crowding around, so I couldn't see. I was at the end of the Bridge of Lions and only got a glimpse. Ooh—a little, crisp, roasted suckling pig!"

"Mr. Shao must be rich indeed."

"That goes without saying!"

"That need not be said. They've got those two big stores on Long Street!"

"Ssh! Keep your voice down!"

"Oh, I'd forgotten! The little Zhou girl is here—"

"Ssh!"

This was followed by peals of laughter. But I could no longer make out what they were saying.

They must have been talking about seeing the betrothal gifts being carried to our house. I ran behind the bed. My heart was pounding and I did not know what to do. I was afraid they would come up to look at me, since they knew I was here—but fortunately they did not. The event I had been worrying about had now happened and suddenly I felt exhausted. I had not slept well the previous few nights. I had been feeling too upset and confused. And now it was as if all these things had coalesced and were crushing me. I went to the chaise longue and lay down on my side with my hands over my eyes to rest....

"Baogu, Baogu ..."

A hand was patting my shoulder. I opened my eyes. The lamp had been lit. Grandmother, dressed in blue silk, was standing over me smiling. Mrs. Cheng, also in silk, was beside her. I suddenly remembered where I was. Sleep had let me set aside all that had happened, but now the events of the day came back to me. I got up immediately. Mrs. Cheng took a wooden comb and began to smooth my hair while Grandmother straightened my coat and skirt. Mrs. Cheng offered us some tea, but Grandmother thanked her and said that we had to go home. She took me by the hand and we left.

The cool wind gusted in our faces. A delicate crescent moon hung above the crenellations of the city wall in the distance. The wet cobblestones under our feet reflected the shimmering stars and the moon and looked as if they were floating in water. Our neighbors were resting and cooling off in front of their gates. As they chatted, their voices blended with the chirping of the crickets. As soon as we reached the house, I hurried upstairs without daring to look at the people relaxing in the courtyard.

Upstairs looked the same as always except for all the things on the long table against the wall and the dining table. I did not look at them, but went right to my own room. Grandmother followed me and turned up the light. The room was full of bright red and shining gold. Big parcels and little boxes were piled all over. I turned my back on them and stared at the mosquito netting on the bed. Grandmother came over behind me and murmured, "Look at the betrothal presents they sent—four sets of gold ornaments, a pendant, a set of gold buttons, a pair of rings ..."

While she was still talking, I crept behind the curtain onto the bed. She asked me again if I wanted anything to eat. There was much rice and good food left over from the banquet. I said I was not hungry. Grandmother sat down on the square chest next to the bed, lit her paper spill in the lamp, and puffed silently on her water-pipe for a long time. Then she got up and began sorting out all the gifts.

I do not know how many times I woke up that night, but every time I woke up, I would involuntarily look at all the silk brocade boxes, fastened with strips of red paper and tied with gold cord, that lay outside the curtain. I would eye them stealthily. The brocade boxes gleamed in the dim light of the lamp. I kept asking myself, "Am I really engaged?"

For the past few days, the idea of becoming engaged had made me feel afraid and hurt, but the words, "really engaged" seemed to contain some other meaning, one I could not understand or even perceive. I had never had such feelings before—there was wonder and excitement, happiness and sadness, all at the same time. I felt as if I was carrying a secret deep in my heart, and I feared that people might discover it. Whenever I woke, I could feel my heart pounding.

Chapter 17

ONLY a month had passed since my graduation from the convent school, but within that time I had experienced many things. I now felt calmer because the Shaos had promised Grandfather that I could take the school entrance examinations, and that they would be willing to let me go there if I passed. The decision about my moving into their house would not be brought up again until after the examinations.

Grandmother too seemed to feel reassured because of this. She said that from now on I belonged to his family and that they had to consent to any decision concerning me. I tried to set aside all my worries and concentrate only on the examinations. I was afraid that if I did not pass, it would be even harder to continue my education. In those days, there were only three or four women's normal schools in the whole province. Because of this, young women came from far and near, from all over the county, to take the examinations the Women's Normal School gave each fall. The school would accept only forty students in the entering class of the lower school, and I had heard that there were already more than four hundred applicants. On the first day of the examinations, I got up early and put on my blue-and-white striped linen coat and skirt. After combing my hair and washing my face, I had my morning tea and cakes. Then I again checked my writing brush, ink and ink stone, wrapped them carefully in a big blue kerchief, and went out the front gate with Grandfather.

The school was in the western section of Wuhu, a long way from my grandparents' home. Because it was still early, we could take our time. When we reached the city's west gate, we turned left and walked along a narrow dirt lane at the foot of the wall. Halfway down the lane was a walled compound with many spacious black-tile-roofed buildings. During the Qing Dynasty, it had been the home of a high official. When the Republic was founded in 1912, it became public property. Now it was the Women's Normal School. It had not been repaired for many years. The whitewash had flaked off and the walls were a patchy grey. Grass and moss had grown up among the roof-tiles and on the brick walls. The only remnants of the compound's original might and dignity were the main gate, its freshly-painted doors, studded with large iron nails, and two lively-looking unicorns that guarded it. A long wooden sign hung to the right of the gate. We went through the gate and followed pointing fingers printed on paper and pasted on the walls and ends of the buildings through several moon-shaped gates. We came to a large unpaved courtyard that surrounded a raised flower bed three feet high. A tall locust tree stood nearby. It was cool and shady under the tree, whose leaves and branches spread out like an umbrella. About ten feet from the flower bed was a large building with carved wooden doors. This was the hall where the examinations were being held. It was filled with rows of chairs and tables and was already half full of young women who were roaming up and down the aisles trying to match the numbers on their registration cards with those on the seats. After hunting for quite a while I found the hundred and fifth seat. It was in the middle of the twenty-first row.

During the morning we were examined in Chinese. Seven or eight men teachers monitored us. When we were all seated and it was time to begin, a young man teacher wearing a light blue cotton gown and gold-framed eye glasses walked onto the platform and wrote three topics on the blackboard. They were "Discuss the Women's Rights Movement," "Discuss Whether Books Should Be Written in the Language of the Classics or the Vernacular," and "Discuss the Value of an Education." Next to them he wrote, "Choose one of these three topics." Although the first two subjects were very topical, I had had no opportunity during my years at the convent school to hear them debated, so I could not write about them. I chose the third subject. After all, the question of my own education had been of great concern to me. I had never been able to set it aside, and had worried about it a great deal. How difficult it had been for me to get there that day for the examination. As I thought about the topic I felt I had been suppressing many ideas and feelings because I could not talk about them with my father or my grandparents. Now I could set them all out on paper. I quickly opened my ink box, ground my ink, and spread out the book of red-lined paper that they had handed us. I wet my brush in the ink and then I sat and thought for a while. First I wrote about the many advantages of an education. Then I described my family's coolness and objections to my desire for more schooling. I also wrote about how families too often favored sons and ignored daughters, and why it was wrong to consider it unimportant to educate girls. I wrote it all down, little by little, and when I got to the end, I could not stop myself from adding a radical section, saying I hoped that there would soon be more schools for girls everywhere so that daughters would be taken as seriously as sons and prejudice against girls would be done away with. I added several exclamation marks at the end of each sentence. My feelings were so strong that I could not control my pen, and I saw that I had written more than three thousand words without stopping. After I finished, I reread it carefully three or four times and corrected a few words. I felt that although my essay might not be profound, it had flow and unity and was full of sincerity and passion. I hurried up and gave my booklet to the teacher. When I went outside to the courtyard, I realized I had been the first to hand in my paper.

The mathematics examination that afternoon was very easy. On the second day, we were examined in history and English, and on the third day we were tested on general knowledge and given an oral examination. Then it was finally over. I felt somewhat relieved, but still anxious and impatient as I waited for the list of successful candidates to be announced. One morning two weeks later, Grandfather was sitting in the living room reading our local morning paper. I saw that the list of the successful candidates was on the last page. In big characters right at the top were the words, "Zhou Baowen and thirty-nine others have been accepted for the first year of lower middle school." I snatched the paper from Grandfather and stared and stared, and still could not believe it. I told Grandfather and Grandmother and then I ran to the school to see if I could learn more. When I reached the dirt lane, I saw a large crowd of young women students reading the notice posted on the main gate. I squeezed in among them. Pasted on the grey brick wall was a large sheet of white paper on which all our names were written, and mine really was the first. Suddenly I felt calm and full of peace.

Grandmother did not say anything but cooked two extra dishes for dinner that night. I understood. Although she did not think much of my wish to study and disapproved of my going to school, she was still happy that I had placed first in the examinations. She refilled my dish several times and urged me to eat more meat and vegetables, because I had lost weight studying. Grandfather smiled too, but said only, "Good. You really hit the bull's-eye by coming in first."

I felt happy but troubled—I wanted to laugh and cry at the same time. As I ate, I could not keep my eyes from smarting, but a little later I realized I had a smile on my face. This was the first time in the month since I had been at home that I could smile with peace in my heart. Although I could not look forward to a smooth, easy path laid out for me by my parents, like more fortunate girls my age, and had not dreamed that my future would be beautiful, at least I knew now that I could go to school in the fall. How difficult it had been! I also felt proud of myself because I could say, "This was due to my own efforts." However, I was under no illusions, and hoped only that nothing more would happen before school opened. It would be best if I could be allowed to be a boarder like the other girls, but if not, going as a day student would also be good. I hoped that there would be no more talk of my moving to the Shao family's.

A month remained before the start of school and the Shaos seemed much concerned about my affairs. A few days before the examinations Mr. Shao had come over to talk with Grandfather. They had sat in the living room, but I had gone into the bedroom to avoid meeting him. I heard him ask about my taking the examinations, saying, "My wife is not entirely at ease. She asked me to come especially to make inquiries. If there is anything Baowen needs, tell us and she will buy it for her."

The afternoon after my name had been posted, Rolan paid me a surprise visit. Although she and I had both attended the convent, we had never been close. Now, because we had not seen each other for a long time and our relationship had suddenly changed, I felt ill at ease and embarrassed to see her unexpectedly. I did not know how to greet her and was grateful when Grandmother came to help. Rolan was at ease and the same as she had always been. She smiled and called me "big sister" and showed me more affection than she ever had before.

We talked for a while. Then, as she was getting ready to leave, she waited until the two of us were alone and whispered, "Big sister, Mother told me to congratulate you for achieving first place in the examinations. Our whole family is pleased. She told me to come and see you and ask you face to face if you need anything. She said that you have no mother and that not enough people are concerned about you. Now my mother is your mother." As she spoke, she took a little parcel wrapped in a handkerchief out of her pocket. She unwrapped it and handed me an embroidered silk handkerchief and five bright new silver dollars. "My mother said that this is for you to use, to buy whatever small things you need."

When she said this, I was filled with gratitude, but also tongue-tied. I also felt too embarrassed to reach out and take the gift. Rolan placed the handkerchief and the coins on the arm of my rattan chair and murmured, "Put them away and don't let anyone see them."

From then on, she started coming to see me every two or three days, and every time she came she would bring me a gift—silk stockings from their general store, embroidered slippers, a little silk fan from Hangzhou, or a message from her mother. Sometimes she would mention her elder brother, but only when we were alone. Without realizing it, I started developing a warm affection for the whole family. Then, one day, she brought a little pink envelope. I knew as soon as I saw it that it was a letter from Zhongyao. I waited until she left then I went into my bedroom, opened and read it. On the pink notepaper were formal ideographs written with a fountain pen. He had addressed it to "Miss Baowen," and in the letter he asked me if I was well and said he hoped that from now on we would often exchange letters. After I read the letter, I hid it under my pillow. A little while later, I took it out and read it again—I don't know why. Although the words were commonplace, I now understood one thing, that this betrothed husband whom my parents had chosen for me had no ill feeling towards me. I seemed to read between the lines and words that he felt some affection for me.

During this period, I spent a lot of time by myself. The days were very lonely. The joy I had felt while growing up in that old racetrack apartment could never come back. Some of the families we had known had left and others had moved in. Also, I was older and had different interests, and we had nothing in common to talk about. Because I was engaged, I could not go outside the main gate. All I could do was walk from morning to night, day after day—around the upstairs gallery and downstairs in the courtyard—or go to the kitchen. My grandparents also had more problems and they did not talk much. Sometimes I would visit schoolmates who lived nearby, or Mrs. Cheng's daughter. During that period there was so much fear of idle gossip that young women were not allowed to go out of their homes. The only thing we could do was visit one another's homes and talk. So I looked forward to Rolan's frequent visits.

A few days later, she brought me a second letter from Zhong-yao. It was longer than the first, on two pages of notepaper. Besides his words of greeting, he wrote about how he was spending the summer vacation and how he studied. He also wrote that he hoped every day for an answer from me and that he often thought of me. After reading this letter, I hid it under my pillow and hid the first one in my clothes chest. Then I sat down to write a reply, a few lines of guarded greetings. I knew that since our parents had betrothed us we were permitted to exchange letters, but I dared not write freely or much.

About three weeks before school began, Grandmother again brought up my move to the Shaos', about which I was so apprehensive. But this time her attitude was different from the first, when she had called it unjust and had suggested a plan of action. She said only, "Baogu, Mrs. Shao still wants you to move there soon. Mr. Shao has told your grandfather that your studies and everything else can be planned better if you are living with them. The family has already chosen a day. Mrs. Shao says they will invite only a few close relatives and women guests, and no outsiders." She sighed. "Why don't they wait another two or three years and carry you through their gate formally, in the red embroidered sedan chair and with the horns blowing and gongs beating? Then our family also could add something at least to your trousseau. It'd be better for our reputation. Zhongyao has many younger brothers, and a formal wedding would give you more standing among your sisters-in-law.... But your father and stepmother are faraway. They can't even manage their own affairs —I'm afraid they have no attention to spare for yours. If your third uncle were not sick in bed, it'd be easier to make arrangements. Your grandfather and I have no say in it, however—it would only create difficulties if we refuse them. After all, it's too late now—you're now a member of that family and you'll spend your life there. We've put it off for quite a while because you were so unwilling to go. But if you get on Mrs. Shao's bad side now, she may not say anything, but once you go to live with them she could make your life difficult.

"I can't blame them. We can only blame your father for planning it so badly. The Shaos seem to be up-to-date. They will let you study after you move there. Then, when you are both sixteen or seventeen, you'll be married."

Grandmother lit her paper spill, but instead of smoking her water-pipe she held it in her hands as though she was thinking about something or waiting for my answer. I understood what she had said and knew that every word of it was true. Grandmother herself had faced no small amount of trouble and tragedy in her lifetime. She knew the situation women had to face, both in their homes and outside. Throughout her entire life, she had always made the best of adverse circumstances. She had been patient and yielding in everything and had never rebelled against her fate. And now she was hoping that I would knowingly and conscientiously follow her along that same road—because even if we suffered injustice it was better to bear it than to resist, for resistance might mean only more trouble and suffering in the end.

Still, I was two generations younger than she. Although I had come to feel some affection for the Shaos, I remained unwilling to go to their home as a child bride. I knew that child brides had even less standing and protection than slave girls. Although Mrs. Shao seemed to be treating me well now, I had no way of knowing what would happen once I had gone to live with them. And once I was in her home, I would have no control over my own decisions. She would hold all the power, and I would have to obey her in everything. What would happen if I were to refuse to go? I had already been accepted at the school. If I did not have enough money to pay the boarding fee, I could go as a day pupil. My grandparents would soon be moving to a new place and, though it was smaller than this one, I knew they would have room for me. The real burden would be to feed me, because their financial situation was getting worse and worse and they had to borrow money to get by. They were no longer able to find or borrow enough money to pay for Fourth Uncle's hospital care and medicine, even though they were getting them for half price. They planned to bring him home and nurse him there once they moved. If I went away, it would save them the cost of one person's food. Perhaps the Shaos knew this, and that was why they wanted to have me come and live with them sooner.

I thought and thought and in my frustration I thought about flying out of this big iron cage to a new way of life, one different from the old one Father and my stepmother had chosen for me. But where could I fly? Not a single road was open to me. I did not know where to go. Though Grandmother and I were two generations apart and the world had changed since she was young, the rules and customs of society and of our family had changed very little. From my earliest childhood on, I had been surrounded by circumstances that were like high walls, so tight and close that not even one breath of air could reach me. New currents had been stirring in the outside world, but I had never felt them. And even if I had, what use would it have been? I had no idea how to take care of myself. In those days, the professions open to women were pitifully few. Suppose I were to give up the idea of going to school and instead do as Xiulian had done, teach in a lower primary school. But no school would accept me without my family's permission, even if I offered to work for no pay.

I also realized that no matter how unfair everything was and how unwilling I was to go I could say nothing to Grandmother. She had already said all there was to say. She was a prisoner of the old ways. Even my own father did not care what happened to me. I was alone. My mother was dead. There was no one who cared about my pain.

Grandmother said nothing more. We both understood that I would walk the same road that she had walked. But because my road was to be that of a child bride, it would be even more difficult than hers, for she had been formally married into our family. I took out my handkerchief and kept wiping my eyes and nose. Grandmother said, "Baogu, if it makes you so unhappy, I'll ask your grandfather to go back to the Shaos once more and ask them to delay your move to their home even longer." Her voice was trembling.

"Delay ... it's no use. I know it's no use...."

Grandmother sat there a long time. Finally my weeping subsided. Then she sighed again and, as if talking to herself, said, "Child, you don't have any appropriate clothes to wear for the move to their home. I must have some made for you...."

Chapter 18

THE day I moved to the house of the Shao family, they held a banquet for about twenty guests. They said they had invited no outsiders, only close relatives and women friends they wanted me to meet.

Early in the afternoon, Grandmother began helping me dress and get ready. She told me I should wear the betrothal rings the Shao family had given me. One was solid gold and the other was set with a ruby. She said that if I did not wear them I would not display any wealth. She said that would look bad and that she was afraid Mrs. Shao would be displeased. I wore a new coat and skirt of pomegranate-red silk printed with tiny pomegranate flowers and green leaves, silk stockings, and embroidered shoes. Grandmother fastened fresh jasmine blossoms, wired in the shape of flying butterflies, to the black-and-white knotted shoulder button of my coat and in my braid, which she had combed until it hung gleaming down my back. Grandmother herself put on a finely-woven light grey, gauze-lined jacket and a pleated black gauze skirt that she had kept stored at the bottom of her chest for special occasions. She replaced her ordinary hair clasp with one of gold-plate and put on earrings of solid gold. While she changed and dressed and helped me to dress and look my best, she talked to me and told me in detail how I must behave.

It was like any other day, except that Grandmother and I were both all dressed up. Just before sunset, Grandmother summoned a rickshaw and took me, my little rattan box, and a bundle of clothes wrapped in a flowered kerchief to the Shao family's gate. Tears stood in the corners of my eyes and my head drooped almost to my chest. I followed behind Grandmother, taking a step and then hesitating, taking another step and stopping again until we reached the living room. The living room was brightly-lit. A pair of tall red double-happiness candles burned on the long red wood table along the back wall. The cloth on the square table and the chair cushions were of embroidered red satin. The room was full of guests, all of them wearing pearls and bright jewelry.

The perfumes of their rouge and powder mingled with the acrid smoke of the firecrackers that had just been set off. The smells circled around us and filled our nostrils, and laughter and conversation filled our ears. Grandmother stepped forward and led me towards the dining table. Then she said, in a slightly louder voice than usual, "Baogu, bow to your new grandmother."

"No need to stand on ceremony!" a woman's laughing voice called from nearby.

I did not know what to do.

Grandmother, on my left, tugged gently three times at the corner of my jacket and pushed me forward so I could do nothing but bend forward and make three deep bows.

After I made the three ceremonial bows to Zhongyao's grandmother, my grandmother led me over to his parents. Again, that laughing voice told me not to be so formal. I know it was Mrs. Shao who was talking to me. After I had bowed to them, Mrs. Shao led me over to bow to and greet their relatives and friends. My grandmother stayed right behind me, and if someone belonged to an older generation she would gently tug my jacket three times. If the person was of my own generation, she would tug once. So, although I was frightened and confused, Grandmother's secret signal told me how many times to bow. In this way, like the monkey in the monkey shows I had seen so often when I was small, I was led around the room. I never once lifted my eyes, but kept them glued to the floor. I knew, however, that everyone was looking at me, and I could hear their murmurs as they praised me. They commented on everything about me—my age, the shape of my feet, my hair, my ears, my nose and all the rest of my features, all of me, from head to foot. When the ceremony was over they paid me polite compliments and laughed for a while. Then they all went to the banquet tables.

After much polite hanging back and many urgings, everyone was finally seated in the proper order. Zhongyao's grandmother, her aged sisters-in-law and friends, the young granddaughters, and the little children all sat at the table on the left. His mother, her sisters-in-law, and her friends of her own age sat at the table to the right. Mr. Shao had left after accepting my ceremonial bows. Mrs. Shao wanted my grandmother to sit with Zhongyao's grandmother but my grandmother wanted to sit near me, so she was moved to my table. I had been seated to Mrs. Shao's right, the lesser side, and Grandmother sat next to me. The dishes, course after course of cold and hot meats and vegetables, arrived continuously. Mrs. Shao went around the tables several times and urged the guests to drink more wine. Whenever a new dish arrived, she would pick up some of the food with her chopsticks and put it on my plate. Grandmother would secretly press her knee against mine under the table as a signal, and I would half rise, bow, and take the plate with both hands. Before long, my plate was piled with all kinds of food but I never knew what it tasted like. I could not eat, but I kept holding my chopsticks so it would not be obvious. All the guests except Grandmother and I were laughing and talking gaily, and offering good wishes and compliments. They always began by talking about the wine and food and then edged around to Mrs. Shao and to me. First they praised her, saying it was fortunate that a woman so young had so prosperous a husband, and so many sons, and that she knew so well how to manage her household and build the family's wealth. They said it was rare to see someone so accomplished. Then they praised me, saying that I was pretty and graceful that my eight characters were auspicious, and that my destiny had to be fortunate, since I had come to this wealthy home as daughter-in-law to such a worthy father-in-law and virtuous mother-in-law.

Grandmother said a few modest words—that I was still young and inexperienced, and that from now on the Shaos and my new grandmother would guide me in everything. Mrs. Shao also pooh-poohed her guests' compliments, saying they had praised her too much and that their good fortune was due to blessings of the ancestors and the heavens. She said she only hoped that the family would continue to enjoy peaceful lives, and that all the relatives and friends would often honor them with visits. I heard what everyone was saying, but my mind was on other things. I felt a bit dizzy. By the time the second sweet course and the real banquet dishes arrived, I was starting to feel frightened. I knew it was late and that the feast would soon be over. That meant Grandmother would be leaving. I glanced over at her, but she was in the midst of a courteous exchange of food with the person to her right. She was dearer to me that day than she ever had been! I wanted her to stay longer—every minute was precious. I wished that she could take me back with her when she left. While I was thinking these confused thoughts, the maids and slave girls began handing around hot towels and tea. Then everyone got up and left the tables. When Grandmother stood up, I stood up too and clutched at her sleeve. She waited until no one was looking and then whispered into my ear, "Be well and be good. Take care of yourself. Soon Grandfather will come and bring you home for a few days."

The tears I had been suppressing for so long sprang from my eyes when she said this. Just then, Mrs. Shao came over to us and began talking with Grandmother. I dodged behind Grandmother and dabbed at my cheeks with my handkerchief, letting go of Grandmother's sleeve.

Amid the noise of footsteps and farewells in the courtyard, I heard a gentle, melodious voice—my grandmother's. "In-laws, she is still young, and she lost her mother when she was very small," Grandmother said. "We hope that you'll teach her and be patient with her."

"Oh, yes, yes! That's right, Grandmother Zhou. Don't worry. She'll be like my own daughter." Mrs. Shao's loud, harsh voice, still tinged with laughter, drowned out everyone else's.

Everyone had left. The sounds of the rickshaws died away. In the living room, the maids were clearing away the dishes and sweeping the floor. I remained where I was, near the long table. Rolan came over to talk to me, then she and her mother led me across the front hall to a back room set off by a wooden partition. Mrs. Shao lifted the door curtain and said, "This is my mother's room. You will share it with her."

The room was crammed with massive, old-fashioned furniture. A high bed of carved sandalwood took up half the room. A large oil lamp with a glass shade the color of white jade stood on a small table next to the bed. Along the side of the bed was a long, narrow bench of red padauk wood that was used as a step. A small tea table stood on one end of the bench and next to that was a tall copper spittoon. The white linen bed curtains, stencilled with blue flowers, were looped over two large, carved silver hooks.

Mrs. Shao's mother, a large woman who looked about sixty, was sitting on the edge of the bed. She was smoking a long silver water-pipe. Mrs. Shao led me over to the bench and said with a smile, "Baowen, you now belong to our eldest son, Zhongyao. As soon as he was born, he was adopted by my mother and given her surname. She loves him best. Now you too belong to her family. From now on you must take good care of her and show her filial respect. Zhongyao's father and I come second."

The grandmother, who was blowing on her paper spill, was pleased with her daughter's words, and smiled so broadly that her eyes became slits. She gestured at the side of the bed with her paper spill and asked Mrs. Shao, "Are you tired? Sit down."

"No, no. I must go upstairs and make sure all the children are covered."

The door curtain moved and the slave girl who used to bring Rolan food at the school came in. Mrs. Shao said, "Xiao Lazi (Little Wax), have you lit the opium lamp in the master's room?"

"It's been lit, mistress," the girl answered. She went over to the bench and lit the opium lamp on the opium tray, which was on the bed.

"Mother, smoke a couple of pipes of opium and then go to sleep with Baowen," said Mrs. Shao. She yawned twice as she spoke. "It's late. I'm going to bed, too. Rolan, come with me. See you tomorrow."

"Baowen, big sister, see you tomorrow," echoed Rolan as she left the room behind her mother.

As they left, I watched Mrs. Shao from my place near the side of the bed. Her hair, as smooth as satin, was in a round chignon that touched the high collar of her jacket. She was wearing a tight-fitting suit—the square-cornered jacket was of fine light jade green linen and under it was a long black skirt of soft gauze. Although she was not slender, she walked gracefully. It was only since we had come into this room and she had been standing and talking that I had been able to get a good look at her. Unlike her guests, who had powdered their faces chalk-white and rouged their cheeks deep red and worn many jade ornaments on their heads and hands, she wore few ornaments. Her oval face showed no trace of rouge or powder, and her only jewelry was a round gold bracelet on her left wrist. Both her shoulder button and the button at her collar were of green jade and as big as beans. Perhaps because she had drunk two cups of wine, the corners of her eyes were slightly red and she had spots of color on her cheekbones. She was polished and elegant and had been born knowing how to dress. My grandmother had guessed her age at thirty-four or thirty-five, but she looked no more than thirty. As I remembered, her eyes turned upward at the corners, giving her a shrewd, alert look, and the hair at her temples had been plucked as evenly as if it had been cut by a knife. I could not understand why I could not feel close to her, even though she was so attractive and kept smiling at me. Maybe it was that harsh voice. I never felt any warmth or kindness in it, only a sharp, cold edge.

After Mrs. Shao had left, her mother told me to sit down on the bed. She got up, put the water-pipe on the tea table, and brushed the ashes off her coat. She went over to the high wooden chest, bent over, and opened its lower doors. She took out a porcelain plate. Then she brought out a large drum-shaped red-and-green-flowered jar. She put it on the side table, took out several handfuls of big honey dates, and piled them on the plate. Then she replaced the jar and shut the chest. As if talking to herself, she said, "I can't leave any of my things out. Those little brats get into everything as soon as I turn my back." As she spoke, she handed me several honey dates. "Eat them, eat them," she said. Then she set the plate on the middle of the bed beside the opium tray. She lay sideways on the other end of the bed and picked up a fine, sharp, iron stick about five inches long from the opium tray. She used the stick to dip out some earth-colored opium paste from a tiny copper box about an inch square. She slowly heated the opium over the pea-sized flame of the glass lamp, which was as big as an egg.

Her face, figure, and voice resembled her daughter's, but because of her age she was stouter. She had very little grey in her hair, only a few patches at her temples and on top of her head. She was wearing four or five wide, heavy gold rings, which gleamed in the lamplight. Her voice was slow and direct, and her easy manner had none of her daughter's hardness.

"Last year, when I had heart pains," she said casually, turning the iron stick around and around to cook the opium. "I got into the habit of smoking this stuff. I've thought about stopping, but your father and mother said, 'You're old, you don't have any other bad habits—why give it up? Perhaps if you got rid of this, you'd develop some worse habit. We don't care about the cost—we can afford it. Use it to cheer yourself up—smoke a couple of pipes and get rid of your boredom.' Now, whenever they buy it for your father they always bring me a little, too. I don't smoke much, only in the evenings, and only a few pipes.

"Your mother's only fault is that she's a little impatient. When she gets impatient, she has a sharp tongue. When she's in a good mood she's very dutiful, but when she's angry no one can stand up to her. Even your father doesn't dare open his mouth. But she doesn't hold grudges, either."

She was smiling. Her eyes were partly closed. Then rolling the stick, she moved the bead of hot opium to the bowl in the center of the foot-long pipe, held the bowl near the flame, and drew in the smoke. The strong, slightly sweet smell of the opium filled my nostrils. The door curtain moved and Xiao Lazi came in carrying a big pot of water. She went over to the small table and filled the thermos bottle with boiling water. Then she came over to the bench. As she spoke, she eyed me smilingly.

"Honorable old mistress, Mrs. Zhang wants to know what you want for a midnight snack."

Zhongyao's grandmother had just finished inhaling the opium. She had her lips clamped together and she did not reply. She sat up a bit, picked up the teapot on the opium tray, and drank several swallows of tea from the spout. Then she took a deep breath and swallowed both the tea and the smoke. She exhaled the leftover smoke. "What is there?"

"Lotus seed and red date gruel. There's a small pot of chicken and ham soup left over from the banquet. Mrs. Zhang has added thin noodles to it."

"I think I'll have the gruel. Put in some extra white sugar. Baowen, what about you?" I shook my head because I did not want anything, but she told Xiao Lazi, "Bring her a small bowl of the soup."

The slave girl answered, "I understand." She refilled the teapot on the bed with hot water and left.

Zhongyao's grandmother picked up the iron stick again and began cooking a second bead of opium, chatting with me the whole time.

"Now that you are here you must learn to understand your mother's personality—I'm helping you because you're a member of my own family now—so I will be partial to you. When she speaks, you must always listen, and if she gets angry you must not answer and must pretend nothing's wrong. That will please her.

"Now, about Rolan—she's still young, but she's mature for her age. She's very aggressive and always wants to be first. Your mother loves her best, and your father loves his sons, but even the boys have to give way to Rolan half the time. You must try never to contradict her, and let her words be gone with the wind. Forget them. I'm telling you all this so you'll know what's what. But you must believe we all love you!

"Everyone in the family says I'm partial to Zhongyao and love him best." When she spoke his name, she smiled even more broadly. "I feel he's special, different from the others. He's mine. As soon as he was born, he was given to me, and has my surname, Shen. I've raised him myself. He's perceptive, and respectful to me. He's more attached to me than to his mother, and I'm very attached to him." She had begun smoking her second pipe of opium. When she finished, she swallowed more tea. Then she changed sides of the bed with me and lay down on her side. Xiao Lazi came in with the food. Zhongyao's grandmother sat up and took the bowl of gruel. Xiao Lazi handed me the other bowl.

I was sitting stiffly on the edge of the bed. I felt dizzy. The smell of opium was suffocating. My head ached and my stomach was churning. I felt nauseated and did not know how I could bear to swallow anything with oil or meat in it. Besides, we had never been in the habit of eating at night at my grandparents'. But I had to take the food, even if I could not eat. I forced myself to eat a couple of mouthfuls, then set the bowl down again.

Zhongyao's grandmother ate her gruel hungrily. After she finished, she washed out her mouth with tea and spat it into the spittoon. Then she lay down again and began heating her third pipe of opium. She seemed more awake than ever and asked me many questions about how my grandparents and I had lived —what time we went to bed at night and got up in the morning, and whether Grandfather and Grandmother were in good health. She also asked about my third uncle. It was because my grandparents had decided to bring my uncle home for nursing that they had sent me to live with the Shao family—they were afraid that his lung trouble might be contagious. She also told me that she did not want me serving her but that every day before I went to school and when I came back, I should go to Mrs. Shao and see if she wanted me to do anything for her. She said Mrs. Shao was insistent about things like that, but that she herself was not. Then she warned me that my mother-in-law was very particular about cleanliness. "When you do anything for her, remember to first wash your hands very clean with soap," she said. The last thing she told me was that if I needed anything when I started school, I should tell her and no one else and she would give me the money.

I listened to all of this as carefully and attentively as I could. Although Grandmother had warned me to be on my guard all the time, and to observe my father-in-law's and mother-in-law's expressions and to act accordingly, her advice had all been too general. She could not tell me all the details about how the Shao family actually lived. The old woman seemed to be lighting a lantern for me that would lead me on my path and guide me as I walked the steep, uneven road that lay ahead. And, as I listened, I felt, though I tried to resist it, a blanket of cold sadness creep over me.

It must have been after two o'clock before we went to bed. When Xiao Lazi brought in the wash water and tidied up the opium tray, she put a thin quilt at the foot of the big bed, towards the inside. I realized that I was to sleep with my head at the foot of the bed, while Zhongyao's grandmother would sleep at the head of the bed. I also noticed that my little rattan box and bundle of clothes were both on the rattan chair at the foot for the bed. I opened the bundle, took out the flowered cotton long underwear my grandmother had made for me, and went behind the bed to change. Zhongyao's grandmother waited until I had rolled myself up in the quilt before she turned down the lamp. She sat up at the head of the bed and smoked her water-pipe several times. Then she lay down to sleep.

I was curled up with my head at her feet and my face to the wall. Although the bed was big and wide, I dared not move for fear of touching her. But I was feeling a little less upset. In this dark corner of the bed, I seemed to have found my own heaven and earth—my own small universe. Suddenly tears gushed from my eyes like water from a bottle that had been turned upside-down. I could not stop crying. My nose immediately became stopped up, and I could not breathe. I had to try to breathe through my mouth without making too much noise because I was afraid that if I breathed too loudly, Zhongyao's grandmother would hear me. Fortunately, however, she fell asleep quickly and in a very short time was snoring deeply. I was exhausted in both body and mind, but late as it was I could not get to sleep. The sticky, slightly sweet smell of the opium filled my mouth and nose, and bung in the air. After a while, I heard Mrs. Shao, in the room off the living room, telling Xiao Lazi to pour the wash water. I also heard her ask the little slave-girl what her mother and I had been talking about.... So late, and they were still not in bed! But Mrs. Shao also smoked opium, and I had often heard that people who smoked opium always went to bed late and were at their most wide-awake in the middle of the night.

My brain felt as tightly wound as the springs of a clock, and my thoughts swung back and forth like a pendulum, thinking of the future, of the past, and of the present. I kept seeing Mrs. Shao and hearing her voice. and I also thought about how she had told the guests that her two oldest sons had left for the school on Haojia Hill the day before. So I knew that Zhongyao was away and that I would not see him the next day. But I felt that was all to the good—it would have been hard on me to have him there.

Because his grandmother had told me I had to go and greet Mrs. Shao before and after school each day, I realized that the family had decided against letting me live at the school. I thought about what the grandmother and my own grandmother had said and realized clearly that, if I was to have any standing in this household, the most important thing was to please my mother-in-law. I was now living in their home and had no mother of my own. I was truly willing to consider Mrs. Shao as my own mother —and had she not told Grandmother that she would treat me like her own daughter? I could only hope that she meant it and was not just being polite.

I thought of all that had happened and all that could happen. My thoughts darted every which way. I found myself thinking about the grandmother holding her long opium pipe and twirling the slender rod in her fingers. I thought about the toy man I used to see outside our gate when I was small. He shaped figures of dough with a long bamboo stick the same size as the opium rod, and twirled it just as quickly. How skillfully he worked the dough, and how finely detailed his ancient operatic heroes and famous generals were! And he dressed all the little figures in full costume —the soldiers were in armor and carried spears, the old men had long beards, and the Western women characters had long sleeved dresses with pleated skirts, wide-brimmed foreign hats, and foreign parasols.... All these irrelevant thoughts and strange ideas drifted in and out of my mind.

From the street came the faint sound of the bamboo stick that signaled three o'clock. The room was sunk in silence except for Zhangyao's grandmother's snoring. Everyone but me seemed to be fast asleep. It was pitch-black outside the bed curtains. I had not noticed when the lamp had gone out. The deep night was cool enough that I felt a bit chilly. I pulled the thin quilt closer around me.

Chapter 19

BEFORE many days had passed, I began to understand the Shao family's household and personalities.

Zhongyao's grandmother was kind to me. She kept the promise she made the night I arrived. She always favored me, helped me, cautioned me, and counselled me. When I had been living at home, I had never had to be very cautious, but now that I was with the Shaos, I had to remember to constantly be on my toes.

My first few days there, I was startled awake early each morning by the dawn light that slanted through the bed curtains from two small glass skylights in the ceiling and by the clattering footsteps of the shop apprentices and clerks, who slept in the loft over the shop, as they came downstairs. The two sections of the family living quarters were attached to the back of their general shop. No matter how sleepy I was and how unwilling to get up, I dared not linger under my quilt. I would get up quietly and go behind the bed to comb my hair and change my clothes. Then I would take the wash basin across the courtyard into the kitchen to get hot water so I could wash my face. Except for Da Biao Sao (Older Cousin Sister-in-law), a distant niece of Mr. Shao's whose real name I never knew, and the servants, everyone in the family would still be comfortably asleep.

I would have breakfast with Da Biao Sao in the living room. Then she would station herself at a small table in the hallway, across from the grandmother's room, and sew shoes for the children. I would go upstairs with Xiao Lazi and help her get Rolan and her seven-year-old brother up and ready for school. They both attended primary schools that opened earlier than the Women's Normal School. Xiao Lazi and I would fetch the wash water, get out their clothes, put on their shoes and socks, and put their book-bags in order. Then Rolan and her brother would go downstairs for breakfast. I would stand behind Rolan and comb her hair. By the time they had been prodded out the door, the five-year-old would be up. Children like anything new, so he wanted me to do everything for him and refused to let Xiao Lazi help him. The Shaos also had another son, one-and-a-half years old, but he had a wet nurse. By the time the five-year-old was washed, dressed, and helped with his breakfast, the sun would already be high above the brick wall of the back courtyard. Then Zhongyao's grandmother would get up. Da Biao Sao would put down her sewing and help her. A short time later, we would hear my mother-in-law stirring in her room. Xiao Lazi and I would hurry out to the backyard, where we would wash our hands thoroughly and share the chores of carrying the hot and cold water, the white porcelain wash basin, the yellow wooden foot tub, and the large and small bath towels to her room. We would help her get up and wash her face and feet.

Mrs. Shao treated me warmly and good-naturedly and did not give me any orders. When Xiao Lazi and I came into her room each morning, she would say, "Baowen, let them do it." But I went on helping, and she did not stop me. I could see that what her mother had told me was correct—Mrs. Shao was very particular about cleanliness. All the furniture in her room—the tables and chairs, the long step-bench, the spittoons, the stools, the knickknacks, the sheets and quilt covers, and the silk gauze bed curtains with their silver curtain hooks—were all in perfect order. Everything had to be neat and clean without a speck of dust. Needless to say she was just as immaculate about her own person. Everything she wore, even her handkerchief, had to be pressed perfectly smooth and without a crease. Every morning, a professional hair dresser who went from house to house came and combed her hair until it was as smooth and glossy as black satin. She also liked to wear fresh flowers. Every morning, the woman flower-seller would bring a big basket of seasonal flowers and ask her what she wanted to wear that day. Although Mrs. Shao was so particular about her own appearance, she did not pay much attention to her children or servants. The five-year-old and seven-year-old often had their noses running down to their lips, but she did nothing for them. Da Biao Sao, Xiao Lazi and the women servants were all kept so busy all day that they never had time to tidy their hair and clothes or to wash their faces, but she never said anything. The only other person she paid attention to was Rolan—she was very concerned about her daughter's clothes, shoes and socks, and hair.

Mrs. Shao exerted strict control over the household. Everything ran according to a rigid plan. Although she never lifted a finger to do anything herself, no one else ever had a moment's rest. Everyone—Da Baio Sao, the women servants, Xiao Lazi, the wet nurse, and the cook—had specific duties. Rewards and punishments were also clearly spelled out. When any of the servants saw her, they seemed slightly afraid of her. They were less afraid of her mother and Mr. Shao.

Mr. Shao was seldom home during the day. He was kept very busy with his two stores. It was only when he came home for dinner that he had time to talk and laugh with the children and watch them argue, fight, and play with one another. After dinner he would drink tea in the living room and talk for a while. Then he and his wife would go to their own room to smoke opium. Mrs. Shao's mother would then whisper to me, "Baowen, follow your mother and take care of the tea water. Even if there's nothing to do, sit in a corner and don't leave until she tells you to." There was nothing I wanted less to do, but I had to follow them and sit on a little stool near the footbench and watch idly as they heated the opium and talked. The children, talking and laughing, often surrounded their parents' bed. They would play for a while, eat something sweet, and then go to bed. After I had helped put them to bed, I would return to Mr. and Mrs. Shao's room, where I would sit and wait, until my mother-in-law told me to go to bed. Then I could leave. It was like receiving a pardon.

Mr. Shao was tall. His face thin and square, his skin was yellowish, and his forehead bulged a little. He looked about forty, and his temperament was in many ways the contrary of his wife's. He was not very particular and was casual about his clothes, his food, and how he lived. He was always amiable to everyone in the household. But his amiability was an expression of his own self-confidence and self-satisfaction, as it often is with successful businessmen. This was most obvious when he smoked opium and when he was with his sons. When he was smoking opium, I would hear him talking with his wife with mingled pride and amusement, saying, "Xiao Lao Wu (Little Old Five)—he's certainly strong. I'm afraid Xiao Lao Si (Little Old Four) will never be able to beat him in a fight. They certainly are lively, our little ones! Some of the things they come out with make you split your sides laughing!"

Mrs. Shao would smile and nod in agreement.

Although Mr. Shao seldom spoke to me, he would nod and answer my greetings whenever we met, and it seemed to me that he would treat me well. On my third day in their home, he happened to see a woman flower-seller passing his store. He bought some fresh flowers for me. Zhongyao's grandmother saw him, and bought some flowers too. She gave Rolan the ones Mr. Shao had bought and gave me the others. Once we were alone she said that Mr. Shao seldom spent money on such things and that when she had seen him buying flowers, she knew they had to be for me. She had bought some more because she was afraid that Rolan would be jealous if she didn't get any. That same evening, my mother-in-law told Mr. Shao that she wanted to have a couple of new suits made for me because I would be starting school in a few days. She asked him to bring home enough light-grey alpaca from the drygoods store so she could have a coat and skirt made for herself and for me. He agreed. He also asked me if I had made all the arrangements for entering school and if I needed anything else. He said that if I did I was to tell Mrs. Shao. Then he added, "Baowen, this is now your home. From now on, no matter what you want to do, you must first ask your mother. If you make any mistakes or say anything wrong, she'll correct you. But you must never answer back. Your mother's heart is soft but her tongue is sometimes sharp. After she reprimands you, she won't hold a grudge against you."

"What a thing to say!" My mother-in-law seemed to disagree. Her voice was a bit louder than usual. "Why meddle in what doesn't concern you by bringing up things like that?"

"I'm just trying to be helpful. There's always a chance that someone as young as she is might be a bit thoughtless...."

"That's no reason for a scolding!" She interrupted.

He smiled at her and handed her the opium pipe he had just finished heating. "Try a whiff and see."

She said nothing more, but accepted pipe, held it over the opium lamp, and smoked it. Mr. Shao picked up the little teapot and sat up on his elbows to drink from the spout. Suddenly he seemed to think of something. He put down the pot and said to me, "Your mother doesn't have the slightest compulsion to smoke opium. She just keeps me company sometimes by smoking a whiff or two to relax."

Whether Mrs. Shao had a compulsion to smoke opium or not I was never sure. Every evening when Mr. Shao was smoking, he would heat a pipe and give it to her. I never saw her refuse it, and I never saw her smoke more than one.

Mr. Shao seemed to obey his wife in everything, no matter how minor, and to agree with her about all things at all times. In the evenings as they leaned face-to-face on the bamboo couch smoking opium, he would always listen with great interest as she recounted, in the most minute detail, everything that had happened that day. How mischievous Xiao Lao Si was! Coming up with pranks a grownup would never think of, such a head full of ideas. How perceptive Xiao Lao Wu was! If anyone said his nose was too flat or that he was not handsome, it meant an immediate fight. How clever Rolan was, nothing escaped her! If she said a catty was a catty and an ounce an ounce, no one could out-argue her. How thickheaded and clumsy Da Biao Sao was! No matter how often she was shown how to make shoes, she never learned —she just sat there with her sad face from morning to night. Mrs. Shao would also complain about how Xiao Lazi and the servants wasted time and were lazy when she was not around and how she could not turn her back on them for a moment.

Mr. Shao would listen, nod when he should nod, and compliment her, and shake his head emphatically, many times, when what she was saying called for it. When she left off, he would recount his day, what he had done and the people he had seen, and recount, also in minute detail, how business had been, how much had been taken in and spent. If he came up with any plan or wanted to do something, he would always consult her first, saying, "What do you think? Do you think it's a good idea to do it that way?"

Though she did not nod or shake her head or praise her husband the way he did when he listened to her, Mrs. Shao always heard him out with a mixture of appreciation and admiration. When he asked for her opinion, she would speak slowly, as if her reply were the result of long deliberation. "I think it will be all right that way."

"Then that's what I'll do."

"Then it's settled." And so the matter would be settled.

Mr. Shao did not need to concern himself about the everyday details of his life because his wife took care of everything. Each morning when he left the house, no matter whether it was cloudy or clear, cold or warm, his clothes and hat were ready; and when he came back each afternoon his pipes, his tea, his meals, and everything else were prepared as they should be. He had no need to open his mouth because Mrs. Shao had long since given orders to the servants. People said he valued his wife not only for her skill in managing, but also because her own favorable destiny had given her husband wealth and many sons. During my first few months with them, I learned little by little from Zhongyao's grandmother that all of Mr. Shao's property, his house and his shops, had come to him from her family. Mr. Shao came from a poor family and had been an apprentice in his father-in-law's general store. Mrs. Shao's mother said that because he was intelligent, did his work well, honestly and thoroughly, and endured misfortunes bravely, her late husband had gradually come to favor him and promoted him from a clerk to an accountant. Then her husband began having breathing problems. He was no longer able to oversee the business, so my father-in-law gradually took over.

One day Zhongyao's grandmother talked about how her daughter's marriage to Mr. Shao had come about. "There were I don't know how many wealthy local families that sent people to talk about a match, but her father was reluctant to give her to any of them. He always said, 'If a person has only property, but lacks character and ability, then even if the family has mountains of gold, it could all be eaten up. The most important things are character and ability.' It turned out that he had developed a plan of his own, although he had not said anything about it. He waited until he was on his death bed and then called me over and said, 'I know I'm dying. We have only one child, only our daughter and the shop. I think Shao Anlin will be successful—he's steady and honest and will make good. In him you'll find shelter and protection.'

"When I saw how ill he was and realized he would not live much longer, I said, 'Husband, I will do as you wish. I have no objections!' And that was how their marriage came about. When they were betrothed, I told Shao Anlin that I wanted him to live with us so that I might keep my daughter with me for the rest of my life. I also said, 'I want you to let me adopt your first-born son and let me give him my surname of Shen.' Anlin did not hesitate even a moment before agreeing to everything.

"It turned out that my husband had planned well for the future. Just speaking of our shop, we started out with only one little shop. Within five years of Anlin's taking over, it doubled in size. Later it doubled again, and now it's the largest or second-largest shop on Long Street. A few years ago he opened a drygoods store, so now we're even more prosperous. But he hasn't changed—he's still careful and frugal. As for his opium habit ... it was my daughter who said that he had worked too hard year after year to have any leisure. She said that men who reached middle age and had money to spend might get up to things they shouldn't, if there's no reason for them to stay at home. It took her two years of prodding and urging, but she finally got him to take up opium."

Zhongyao's grandmother had nothing to do all day. After meals, she would always take her silver water-pipe and have someone carry her chair out to the back gate, where she would sit, smoking and watching the stream nearby. She would watch the little wooden boats sailing back and forth and chat with the wife of the owner of the rice shop across the way. Or she might go out to the front and walk around the shop, watching the customers and the passers-by. She never questioned anything about her daughter's management of the household. As far as her own food and clothes were concerned, she was like her son-in-law, agreeable to whatever came. She always kept a little supply of money in her own purse. She also had a number of gold ornaments. Ordinarily, if she wanted to eat or buy something special, she would dig into her purse and send a servant out to buy it. When she was happy, she would recall things that had happened many years ago and tell about them in detail. If she felt depressed, she might not open her mouth all day. Sometimes, if the children annoyed her or if she and her daughter quarrelled and her daughter shouted at her, she would be angry and shut herself up in her room, or go out to the shop instead of staying in the living room. She would not come back until Mrs. Shao's anger had subsided and one of the children had been sent to invite her.

As my mother-in-law had told me my first evening there, I belonged to her mother's family. I still slept in the same bed with her mother. At night, when Mrs. Shao dismissed me and I had returned to our room, taken off my clothes, and gotten onto the bed, Grandmother would just be finishing her opium. She would be at her liveliest and would start talking about all her thoughts and feelings and everything that had pleased or angered her. I had been so busy all day that I was too sleepy to move. But she would sit at the other end of the bed and talk and talk. If a long time passed without my making a sound, she would ask, "Baowen, what is it? Have you gone to sleep already? I've been talking for a long time and you haven't heard a word."

"No, no ... I'm listening," I would force out a reply.

"Never mind. Go to sleep. It's not surprising that you need so much sleep—teenagers are so full of energy. And tomorrow you have to get up early. Go to sleep." She would mumble to herself for a while and then fall silent.

Of all the people in the household the only one whose position it took me a long time to understand was Da Biao Sao. I knew she was not a hired servant, but it was even clearer that she was not on the same level as the rest of the family. Mrs. Shao often acted as if she disliked her. One afternoon soon after I moved there, Da Biao Sao took a black cloth shoe upper she had just finished to her for her to look at. But Mrs. Shao was much displeased with Da Biao Sao's work. She said the stitches were uneven and that the rolled edge was crooked. She threw it on the table and told Da Biao Sao to rip off the edge and do it again. "I think this life of luxury has muddled your brain," she snapped. She went over to the carved, latticed door of the living room and exclaimed to the servants, who were eating in the courtyard, "How much better can I treat her? You've all seen it. When Baowen, our new eldest daughter, came, I told her to call her Da Biao Sao, I've never slighted her. I treat her same way I treat Baowen, but she always looks as if she's at a funeral. She doesn't know when she's well off."

Da Biao Sao did not say a word. She just picked up the shoe upper, went back to her table in the hallway, and went on with her sewing. But her thick lips were pressed tightly together and turned downward at the corners, showing that she thought Mrs. Shao had been unfair. Her complexion was greyish and dull and her face was expressionless. She looked older than Mrs. Shao, and I thought she was about forty, but in fact she was only twenty-seven. She had a large build, coarse hands, and big feet. Her cheekbones were high, but her eyes were small and because she was somewhat near-sighted she seemed to narrow her eyes to see better. This made them look even smaller. She always seemed sleepy, half-awake, and indifferent. She sat sewing in the hallway all day and seldom opened her mouth.

Once, when Grandmother and I were alone, I asked her about Da Biao Sao's husband. She told me that Da Biao Sao had been married off to a distant nephew of Mr. Shao's. They had been living in the country, where they ran a peddler's stand. But then misfortune struck—one day, when they were selling things at the roadside, a band of soldiers came along and forced her husband to go with them as a porter. She had not seen him since. She had received letters from him for a few years, but in the last year or two they had stopped. Mrs. Shao had felt sorry for her because she was young and orphaned and had been sold to a wealthy family as a slave and they had brought her to Wuhu to live with them and to sew for the children. Grandmother quoted Mrs. Shao as saying, "There's plenty of food for one more person. We'll never miss it. Besides, if we hired a stranger to do the sewing, she would eat, and we'd have to pay her besides."

I noticed that Mrs. Zhang was my mother-in-law's favorite servant. She was about thirty and was thin, clean, and quick. She was smart and had a sharp tongue, and she knew how to flatter my mother-in-law. She was quick to read her expression and to act accordingly. Even when my mother-in-law needed nothing done, Mrs. Zhang would go to her and flatter her with "Mistress" this and "Mistress" that. She cooked all the special meals and the family meals; the meals for the shop clerks and apprentices were cooked by a man cook. She also did little things for my mother-in-law, who trusted her completely.

The wet nurse was different. She was plump and honest and had just arrived from the countryside. She was tongue-tied and did not know how to flatter anyone, but my mother-in-law liked her because she was strong and had enough milk to feed the baby.

Xiao Lazi had to do all the odd jobs. Although she was my age, she looked only twelve or thirteen because she was undeveloped and her hair was thin and sparse. The children had nicknamed her Xiao Lazi because she had a bald spot on her head. No one ever used her real name. In addition to doing all the odds and ends of work, she also had to play with the little masters and the young lady of the house.

Over time, it just happened to come about that I became Xiao Lazi's assistant.

Chapter 20

TWO weeks after I moved into the Shaos' home, I started attending the Women's Normal School.

My mother-in-law had said at first that she was thinking of sending me to board there because it would be improper for a young woman of my age to walk down Long Street every morning and afternoon. But a few days later she changed her mind. She said that because I was such a new member of the family and because she did not yet know me very well, she wanted me to continue living with them for six months or so. She said she could then feel more secure about having me board at the school for the spring term.

A few days before school opened, she had a tailor come to the house to make me two skirts and jackets of light blue cotton, the school uniform. She also picked out two stylish new rattan book boxes, one for Rolan and one for me, from the family shop. Zhongyao's grandmother gave me the money for the other things I needed, paper and pens, and pocket money. But even after everything was almost ready, my mother-in-law seemed uneasy about my going back and forth to the school alone. Then she remembered that the Xiao family, who owned the silver shop across the street, had a daughter who was also a day student at the school. My mother-in-law took me to call on them so I could meet Mrs. Xiao and her daughter, Xiao Ming, and discuss our going back and forth together. That way, we could be companions and could look out for each other. Both Mrs. Xiao and Xiao Ming were very pleasant and happy to take my mother-in-law up on her suggestion.

The afternoon before school opened, Mrs. Shao and her mother were sitting in the living room drinking tea and cracking watermelon seeds and chatting about my starting school. And it was then, when everything had been decided and all the arrangements made, that my mother-in-law appeared to change her mind again. As if she had just thought of it, she chose that moment to ask me, "Baowen, tell me the truth—do you want to live at the school, or do you prefer to live at home and go as a day pupil?"

I knew she was asking me this to test me and to see if I liked what she had arranged for me. I knew that I ought to reply, "Mother, I am happy to live at home and go to school each day," but it went against my wishes too much, and I hesitated, unable to get out the words. Then her mother spoke up, saying with a smile, "How can you ask? Of course she's happy to go on living at home—if for no other reason than that the food and drink are so much more nourishing."

Perhaps it was true that Mrs. Shao's mother liked having me around as company. But I knew she had taken it upon herself to answer at that moment because she feared I would say the wrong thing.

Mrs. Shao's displeasure was clearly and immediately visible. Her eyes narrowed. She turned to her mother and said in a slightly louder voice than usual, "Mother, no one asked you. Baowen isn't a three-year-old baby. She's old enough to speak for herself. She doesn't need any help from you."

"Mother," I stammered, "I ... I'm happy to be living at home." I wanted to smile as I said it, but the displeasure on her face made my heart sink and my face freeze, and I could not force a smile.

Although my mother-in-law had never, from the day I arrived, said a harsh word to me, I had been a little afraid of her from the start. That fear had grown during my first two weeks there, once I had seen how submissive everyone in the house was to her and how she treated Da Biao Sao and the servants. I could not keep my heart from sinking. I had been anticipating going to school. But even if I had to be a day student, it would still be better than having to spend every day in the house, not knowing what has expected of me and always in suspense, and without a moment of leisure.

The Shaos lived at the entrance to Long Street. To get to the school, we had to walk all the way down that long, busy street and down two small streets besides. Even walking quickly, it would take us half an hour to get there. Xiao Ming was four years older than I and in the second year of upper middle school. We had originally planned to leave every morning at about eight so we would not need to hurry and would still have a few minutes to rest once we reached the school. I should have been able to manage this easily because I got up at daybreak and by the time I washed my face, combed my hair, changed my clothes, ate breakfast, and got ready it was still only about seven o'clock. But then I had to wait until Rolan and her brothers got up and go upstairs to help them and to comb Rolan's hair. I had to run up and down the stairs so much that I was often late and Xiao Ming had to come and wait for me. And though I was uncomfortable about this, I could not tell her the reason.

If my relationship with Rolan had remained the same, I could have talked with her and told her that, because I was now going to school and time was short in the morning, I wanted to comb her hair as soon as she got up. She could wash and dress afterwards and still not be late, because her school was nearby, while I would be able to leave sooner and not make Xiao Ming wait. But within a few days of my move into the Shaos' home, my relationship with Rolan had begun to change.

Before, when Rolan had come to see me at my grandparents' she had been the guest and I the hostess. We had gotten along as well as if we had been older and younger sisters, and had felt even warmer towards each other because we knew we were going to be members of the same family. Now that I was in their home, my relationship to her and my position in the family had both changed. She was the apple of her mother's eye, the complete little princess of the family, and I was an outsider. Not only that, I was a child bride. She and I could never be equals, all the more so because as the daughter of the family, she had all the advantages and would always outrank me. It became my duty to look after her and wait on her, even though I had not been brought there to be a servant. When I first came, her father and mother kept saying they would treat me like a daughter, but this undercut her position as the only daughter. Also her own grandmother treated me well and was partial to me. Rolan resented me —though she said nothing, I had no difficulty understanding what her sour, arrogant frowns meant.

Rolan was not yet twelve years old, but, as her grandmother had said, she had a mature mind, her speech was clever, and she always had to win. Because her mother had always let her have her own way, she was usually unreasonable and overbearing towards the servants, towards Da Biao Sao, and even towards her younger brothers. Young though she was, she woke up in a bad mood every morning. She did not yet feel free to lash out against me, but Xiao Lazi was a convenient target for her anger. And though she obviously disliked me, it was Xiao Lazi who had to bear the brunt of her displeasure, and of course had to swallow it all without daring to answer back. I pretended not to notice how she looked at me.

Sometimes when Rolan was bored, she would turn her bad temper on Xiao Lao Si. But he was not Xiao Lazi or me—he too was his mother's little darling, so he would not put up with her. When Rolan began berating him, he would glare at her and not yield an inch. "Pooh!" he would shout at her as if spitting. "You're just a girl—what's so special about that? Pooh! Do you think I'm afraid of you?"

The two of them would start hitting and kicking each other, shouting and running up and down the stairs. We would stand aside and watch, feeling annoyed but also amused, though of course we dared not laugh. We wanted to try to make peace, but dared not say much, because we would be blamed if we failed —however, we would also be blamed if we did not even try to stop them. Mrs. Shao, who would be on her bed, would hear her precious son and daughter fighting, and would start scolding us without even trying to find out who was to blame.

"What's wrong with you? Are you all dead? Are you good for nothing? They were fine. Who got them all upset, making them yell and hit each other?"

Those of us who were "dead" were, of course, Xiao Lazi, the wet nurse, Da Biao Sao, and Mrs. Zhang—all of us who rose early. I was included as well.

"Rolan! Xiao Lao Si! Stop fighting! Be good now and go to school quietly, and when you come back this afternoon I'll buy you something good to eat."

The two of them, hearing their mother and seeing that all of us were pleading with them to stop, would stop, but they would go on pouting and glaring at each other while they got ready for school. Then they would thrust their book-bags at Xiao Lazi and march out the front gate. Xiao Lazi would follow behind, a book-bag in each hand. Her thin, yellowish braid, which looked like a rat's tail, would swish back and forth against her dirty, greasy collar.

Although Mrs. Shao missed nothing when it came to managing the household and controlling all the people in it, she was over-indulgent and over-protective towards her children. Her attitude towards the two other boys was an example. She found Xiao Lao Wu, who had a bulging forehead and stammered, amusing and interesting because of his speech defect. And she said Xiao Lao Liu, the plainest of the children, had the loveable-ness of his ugliness. Not only did he have a bulging forehead, but his nose was also too short and it turned up at the tip. She would often laugh and say, "Oh, my little piggy, my little piggy, my little ugly one! How did you get to be so homely? Oh, I love you so much!" No one else, however, not even Mrs. Shao's own mother, could criticize his looks. Her sons and daughter were perfect and beautiful and without fault. If they quarrelled with others, it was of course the others who were at fault, and if they quarrelled among themselves it was also the others' fault because they had not taken good enough care of them and had provoked the yelling and hitting. Whenever she saw Rolan pouting and looking angry, she would call her gently by her milk name and croon, "My little pearl, my little precious, who's been mean to you? What's bothering you? Tell Mother—let Mother console you...." If she had not talked so much about easing Rolan's anger, Rolan might have gotten over it sooner, but because Mrs. Shao made such a fuss, Rolan used her anger to get more attention.

Under the circumstances, I thought myself lucky to have kept peace with Rolan. Even if she inconvenienced me in the morning, I did not want any trouble. And I wanted even less to humiliate myself by asking her for any favors.

In good weather, Xiao Ming and I could still reach school without hurrying too much, even if we left late, by walking faster. But on rainy days it was more difficult. The cement pavement on Long Street would get slippery, but it was still easy to walk on. The side streets, however, turned into mud in the lightest rain. Our rain shoes were heavy and clumsy and it took us three times as long to get there. We had to hurry to arrive on time, and whenever I saw Xiao Ming run into her classroom out of breath I felt apologetic. I felt like calling after her, "Xiao Ming, from now on, don't wait for me. When it's time to leave, go on ahead." But I could never get the words out of my mouth—because I did not want anyone to know about my situation, or because I did not want to lose my loveable and warm-hearted friend? I think it was some of both. Xiao Ming seemed to understand my difficulty and my unhappiness. Each afternoon when we arrived home and were about to part, she would smile at me and say, "I'd better come again for you tomorrow. See you then."

We never had to hurry on the way back. Xiao Ming and I would saunter along and chat. She was an officer of the student self-government association and she would explain its principles to me and tell me about its activities both inside and outside the school. I knew that my schoolmates who ran the self-government association were able young women who had new ideas and were respected by the rest of us. Xiao Ming often asked me about my impressions of the school—what courses and activities outside of lessons I liked, and what musical instruments I liked to play—but she never asked me anything about my life with the Shao family. For this I was grateful, because if she had, I could not have told her. People are often that way—if something pleasant and happy happens to them, they want everyone to know, but if they experience something unpleasant or humiliating, they will not talk about it, even with their closest friends. My situation in the Shaos' home was a pain I kept hidden in my heart. I wrapped it up well and did not want anyone to touch it.

Xiao Ming seemed to realize when we were approaching these subjects and was careful not to hurt me. Once, for instance, when I happened to mention that I knew how to play the flute and the *xiao*, a straight bamboo pipe, she invited me to join the flute and drum band at school. I hesitated a long time without being able to give her a definite answer. She considered for a while and then said, "Do you want to ask your family before you decide?" I nodded, unable to speak. Then, trying to make me feel comfortable, she added, "It doesn't matter. It's only an extra-curricular activity. It'd be nice if you could join, but it's not important if you can't."

At first, no one at the school except Xiao Ming knew about my situation, and she knew only a little. Perhaps because I had placed first in the examinations, my classmates always wanted to choose me to represent them whenever there was anything to be done. I could not accept, and my pride would not let me divulge anything about my real difficulties. I was therefore caught between acceptance and refusal. Sometimes, if it was something that did not require a public appearance and was not too time-consuming, I would let myself be forced into accepting—but I never dared say anything at home.

Before school began, my mother-in-law had told me several times, "Going to school is fine—our family is enlightened, not like those from the lower classes. In our family, daughters-in-law are the same as daughters, and must go to school and learn. But there must be limits, even to learning. Baowen, remember and never forget—you must not get involved with the fad for making disturbances and holding meetings and having demonstrations in the streets. Imagine—girl students on the streets with boy students, shouting and yelling with them, standing up straight with

175

no sense of shame, and not behaving like ladies! Think how that looks! You must behave and go only to classes. You must not even think about getting involved in any other activities."

So though I loved music and loved to play the flute and *xiao*, I knew I could not join the band. Not only would I have needed time to rehearse, but whenever the school had an outside activity and the students marched out in formation, the band led the way blowing and drumming and attracting the stares of the people on the streets. And no matter where we were going, we always had to go down Long Street. The Shaos would never give me permission. Sometimes, on my way to or from class or during the rest period after lunch, I would go to the courtyard outside the big hall where we had taken the examinations and which was actually the music hall, and sit in the flower bed under the locust tree, and listen to the band members practicing the program for the autumn school reunion. They would play new and ancient music. I felt the ancient rhythms and melodies were more beautiful and pleasing to the ear when played on the *xiao* or on the *erhu*, the two-stringed fiddle, or the organ. Sometimes, as I listened, I would forget the difficulties that confronted me, but at other times the music would make me feel especially sad and lonely.

If there was any activity at school that made me even a little late, Mrs. Shao would question me almost before I got through the door. "Baowen, why are you late? Have you been out playing with your friends?"

"No, I had something to do at school and it kept me late."

"What was it?" Mother-in-law would persist.

"The student self-government association called a meeting of the whole student body."

"A meeting! Why doesn't everyone just study hard? Why should there be meetings?" My mother-in-law's manner of speaking may have been slow, but she would not let things drop until she knew everything.

"It was called to discuss nominations for delegates to the provincial students' association and to elect officers for the self-government association."

"Oh." She was sitting in one of the dinner chairs and I was standing near the door. Because I was late and had hurried, I was hot and out of breath. Mr. Shao was sitting at the tea table drinking tea and smoking a cigarette. He said nothing, but only listened as his wife questioned me. She glanced at me a couple of times and, tapping lightly on the table, asked, "Were you elected?"

"No."

"If they should elect you, remember, you must never, ever accept."

I did not answer.

Then my father-in-law decided to take over. "Don't worry," he said. "I'll tell you a good way to get out of these things." He smiled as if he was pleased with himself for knowing a "good way." He put down his tea cup, inhaled a couple of big lungfuls of smoke, opened his mouth wide, and blew several big smoke rings. "If they ever elect you, you must stand up and say, 'My family has spent money to send me to school. They have sent me here to study and learn, not to attend meetings or to be a delegate.'"

What was so good about that? I was angry and I also wanted to laugh. I felt rebellious. I was not a baby. I bit my lips and did not make a sound.

My mother-in-law said, "I think it would be best if you did not even go to the meetings. When school is out, get your book-bag and come straight home."

"Even if I don't go to the meetings, I couldn't leave right away." I could tell that my voice had an angry edge to it and I swallowed to make it sound better. "I'd have to wait for Xiao Ming. She has to go to the meetings because she's an officer of the association."

"I never would have believed it! She looks so cultivated. I'd never have guessed that she liked to go to meetings."

"Well, even if you go, let them do the talking. Let them make the noise. You mustn't say anything or stir them up. That way they won't be able to get at you." Father-in-law did not want me going to meetings, but he was even less willing for me to walk home alone.

Rolan, however, was treated quite differently. If she came home on time, Mrs. Shao would worry that she was bored and would ask her gently, "Why are you home so early today? Why didn't you go to play with your schoolmates?" And if she came home late, her mother would worry that she had tired herself out playing. "Was there something going on at school? Did you have a good time with your schoolmates? How did your classes go? Did the teacher scold you? Are the two of you hungry? Go and tell them to bring you water so you can wash up. Then have something to eat and rest a while and relax."

"Xiao Lazi!" Rolan would shout impatiently. "Hurry up and bring me some water so I can wash my face!"

"Baowen!" Xiao Lao Si would bellow as if trying to out shout his sister. "Hurry up and pour the tea! I'm thirsty!"

Xiao Lazi and I would run around trying to keep up with them and take care of them until we were both going around in circles.

Chapter 21

EACH day when I got back from school, my mother-in-law had more and more sewing for me to do. So I had less and less time to prepare my lessons.

She told me, "This is for your own good, no one else's. You are our oldest daughter-in-law, so you must be a model for the rest of my sons' wives. If you don't even known how to thread a needle or do housework, you'll be a laughingstock and your sisters-in-law won't respect you. No one will make any allowances for you, even though you lost your mother when you were small and there was no one to teach you. Now that you're in my home you must learn all you can."

Then she asked, "Baowen, do you know how to knit?"

"Yes, Mother."

"Good. When it gets a little cooler I want you to knit one or two sweaters for each of the children. Hand-knitted clothes are always warmer and more durable than machine-knitted ones. And about your sewing—do you know how to make shoe uppers? Do you know how to roll bindings? You don't? Tsk, tsk!" Then she called out, "Da Biao Sao, hurry up and find some old cloth and teach Baowen to paste the stiffening for the uppers. Teach her to roll bindings too. Really! To not even know how to make shoes! Even if I didn't want you sewing for my children, would you want to have to call in others to make shoes once you have children of your own?"

I did not say a word. I just took a chair and went into the hallway, where I sat across the table from Da Biao Sao and began learning how to make shoes.

From then on, every day when I came home from school I would put down my book-bag and go to greet my mother-in-law and the others. Then I would go to the kitchen, boil water, and make a flour paste. I would pick over the scraps of cloth, paste them into a board, cut the paper patterns, and paste them onto the boards. My hands began looking like Da Biao Sao's, black and sticky. The little table in that long, dark hallway became our universe, hers and mine.

It was not that I was unwilling to learn how to do housework or make shoes—ever since I had moved there, I had tried to behave properly. How I had hoped that I would be able to treat her like a real mother. Although I had never put much stock in her promises to me and others to treat me like her own daughter, I had hoped for some warmth, some affection. I had hoped that she would treat me with respect and not insist on keeping me in my unfortunate and humble place of a child bride. For me to be learning housework and sewing, to be constantly waiting on Rolan and her brothers, and to be standing by in Mr. and Mrs. Shao's room to light their opium pipes and pour their tea and all those other tasks—these were no more than my duty. But the way these duties were being imposed was forcing me inexorably into the position of a servant or a slave. If my mother-in-law had been able to treat me even a little more kindly, I think I would have felt grateful to her, from the bottom of my heart, my whole life. But instead, I was as afraid of her as a mouse is of a cat or as a chick when it sees a weasel. In the years that followed whenever I thought of her, it was like remembering a nightmare. I would feel nauseated and cold. Even now, some of that fear is still with me.

As we sat in that dark hallway, Da Biao Sao and I spoke little except to ask each other essential questions about the work that had to be done. We all avoided talking among ourselves because Mrs. Shao was so suspicious of all of us. Our table was across the hall from Grandmother's room and near the living room—if we raised our voices in the least everyone could hear us. Often, when my back and head and neck began to ache from bending and I would lift my head and straighten my back, my eyes would meat Da Biao Sao's dull, lifeless glance. She would purse her thick lips and smile at me, a smile flavored with bitterness. I would return her smile silently, well aware there was no cheerfulness in it. I would look at her sallow face, at her lips, at her lifeless expression, and at her big, coarse, black-stained hands and then at my own dirty, paste-covered hands, and I could not help wondering, "Will I end up looking like her one day?" These thoughts frightened me, and I would quickly turn back to my sewing and think of other things. But Da Biao Sao was like a shroud over my future. As I sat across from her, I could not help seeing myself in her.

Now when I came back from school I had no time to study.

Since school had started, Mrs. Shao had let me leave their room before their midnight snack and Grandmother had moved the opium tray from the middle of the bed to her end so I could sleep on the inner side, but by the time I had helped Mr. and Mrs. Shao with their opium and tea and had attended to what I must do for myself—sometimes washing the clothes I had taken off—it would be after eleven o'clock before I was able to get into bed. By then I would be too tired to look at my books. The only time I had left for studying was what I was able to seize in the mornings, after I had gotten up but before having to tend to Rolan.

There were many lessons and outside activities at the school. The accommodations and equipment there were not as good as at the convent school but the teaching was much more progressive and there was more life and freedom in the courses because several young teachers, recent university graduates with new ideas, had recently joined the faculty. For example, Mr. Wei, who taught Chinese literature and history, had just come from Beijing University. He was the young man with the gold-rimmed spectacles who had written the three essay topics on the blackboard when I took the examinations. In his classes he often told us that we should not just accept and memorize what was in all the old books of the past but should think for ourselves. When we had questions, he would not hand down a conclusion, but would encourage each of us to get up and express our opinions. About once every two weeks, all forty of us would divide into two groups and debate any question we had not been able to resolve. He and a group of students who had been chosen as judges would make the final decision. In this way, he trained our ability to speak and stimulated our interest in learning.

Another of the new teachers was Miss Hai, who taught us music and physical education. She was only twenty-two or twenty-three and had graduated from a school in Shanghai that had a fine reputation in those fields. She was very lively and full of ideas. In our calisthenics classes, she would pat her own chest and tell us, "Students, students, look! Lift your chests and stand up straight! We are a new generation! We must move beyong the past! Don't be afraid! Don't be like your grandmothers, with bent backs and rounded shoulders. One-two, one-two, lift your heads and throw back your shoulders! One-two, one-two, forward, march!"

All the time she was clapping her hands and calling out the

orders, she would be keeping step. We all admired her strong, beautiful body, proud erect posture, and her quick, light footsteps.

I liked the school. I liked the teachers and my schoolmates. Every day when I left the dull, gloomy atmosphere of the Shaos' home, where there was no life or anything of interest, and entered the bright, shining atmosphere of the school, so full of happy voices and laughing talk, it was as though I had left the clouds and rain behind and was walking in the sunshine under a blue sky, I would immediately feel free and happy. At the school I was just like everyone else and not an inferior. In school I did not need to try to make myself feel cheerful or screw up my courage or be afraid of being watched and spied on and blamed for everything. I did not need to pretend to smile or to try to please others. I could be myself.

But even at school I could not entirely forget the dark shadow that was the rest of my life. Often, when I was at my happiest, listening to a lecture or chatting with my fellow students, I would remember that as soon as school was over I would have to return to the Shaos' home and my heart would sink. It was as if a great stone were blocking my path.

And when I got home, I would go on thinking about school. Sitting in that dim hallway with my head bent over my sewing, I would think about my lessons, about the new song Miss Hai had taught us, about her gay, free manner, and about how she always said, "We are part of a new age and must not be afraid!"

I would also think about Mr. Wei and how he looked as he strode back and forth on the platform explaining the lessons to us. He always spoke quietly, except in history class, when he would talk about China and the foreign powers and the unequal treaties that had followed the Opium Wars and the Kuomintang government, which he said was rotten and corrupt and unwilling to improve the lot of the people. These aroused his anger and his manner became stern. Whenever he spoke we all concentrated, and the classroom would be very quiet because everyone respected him.

I would also think of the meeting of the whole student body that had been called not long before by the newly elected chairman of the student self-government association. She had said, "We women must now awaken and become independent human beings. We must do our duty to our country, to society, and to all people and not just stay at home as complaisant slaves of the family." And my schoolmates often said, "We must stand up and oppose old-fashioned arranged marriages! We must make our own decisions!"

Such talk was new to me, but whenever I heard it, it was as if the words were meant especially for me and were full of truth. If anyone had asked me what those principles were, I would not have been able to say, but whenever I heard this kind of talk or thought about it, I felt stronger and the dullness that surrounded me seemed to lift a little.

There was one other thing that added a little color to my drab life during this period—Zhongyao often sent me letters at school. Though I had been living in his parents' home for nearly two months, I had seen him only four or five times. Whenever we met, we would both hang our heads and pretend we had not seen each other. During my first month there, he and his younger brother had come back from Haojia Hill to spend two weekends. I did not understand why I should feel so shy and embarrassed around someone I had not even met. I would run to his grandmother's room to avoid him and would not even come out to eat, but I could still hear his voice in the living room and his two little brothers calling over and over, "Big Brother, Big Brother!" Although I knew I could not avoid him completely, I could not bring myself to leave the bedroom.

When he came home on the last weekend of the month, his mother called to me from the living room and told me to come out and pour her tea for her. I could sense her smiling as she said, "You're sleeping under the same roof and eating food cooked in the same kitchen. You can't go on avoiding each other for the rest of your lives. You'll have to meet sometime!" So I finally had to leave his grandmother's room. My head felt as if it weighed a thousand catties. I could not lift it. He was sitting across from his mother. I kept my eyes on the floor in front of my feet, set the teacup down in front of his mother with both hands, and then turned and ran back into his grandmother's room. I never expected that after he went back to school he would start sending me letters every two or three days. And when he wrote, he no longer addressed me as "Miss," but as his "Beloved Wife-to-be." The more he wrote, the more loving his letters became. Gradually all the formality disappeared. I would use the rest period after lunch to write my answers. At first I pondered over each word and phrase and wrote with great care because I was afraid I might not write well and he would laugh at me, but later, when more and more letters came, I no longer had as much time and wrote less formally. We wrote about all kinds of things, about what we were learning in our classes and about our other school activities, and also about our feelings for each other and our mutual admiration. This seemed very natural. The only subject we avoided was my life in his parents' home. In one letter he asked me, "Are you happy living in my home?" But I did not answer, feeling I did not know him well enough to say anything. After all, it was his home. I knew him very little, and I was afraid that bringing up anything unpleasant might spoil our fragile, newborn friendship and affection. Perhaps my adolescent desire to handle everything myself and my pride also made me unwilling to tell him my troubles.

After a while, without realizing it, I started secretly looking forward to his return as each monthly holiday approached. But even when he did come home, it would have been improper for us to say a single word to each other. Our happiness in seeing each other again had to remain hidden. He would greet everyone and talk with them, and all of them, even Xiao Lazi sitting in the corridor, could greet and talk with him. Only I would see him walk by and not even be able to call out in greeting. He would sit in the living room laughing and talking with his family. It was so warm and affectionate. But I sat outside that warm circle and could not enter it. Sometimes he and I would be in the living room at the same time—though of course never alone—or eating at the same table. Sometimes we would pass each other, and if there was no one nearby we could look at each other for a moment. But we dared not linger. All day long, I could see him and he could see me, I could hear the sound of his footsteps and he could hear mine, and I could hear him talk and cough and laugh and he could hear me. But though we were within inches of each other, there might as well have been an ocean between us.

No matter how much we had to say to each other in our letters, no matter how much affection we felt for each other, and no matter how much we longed to see each other, when he came back there were always too many eyes watching us and we could not say a word to each other. It would have been easier if there had been a mountain or ocean between us. We could have accepted that. But to be kept apart even though we were so near made us feel helpless, as if we were bound by invisible chains.

At first his mother had ridiculed me for hiding from him, but now, when he came back and I did not avoid him, it seemed to make her uneasy. She seemed to sense that Zhongyao and I were not indifferent to one another, and began guarding us at every turn. Whenever Zhongyao came home, she not only prevented us from being alone together but also sent Rolan to keep an eye on us. The Shaos were converts and Mrs. Shao always went to church on Sundays. But if Zhongyao said he did not want to go, she would leave Rolan at home to watch us or take me with her.

But although they could bind our bodies they could not bind our hearts. Our affection for each other was deeper than words. Now, when he came home he seldom went out again, and he liked to linger near me. If I was sitting and sewing in the hallway with Da Biao Sao he would saunter past us and go back and forth between the shop and the living room whether he had any reason to or not. He was tall and strong, and his face was sunburned from living on the hill. He looked even healthier compared to the shop apprentices, whose faces were sallow and who did not get enough good food. Although he had his father's bulging forehead, he seemed manly, handsome, and loveable to me, perhaps because of the affection we shared. His eyes seemed to burn with the warmth of his feelings, and behind those feelings I could see something I had not seen before, a cherishing intimacy and the light of happiness.

These things could only be felt, not put into words. But, unlike our letters, they could not be hidden from his family. There were only so many rooms in the house, and every time we moved a hand or a foot it would be observed by many eyes, even if they were not trying. My mother-in-law was not the only observant one. Zhongyao's grandmother also understood. But unlike her daughter, she did not act as if she mistrusted us. She seemed to look on our behavior as the amusing antics of two adolescents. Also, since we were betrothed, even if we did delight in each other it was not a crime, but correct and even proper. So she would quarrel with her daughter when she saw that Mrs. Shao was uneasy and had sent Zhongyao off to help in the shop, or to take his younger brothers out for a walk, or to visit his fellow students.

One day, after Zhongyao had again been sent out and I was at the foot of the stairs picking through old scraps of cloth, I heard Zhongyao's grandmother talking with Mrs. Shao upstairs. "Daughter, if Zhongyao wants to stay home, you ought to let him. These days, when he comes home I scarcely get to say three sentences to him before you send him away again."

"Mother, what do you know about it? You should just stay out of it! Look at him these last few times he's come home—who does he have eyes for? All day long—he's so muddle-headed.... If he's this infatuated now, before they're married, how will he have any time later for his brothers and sister?"

"He hasn't done anything. He just likes looking at Baowen. Boys that age always act like that. It's best to leave him alone. No harm ever came from looking."

"Mother, it's none of your business!" Mrs. Shao's voice was loud and impatient. "The older you get the more confused you get. He's my son—I bore him. I know him. He doesn't need you to protect him!"

"You're right—I have no say in it ... I'll be quiet...." I heard Grandmother start down the stairs. She was muttering, "All right, I'll keep out of it. I'll be quiet...." I was afraid she would see me, so I grabbed a handful of scraps and hurried away down the hallway. Just as I reached the end of the hallway, Mrs. Shao's angry voice came from upstairs. "Baowen, where are you?"

My heart lurched. "I'm here, in the hallway." I dropped the scraps on the table and started back towards the stairs when she called out again. "It's all right, I've found it. Never mind. Stay down there."

I went back to the table and began sorting the scraps, but I was thinking, "It's a good thing I hurried. If I'd answered her from the foot of the stairs, she'd have realized I'd overheard her —then she would've been angry and scolded me."

Chapter 22

ALTHOUGH I never wrote to Zhongyao about what my life was like in his home, he began mentioning it in his.

He wrote, "Although I have returned to Haojai Hill, my heart is still at home by your side. Baowen, I don't understand why the parents who made the decision to betroth us should guard us so closely now that we love each other.

"You're living in my home and I have a right to take care of you. But every time I come home, they guard against me as if I were a thief and I can't even say one word to you."

In another letter he wrote, "Baowen, are you happy? Why didn't I see any smiles on your face the last time I came home?"

And in still another, "Do you know that Grandmother called me into her room to talk last night? As I was leaving, I wanted to pull back the curtain at your end of the bed and look at you asleep. Were you really asleep? I've often wanted to ask Grandmother to look after you when I'm not at home, but it's so difficult to get the words out!

"I think about you all the time. I want to give you my whole heart. Baowen, are you willing to give your whole heart to me? Please make your letters longer and tell me more about what you're thinking."

Whenever I got a letter from him, my heart was touched. His letters had changed; they seemed much more sincere, less romantic, and more perceptive and understanding. They had become part of my life, and I could not do without them. During the day I would tuck the latest one in my inside pocket and at night I would hide it in my pillow case and sleep with it against my cheek. When the next letter came, I would hide the old one in my little rattan box and keep the new one with me as my companion.

Whenever I had any spare time at school I would write my replies.

"Zhongyao, it has been cold and quiet at home since you left. Whenever I pass the chair where you so often sit, I seem to see you sitting there. Then when I look again and see that it's empty, that you're not there—how I long for you!

"I used to think I was like that wild duck that lives alone on the river outside the back gate—alone in the world of people. Now that I have you, I have a companion. I don't feel alone any more. Now, even if I have to bear hardships, I can bear them more easily.

"Please don't worry about me, Zhongyao. I didn't realize I didn't smile the last time you came home. Next time, I'll be sure to find a way to smile."

We came soon to the Chongyang Festival (Double Ninth Festival)* and when he came back from school and walked along the hallway, he greeted Da Biao Sao and stood there for a long time. I saw that he could not decide whether to stay or go and that he had a parcel wrapped in flowered paper under his arm. I did not know that it was meant for me and that he had been trying all afternoon to find an opportunity to place it in my hands. He wandered throughout the house with it for quiet a while. He finally put it on the long table in the living room, apparently hoping that I would go and get it myself. I did not know it was for me, but even if I had, how could I have gone to get it with his whole family there? It stayed there until after dinner when he went back over to the table and picked the package up and put it down again, looking hesitant and undecided. His mother, who was sitting nearby, asked, "Zhongyao, what's in that pretty package?"

"Two books of new embroidery patterns and two raw silk book marks," he answered.

"Is it for Baowen? Then put it down and leave it. Don't keep fidgeting with it!"

He said nothing, but put the parcel down.

I never would have expected that his mother would not only not be angry, but that she would smile and say, "You can do anything and I won't scold you—as long as you don't try to hide it from me and you do what I think right."

Still he said nothing. He just smiled and sat down near the table. I hung my head, much too embarrassed to go and pick up his gift. I waited until bedtime, and when I saw that there was no one in the living room I took the parcel and went to my room.

---

*"Chongyang Festival." Double Ninth Festival held on the ninth day of the ninth lunar month, usually in early October.

I was surprised his mother had apparently decided to stop guarding us so closely, but even more surprised that his sister seemed to have turned against us. When Rolan saw that her older brother had given a present to me but not to her, she fumed all evening and pouted all the next day to show she had been treated unfairly, like a person who loans out polished rice but is paid back with unthreshed grain. I knew she was jealous, but there was no way to undo what had been done, or even to talk it over. I reminded myself to avoid her as much as possible.

Rolan had been acting more and more temperamental. When I first arrived, she had contented herself with frowning when she was displeased, but now she had started expressing her displeasure in words. Combing her hair in the mornings became my biggest trial. She could never keep her head still, and I had to try to draw the wooden comb through her hair while following her movements. But if I pulled out a hair, she would shout, "Not so hard!" and if I combed lightly she would shout, "Harder! What are you doing, counting each hair?" I had to swallow my anger and continue combing. When I looked at her in the mirror, her pretty, well-proportioned face looked sour and disagreeable. She looked as if she had just swallowed a glass of vinegar. Her eyes would narrow and her forehead would be furrowed and she would pout so much that her lips looked like water chestnuts. I thought, "What a waste, to make a pretty face so ugly."

I felt like throwing down the comb and walking out of the room, leaving her spoilt young ladyship alone to her tantrums, but it is true that "people who live under the eaves must bend their heads." I had been living with the Shaos for some time now. The freer rein she gave her temper, the worse it got, but the more my temper was suppressed, the weaker it grew. As time went on and she saw her mother treating me more and more oppressively, she began to believe she had the right to do the same because I was so much beneath her. She would even glare at Zhongyao, as if angry that he was paying attention to me. So when he brought me that present, it made her furious and she had to create a scene. Zhongyao seemed to be aware of the tension. He was due to return to school after lunch the next day, so he went out the next morning and bought several beautifully-colored foreign pictures. Smiling, he went over and gave them to Rolan, who was sitting in the living room with one foot under her and the other kicking a table leg. Her eyes swept over the pictures. What are these? Pictures? No, she did not want them.

He invited her to come out for a walk and to look around the streets.

Go out on the street to be amused? No, she did not want to go out on the street.

He asked her what she would like. Whatever it was, he would go out and buy it for her. What would she like?

What would she like? No, there was nothing she wanted.

Zhongyao could think of nothing else to suggest and, deciding it was best to ignore her, went out in front to the shop.

But when Rolan realized he was not going to pay any more attention to her, she became even more aggrieved, and started crying. When her mother got out of bed and saw this, she hurried out and said, "My pearl, my precious, what's wrong? What's bothering you? Tell Mother. Let me help you."

Rolan frowned and pouted but refused to tell her what was wrong. Her mother felt her forehead, but it was normal. So she said Rolan must be bored with staying at home and that after lunch Xiao Lazi and she should go out and amuse themselves. Then she would be all right.

By lunch time, however, Rolan had managed to dissipate her boredom. First she got into a loud argument with Xiao Lao Si, accusing him of having ruined her things. Then she started complaining that she could not find her drawing book and her paintbrush. Mrs. Shao, who was drinking tea in the living room, put down her cup and said in a loud voice, "You there, get moving! Don't just stand around, hurry up and help her find her things."

Da Biao Sao and I dropped our sewing. The servants and Xiao Lazi immediately put down their bowls and chopsticks. We looked everywhere—back and forth, upstairs and downstairs, on the tables and under the tables, and in every drawer, but we could not find the drawing book or paintbrush. Her mother tried to soothe and coax her, saying, "Be patient, my good little girl. If they're in the house we'll find them. Think carefully, where did you leave them?"

"I remember clearly, I left them in my book-bag."

"When you came home from school the day before yesterday, what did you do with your book-bag?"

"I gave it to Baowen."

"Baowen," her mother turned and asked me, "when she gave you her book-bag, did you see the book and the paintbrush?"

"I took it upstairs and put it on the table by her bed. I didn't open it."

"Baowen, you're so careless! You should look after her things better."

"She never puts my things in order for me," Rolan whined. She pointed her finger at me and said, "The last time I gave her my shoe pattern, she didn't put it away for me carefully, so I had to hunt for it for a long time before I found it."

"Baowen, really ..." Mrs. Shao frowned and she refused to look at me. "For someone as old as you are to be so inconsiderate! And you still haven't gone upstairs to look. Don't you realize she'll need them tomorrow when she goes to school?"

I did not answer. Everyone in the family was in the living room, including Zhongyao. I swallowed, turned, and ran upstairs. Halfway up, I heard Da Biao Sao's call from Rolan's room. "It's all right, I've found them."

"Where did you find them?" Mrs. Shao asked from downstairs.

"Under Rolan's pillow."

"Really?. What a girl! What a fuss over nothing," commented Mrs. Shao's mother.

I came back down the stairs, went into my room, sat down on the bed and let the tears run down my face. Grandmother came in a few moments later. She came over to me and waved her hands at me several times, murmuring, "Stop, stop—if your mother sees you crying, she'll be even angrier."

I thought, "Let her be angry! Ever since I came here, she's hated me! I've put up with enough all these months."

At this moment, the curtain moved suddenly and someone came in very quietly. I looked up and saw Zhongyao walk over to his grandmother as if he were going to say goodbye. But he remained silent and just stood there looking at me. I did not want him to see me crying, but somehow his presence made my heart ache even more, and my tears flowed faster. I could not stop them. I felt as if all the tears I had been holding back for so many months were suddenly pouring out of me.

Grandmother pulled out a big handkerchief and gave it to me. At the same time she said to him, "Are you leaving? It's a long trip. It's time to go. Be careful not to get overheated or chilled, and remember to put on your heavy coat in the mornings and evenings."

"I understand," he answered. But he made no move to go.

"Do you need any money?"

He shook his head.

"All right. You'd better go."

But still he hesitated a while before finally turning away to leave.

She followed him to the door. Then she came back over to me and said quietly, "There's some cold water in the basin. Hurry and wash your face. Then rest a little, and when you look like yourself and as if nothing has happened, come back out. Try to smile and look happy—it would be best if you hide any signs of distress."

After I cried, I felt somewhat better. I got up and went over to the washstand and bathed my eyes with cold water. Then I waited until all my tears had dried. I checked in a little mirror to make sure my eyelids were no longer red before leaving the bedroom and going down the hallway to resume my sewing.

But for the rest of the afternoon, I felt drained, as if I had lost something. I felt lonely, smothered, and depressed, and did not know why. Dinner was served in the late afternoon, before dark. Mr. and Mrs. Shao, Grandmother, and the children laughed and talked and ate just as if it were any other day. But Da Biao Sao and I waited until they had all settled themselves before edging up to the corner of the table and squeezing in. Silently, we picked up our bowls and ate with our heads down. We took food only from the two bowls of vegetables right in front of us and did not reach for any of the other dishes in front of the rest of the family. However, my mother-in-law placed pieces of meat and fish in my bowl several times, saying, "Tonight our eldest daughter deserves something extra good."

She always balanced punishments with rewards when dealing with the servants, Da Biao Sao and me; after scolding us, she would always do something nice for us. But that night I could not enjoy the food she picked out for me. Nor did I have the heart to listen to the family chatting and laughing. I wanted only to be left alone so I could think quietly about one person—yes, about Zhongyao. He should have reached Haojia Hill long since. Perhaps he was even now eating dinner too. How cold and uninteresting this house was without him! Suddenly I realized that the depression and loneliness I had felt in the afternoon had been because he was not there, and I was sorry that I had let him see me cry. He would certainly be worrying about me. I hoped that there would be a letter from him when I went to school the next day, or the day after.

I had been so sunk in my own thoughts, with the family's

laughter and talk sounding in my ears, that I was startled to realize that everyone had suddenly gone quite still. I looked up at the doorway and, like them, could hardly believe my eyes —Zhongyao was standing there. He was out of breath and his forehead was beaded with sweat. He looked as if he had run the whole ten *li* back from school.

"What's the matter that you've run back all this way? You're all out of breath—something wrong?" his mother asked.

"I forgot a book and didn't remember it until I'd gotten back. I need it for class tomorrow. So I asked for a few hours of leave and came back to get it." As he spoke, he looked around the table until he spotted me. Then he smiled and seemed to sigh with relief.

"Then you won't have time for dinner. Come and sit down and eat." His grandmother smiled and moved her hair to one side to make room for him. Xiao Lazi hurried to fetch a chair. Mrs. Zhang wrung out a hot towel and gave it to him so he could wipe away his sweat. Then she brought out a pair of chopsticks and filled a bowl with hot rice. He sat down next to his grandmother and started eating.

I was sitting right across from him. A sudden, inexpressible excitement overcame me. It was due not only to his unexpected return, but also to my knowledge that he had not come back just for the book. I could see from his expression that he was worried about something else—something only he and I could understand.

It was strange that, although he and I had never spoken one word to each other, we understood each other better than if we had talked for weeks. Communication between people depends not just on words but also on manner and expression. If two people feel something for each other, they will watch each other's every movement so closely that they will naturally be able to understand the other's heart and spirit. His grandmother seemed to realize that he and I understood each other. That evening, when I was going to bed, she looked up from her place beside the opium lamp, smiled and said, "I thought there was something strange about Zhongyao's coming back tonight. He has never forgotten anything before. And even if he had, how important could it have been? Did he really have to run back as if his life depended on it? And sure enough, before he left again, he called me to the door and asked if there had been any trouble after he left. Then I realized he had probably been worried because he had seen you crying. So he came up with an excuse to run back and see how you were."

She coughed and drank several mouthfuls of tea from the spout of the little teapot. She set it back down, smiled again, and said, "Everything has its causes in a previous life. Before you were engaged, his mother and I conspired to test him. We would tease him, 'Zhongyao, shall we get the Zhou family's Baowen for you? Would you like her?' Whenever we said this, he'd grin and grin. Isn't that proof of a past relationship?"

I said nothing. I took off my clothes and crept into my little quilt cocoon. I did not believe in reincarnation and relationships in past lives, but when I thought about everything that had happened that day, it made me feel both happy and sad. I thought of his affection for me, and of how I had avoided writing anything about my life in his home because I had been afraid that speaking of it would damage that affection. But now that time was over; even if I did not speak, he would know. Perhaps his mother would blame him as well as me. Our affection had now grown even stronger. What people said was true, that "sharing adversity strengthens love." And because he was treating me this way, I thought that even if they continued to mistreat me and grind me down, I would no longer be without comfort....

Zhongyao's grandmother, having satisfied her opium habit, turned down the oil lamp, pulled her quilt over her, and went to sleep. But I tossed and turned for a long time and could not close my eyes for thinking.

Chapter 23

AFTER the Chongyang Festival, the days grew shorter, the nights longer, and the weather colder. Da Biao Sao and I had more sewing to do, and it had to be done more quickly. Every evening we had to sit in the hallway and sew by the light of the oil lamp until late in the night.

When the autumn winds began to blow, Mrs. Shao brought me several big bundles of yarn from the shop and told me to knit a sweater and a pair of gloves for each of the children. Because she was afraid that I would not get them done by the time winter came, she told me to take the yarn and my knitting needles to school each day and to knit in my spare time. This meant I could no longer rest between classes and had even less time to prepare my lessons. My average marks in the two monthly examinations were just barely passing. Although the teachers did not say anything, I was worried, and mortified as well because there seemed to be no way I could live up to the promise of my performance on the entrance examinations in the eyes of my teachers and fellow students. It was also very difficult to find time to write to Zhongyao and often I would receive two or three letters from him before I had time to write one back. Also, my letters were short and carelessly written. Several times, in his letters, he asked me whether I felt well. I replied only that I was very busy. He seemed to understand and did not ask again, but wrote as he always did.

Sometimes, if his mother treated him kindly during his visits, he would write comfortingly, "I think Mother still loves us. She too has her problems. She is concerned about having grandchildren. But dear one, if she doesn't care for us, after I graduate and we are married, we can be independent and set up our own household so we need not live our whole lives with my parents."

I knew, however, that his words were only half true. I knew that though his mother sometimes treated him sternly, deep down in her heart she loved him, but that though she said she treated me like a daughter, deep down she did not love me at all. She was treating him sternly because she was afraid he would get too absorbed in me and would become too independent and would not take care of his brothers and sister.

One day I overheard her and some relatives discussing how to treat their sons and daughters-in-law. She said, "Our sons, after all, are born of our own bodies. Even if you beat them and scold them again and again when they disobey, they will still listen to you and fly back to you in the end. But daughters-in-law are different—they always try to resist. So to control them, you must clip their wings before they're fully grown, while they're still easy to control. Because if you wait, it'll be too late."

This proverb was very apt. I often thought that no matter how well Zhongyao treated me, he was still his mother's son, and no matter how far away he flew, he would still fly back to her eventually. But his mother treated me like an outsider and no matter how hard I tried to fit in with his family, she would not trust me and certainly would not let me. Because of this, whatever Zhongyao said about her, good or bad, in his letters, I continued to make no comment.

I took his talk about being independent and establishing our own home as an attempt to comfort me, because I knew it would be difficult to achieve. He feared his mother so much and was so much under her thumb that I doubted whether he could stand up to her even if he had the means to be independent.

Mrs. Shao tried to control not only me, a daughter-in-law over whom she had many rights, but even Da Biao Sao, who was only a distant relative living there temporarily because of unfortunate circumstances. Mrs. Shao would get angry at her and warn her, "If your husband ever comes back ... I would be the one to account for you to him about your behavior. If he wants to take you with him, I won't stop you, but as long as you're living here in my home, I'm responsible for you. You can leave if he comes for you, but if you've been having any daydreams about being modern or wanting to be independent and living on your own alone and being disrespectable, they're just that—daydreams! Think about it—if you wanted to go out and try to enter household service without a recommendation from me, what family would dare hire you? If you wanted to shave your head and enter a convent without my consent, no convent would dare take you in! If you were to think about running away with someone ... well, I have money, and money talks. You can run off to Shanghai or Tianjin or the ends of the earth, but I can send people after you to bring you back. If you're thinking about suicide and kill yourself and your husband sees us, I wouldn't be afraid. We belong to the church—what magistrate or official would dare offend the church? They're all afraid of the foreigners! I can get the ear of any official! So if you even imagine you can get away from me, you're dreaming!"

Although these imprecations were directed at Da Biao Sao, she was not the only one who was supposed to be intimidated by them. My mother-in-law knew exactly what she was doing. All of us, especially Xiao Lazi and I, understood. In general, people who lord it over others bluster the way they do because they are insecure. Mrs. Shao wanted us to realize how powerless we were. I think Da Biao Sao's pursed lips and her pale, expressionless face told Mrs. Shao louder than words that she would not submit, even though she behaved like a deaf-mute when scolded and never answered back.

Human beings are made of flesh and blood and feelings, and the human heart can be won only by another human heart, not by force. No matter how great the pressure, it cannot win the mind and heart inside. During my months at the Shaos', I had realized that although Da Biao Sao could not even read or write, her character was as sturdy and strong as her hands and feet. No matter how much my mother-in-law scolded her, I never saw her shed one tear or murmur one word. The most I ever saw was the ghost of a cold smile in the corners of her eyes and on her lips. And when my mother-in-law treated her more leniently, she never made a single move to curry favor with her. Mrs. Shao always said that Da Biao Sao had been born stupid and thick-headed, but I secretly admired her because she had so much backbone. Although we seldom talked with each other and never agreed to become allies, and although I felt like a chicken whose wings had been clipped compared to her, Da Biao Sao and I never made this distinction. Mrs. Shao treated us differently—she had never yet tongue-lashed me as she had Da Biao Sao, and sometimes when there were dinner guests, she would invite me to sit at one of the vacant seats, but Da Biao Sao always had to stand with the servants and wait on us. And at least I could leave the house every day to go to school while Da Biao Sao was never allowed to set foot outside the front gate. Still, we were both like the people in the proverb: we lived under the eaves and had to keep our heads bent.

The months of afternoons and evenings I had spent with Da

Biao Sao, sharing with her the sunless little universe of the hallway and slipping with her into the spaces at the corners of the dinner table, had given rise, without our realizing it, to a deep mutual feeling that we would sympathize and protect each other. When I was first learning to make shoe uppers and would be about to take a finished pair to my mother-in-law for inspection, Da Biao Sao would always reach for them and look them over first. If the rolled edges were uneven—this was the most difficult part—or if the stitches were not uniform, she would silently rip them apart and do them again for me. If I ended up being scolded anyway, she would look up at me when I came back and silently shake her head as if she did not want me to take it too seriously. This always made me feel better.

The weather grew colder. At night, after I helped get Rolan and her brothers to bed and served Mr. and Mrs. Shao their tea and opium, either Da Biao Sao or I would go to the kitchen and heat up some water so we could wash our hands and feet. If water was left over because we had not washed our clothes that night, we would leave it for the wet-nurse and Xiao Lazi. In the mornings when we got up and were at the stove dishing out our breakfast, or when we were washing our clothes together in the wooden tubs out in the courtyard, and no one else was around, we would exchange a few casual words. But we did not confide in each other. I often wondered whether her life would always be as miserable if her husband never came back. She was still young. Twice when Mrs. Shao had had visitors Da Biao Sao had put on an almost-new suit of clean blue cotton and combed her hair until it shone. She had looked neat and attractive. If her life had been just a little smoother and easier, she would not have been so listless and unsmiling.

One evening after Mrs. Shao had been berating her, I murmured in an attempt to comfort her. "It doesn't matter. Just wait until your husband comes back. Then you'll be free."

Da Biao Sao kept her eyes on the shoe upper she was sewing. She caught her lower lip in her upper teeth and, after a long time, gave a soft sigh. "If I were not still waiting for him—poor man —I wouldn't be sitting here grinding my teeth and biding my time like this. But I must know for certain whether he's alive or dead before I'm satisfied. Once I find that out, I'll go my way and I'll still have much of my life ahead of me. I'm determined to make my own decisions."

I thought to myself, "Decisions? Hasn't she already closed off any road you might take? What would you have to look forward to?" But I said nothing.

"When there's no way out, there's always at least one way out." After a while she added, as if to herself, "There are no covers on the rivers and ponds."

When she said this, my heart stopped for a moment. Quickly, I bent my head over my knitting. We did not exchange another word that evening, nor did I ever again bring up her husband's name.

The autumn winds blew the few remaining yellow leaves from the trees. The flocks of wild geese had flown south, their voices sounding lonely as they called and called, lingering on the wind and floating softly down from above the rooftops. Our hearts felt cold. Autumn turned into early winter and the morning and evening dew turned into frost. Our thin padded coats were no longer enough to keep out the cold. It was winter and we were once again busy preparing for New Year's. All the schools let out for winter vacation and Zhongyao and his brother came home from Haojia Hill. Every day they went with their father to the shop in front or to the drygoods store to help out because there was always more business during the holiday season. They always came back home late in the evenings.

About three weeks before New Year's, Mrs. Shao ordered Da Biao Sao and me to put down our sewing, a never-ending task, and to help Mrs. Zhang and Xiao Lazi clean and dust. Every corner of every room in the house was scrubbed and swept. New paper was pasted on all the door and window lattices and holiday couplets were pasted on the doors and lintels. Everything was bright and clean and tidy. Although the Shaos were Christians and usually went to the church to celebrate all the foreign festivals, such as Christmas and Easter and the Western New Year, they also observed the Chinese New Year and the festivals of the Buddhist religion with the same enthusiasm. So when it came time, they all burned incense and imitation money, and worshipped the ancestors and gods according to the old beliefs —they simply did not tell the people at the church. Xiao Lao Si and Xiao Lao Wu sometimes got confused and would ask Mrs. Shao, "Mother, which religion do we belong to anyway? Do we believe in the Jesus religion or do we believe in the Buddha religion?" Mrs. Shao would hush them up, saying, "Remember, in school you mustn't talk in that mixed-up way. It is God we all believe in."

Zhongyao's grandmother was a devout Buddhist but would never say anything against Christianity. She often said, "It's all right to joke about some things, but gods and demons, whether in China or anywhere else in the world, must not be taken lightly and we must do nothing to offend them."

For about ten days, we had no time to be idle. One cloudy afternoon, when a light snow was falling, Mrs. Zhang and Xiao Lazi were in the living room helping Mrs. Shao sort out the holiday decorations and furnishings. Da Biao Sao was in the kitchen making peanut nougat and Mrs. Shao told me to help by keeping the kitchen stove fired. She said I could watch and learn to make the candy at the same time. It got dark early; by three o'clock we had already lit the little old-fashioned oil lamp in front of the Kitchen God. Da Biao Sao had spread the second batch of peanut candy on the kitchen table and was slowly rolling it flat with the rolling pin. When it was almost cold she would cut it into bite-sized squares with the cleaver. She told me to add pine branches to the stove so she could cook the third batch.

Suddenly we heard loud laughter and talking in the living room, as if guests had come. Then we heard several voices calling Da Biao Sao, and Xiao Lazi came running into the kitchen, clapping her hands. "Come quickly! Mistress wants to see you! Hurry up, go out to the living room!"

"I hear you. I'm coming. Why are you shouting?" Da Biao Sao put down her little iron spatula and wiped her hands on her apron.

Xiao Lazi tugged on the corner of Da Biao Sao's tunic and said, "Your husband's come back. Hurry up!" Then she turned and ran into the courtyard, calling, "Young mistress, young masters, stop wrapping up coins and come see! Da Biao Sao's husband has come back!"

This was a great surprise. I pushed the pine branches into the stove so no fire would fall out and stood up, thinking I too would go into the living room to see him. But when I looked over at Da Biao Sao, she was holding onto the edge of the kitchen table with both hands and staring ahead blankly. I went over to her. Her eyes were full of tears and she was frowning to keep them from spilling onto her cheeks. She was also biting her lip to control her silent suffering. I had never seen her shed tears before, or show any emotion, and I did not know how to comfort her. I knew that everyone was waiting for her. I took off her greasy apron, brought out the wooden wash basin, and poured in two dippers of hot water so she could wash her face and hands.

"Don't act like that," I urged her. "It's a happy occasion, that your husband has come back. Now hurry up and wash and go see him."

She did not answer. She wiped her eyes with the corner of her tunic and splashed some water on her face. I moistened my hand with water and pushed back the loose hair on her forehead. "All right, go on!" She nodded and took a couple of steps towards the door that led to the courtyard. But then she turned around and asked, "Little sister, can you tell I've been crying?"

"No. Now, hurry."

She went over to the latticed window and looked at herself several times in the two-inch-square piece of mirror that hung there. Then she smoothed her hair with her hands, rubbed her face, and hurried out of the kitchen.

I was happy for her, but also worried—happy because her husband had come back and she could be free of this house, but worried because Mrs. Shao might lie to him about her. Da Biao Ge (Brother Cousin) had been leading a rough life in the army all these years, and who could say how he would treat Da Biao Sao? This thought made me uncomfortable about going to see the excitement, so I sat down again in front of the stove. I knew it would soon be dinner time and that it would be better to wait until then to go to the living room.

Most of my anxiety evaporated during dinner. Da Biao Ge did not look at all like the rough soldier as I had expected, but rather like an ordinary shopkeeper. He looked about the same age as Da Biao Sao and was wearing a thick, barely-worn long padded gown of coarse grey cotton. His hair, which had been shaved like a soldier's, was beginning to grow out again but was still very short. His face was weather beaten as if from the sun and wind and frost. The only unusual thing about him was a wide, shiny gold ring on the middle finger of his left hand. Mrs. Shao treated Da Biao Sao differently that night, making her sit across from her husband and continually placing food in her bowl. She also spoke to her much more gently than usual.

Da Biao Sao kept her head bent and ate silently. Her husband too kept his eyes on his bowl. They never looked at each other or exchanged any words. Mr. Shao, Zhongyao and his next-oldest brother, who had just come back from the shop, kept asking Da Biao Ge about his experiences as a soldier. Da Biao Ge said tersely that he had been first a bearer then a horse groom, and finally an officer's orderly. Mr. Shao waited until dinner was finished and Mrs. Zhang and the other servants had cleared the table and left. Then he asked in a low voice, "Now that you've come home ... Were you discharged or did you leave another way?"

Da Biao Ge hesitated and then said, "It was after they were defeated and made a retreat. Several of us got away."

Mr. Shao puffed on his cigarette and thought for a while. "They ... won't they try to find ..." He stopped and drew in his breath with a hiss.

"No, they won't. The whole army has retreated northward to the mountain valleys of Henan Province."

"Then what do you plan to do? How long do you plan to stay here with us?"

"I plan to see several people here and then go to the countryside to see how things look. If the situation is good and suitable, I'll set up a peddler's stand. If things look unfavorable, I'll think of something else."

Mr. Shao nodded and appeared satisfied.

"Why didn't you write any letters home these last two years, to keep your wife from worrying about you?" Zhongyao's grandmother asked.

"Every day I thought I'd soon get a chance to escape. How was I to know that it would take so long?"

"Setting up a stand in the country is a good plan." Grandmother nodded. "No matter what work you do, it will undoubtedly be better than the army. You're both still young and if you can endure hardship and work hard, perhaps in a year or two you will have children and a home and a settled, peaceful life."

"Did you manage to save any money while you were with the army?" Mrs. Shao asked. "And when you go back to the country, will you take your wife with you?"

Da Biao Ge nodded.

They talked some more. Then, just as Mrs. Shao was about to go to her room she told Da Biao Ge, as if she had just thought of it, "It's late, and we've all been busy because of New Year's. I'm afraid we can't find a room for the two of you. You can go out in front to the shop and make the best of it with the clerks for a few nights."

Da Biao Ge nodded, jumped to his feet, and said with a polite smile, "Please don't go to any trouble, Aunt. I've already been too much of a nuisance." He remained standing until she had gone to her room. Then he picked up a blue cloth bundle that had been on the floor near the tea table and held it out to Da Biao Sao, who was sitting in a corner in the living room. "I have a few dirty clothes in this. Wash them for me, if you have time."

Silently, she stood up and took the bundle.

I knew that across the courtyard, opposite Mrs. Zhang's room, there was an empty room that Mrs. Shao could have given them. After all those years apart, Da Biao Sao and her husband would certainly like to be alone. I did not know why my mother-in-law would not let them sleep together until later. When I went to the kitchen to fill Zhongyao's grandmother's thermos with boiling water, I heard Mrs. Zhang, who was near the kitchen door, whispering to Xiao Lazi. "Mistress' orders. It's the end of the year and we must all watch out and not let Da Biao Sao and her husband be together. She says it would be bad luck."

Over the next few days, Da Biao Ge worked in the shop out in front and came into the house only for meals. He and Da Biao Sao barely spoke. Da Biao Sao silently helped cook the food for New Year's just as she always had, but her face looked fresher and she seemed more animated and she combed her hair until it shone. Everyone in the household, from Mother-in-law on down to Mrs. Zhang, treated her more kindly. Once, when Da Biao Sao was not around, Mrs. Zhang told the wet nurse that Da Biao Ge's gold ring meant he must have quite a bit of money in the army and that Da Biao Sao would probably have a comfortable life with him.

I thought they would leave in a few days and that nothing more would happen. But the afternoon before they were to leave, as I was on my way back from the kitchen and crossing the living room to go to Grandmother's room to get something, I saw Mrs. Shao sitting in the living room talking with Da Biao Ge. Just as I went out into the hall, I heard him say in an angry voice, "If I find out she's been unfaithful to me, I'll ornament her—with 'the knife that goes in white and comes out red!'"

"No, no—you mustn't!" came Mrs. Shao's voice. "I'm just warning you so you'll be on your guard. If she hadn't been living here with us all this time and hadn't had me to watch her, if she'd been living somewhere else ... not that I'm saying it, but your homecoming just might have been different."

I dared not remain in the hallway any longer. I got the porcelain jar from Grandmother's room and hurried back through the living room without looking up. But for the rest of the day and evening, I kept hearing Da Biao Ge's voice when he talked about the knife. I wanted to tell Da Biao Sao, but there were always people around and I could not get a moment alone with her. Occasionally I would steal a glance at her, but she did not seem worried. Early the next morning, I got up and went to look for her without even taking the time to wash or to comb my hair. I looked in the living room, kitchen, and courtyard, but could not find her. Then I went out to the little room she shared with Mrs. Zhang and Xiao Lazi. As I neared the doorway, I heard the murmur of voices. I stopped and peeped in through a crack in the door. Clothes and other belongings were scattered all over the bed and the floor. Da Biao Sao and Da Biao Ge were squatting on the floor folding the quilts. They were talking. Then I saw Da Biao Ge stretch out his hand. He helped roll up the sleeve of Da Biao Sao's tunic for her and with his hand pushed back the short hair that had fallen over her face. They were both smiling. I crept away without making a sound, but the heaviness in my heart disappeared.

Da Biao Ge and Da Biao Sao waited until Mrs. Shao had gotten up before they left. As they were leaving, Da Biao Sao took a cup of tea to her and to Grandmother, holding the teacups out to them very respectfully, with both hands. Da Biao Ge bowed ceremoniously to Mrs. Shao three times and told Da Biao Sao to kowtow and thank Mrs. Shao for her kindness. He said he hoped Mrs. Shao would forgive his wife all her mistakes. My mother-in-law acted as pleasant and amiable as if the previous day's conversation had never taken place. She told Mrs. Zhang to bring them two packages of cakes and wished them happiness and success. She also warned them to be careful about money. Then Da Biao Ge, with the roll of quilts over his shoulder, went out the back gate followed by Da Biao Sao, who had a bundle of clothes in each hand.

The wet nurse, Xiao Lazi and the rest of us remained in the courtyard, not daring to accompany them to the gate itself. Da Biao Sao said nothing as she passed us, but just smiled and nodded her head. Her small, near-sighted eyes shone with the light of happiness, which I had never seen before, and her lips were relaxed in a small, curving smile.

Chapter 24

NEW Year's came a few days after Da Biao Sao left. Everyone was busy and gay because of the holiday and no one mentioned her, but every time I walked down the empty hallway I felt her absence. I never saw her again, but a few months later, I overheard Mr. Shao say that she and her husband had not gotten on well in the countryside and had moved to Hefei and gone into domestic service. I never found out what became of them after that.

Since about two weeks before New Year's, I had been hoping that Grandfather would come and take me home for a few days before Lantern Festival and the end of the holiday season. I had been living with the Shaos for almost six months, and though my own grandmother had promised to take me home for a visit, they had not because my third uncle had gotten worse instead of better and the two old people had no time to spare for me. I had gone to see them a few times, but could never stay long. Nor had I ever had a chance to talk openly with Grandmother, because Mrs. Shao always sent either Rolan or Mrs. Zhang to accompany me. It seemed to me that Grandmother realized all was not well, that she also knew it was not a good time to question me. I had also written to Father two or three times and had hinted that my life at the Shaos' was difficult, but he never replied. He only included an occasional greeting to me when he wrote to Mr. Shao.

The first few days of the New Year came and went but there was no word from my grandparents. This left me feeling uncertain and anxious. One morning, just after Mr. Shao had finished breakfast—sweet tea mixed with lotus seeds, jujubes and two eggs cooked with soy sauce—he went out to the shop and returned soon afterwards carrying a letter. He said with a smile that it was from my father in Shanghai and that it was no doubt a year-end accounting and a report on their dividends. But when he opened the letter and read it, I saw his smile disappear. In a low voice, he told his wife and her mother that my father's new business had gone bankrupt. His partner, a Westerner, had turned out to be a swindler, and all of Father's securities, all the capital he had put in, including several thousand yuan from Mr. Shao, and capital and securities from other Chinese, had been stolen. They were now in the midst of an investigation to catch the thief, but no one could say whether they would catch him and put him on trial. This news hit the Shaos like a thunderbolt. It was a heavy blow because they had always been a family of merchants. And if keeping track of every penny is important to a merchant, how could the Shaos deal with the loss of several thousand yuan? Mr. Shao, however, took it philosophically and kept telling his wife not to worry, saying, "Anyone who's in business must expect to gain sometimes and to lose sometimes. Let's hope the officials in Shanghai will catch that foreign thief." He said that if only they could get back part of the capital, Father would eventually be able to re-establish the business. But Mrs. Shao thought there was little hope of this because the foreigners had the ears of the officials and were exempt from the Chinese laws, and that no court "had eaten a dragon's liver or a tiger's gallbladder," and would dare oppose a foreigner. The news made her unhappy and depressed for weeks, and she complained repeatedly about Father as if she regretted having agreed to my marriage with Zhongyao. Whenever I heard her, it hurt me as much as if I were being pricked with needles.

I knew nothing about Father's and Mr. Shao's business transactions and they did not concern me. And when the Shaos entertained their second son's in-laws during the holidays, Mrs. Shao was especially kind to me when she told them about it. "We do not blame Baowen," she said. "It had nothing to do with her. We only blame her father for not being careful and for being stupid. What concerns us is not that he lost his own money—but that he lost our money as well...." Nevertheless, I realized clearly that her attitude towards me had become even colder. I knew that if Father did not improve his situation and make good the Shaos' losses, they would take it out on me. My father and stepmother were far away—they did not have to hear the words of reproach or see the anger on the Shaos' faces. But because I was linked with them, the brunt of their anger and humiliation would fall on me.

My grandparents never came to take me home for a holiday visit, probably because they were too upset about Father's failure, nor did Mrs. Shao say anything about letting me go home. And I certainly did not dare raise the question.

Mrs. Shao had decided to let me board at the Women's Normal School when the spring term started, but then she began to reconsider. First she said, "I don't think Baowen needs to keep going to school. Is it as important to study as to learn housekeeping? And since Da Biao Sao has left, we've had one fewer person to do the sewing." Then, a few days later, she changed her mind again. "If I take her out of school now, the people in the church, most of whom take too much interest in things that do not concern them anyway, will say that we are having financial problems because her father lost all that money for us. They'll say we're petty and changed our minds about letting her study because of her father's failure. I think we might as well stick to our original plan, for this semester at least. We've already made all the arrangements with the school. We'll let her finish this semester and then talk about it again.

"But Baowen is too frivolous. I can see right through her. Once she's at the school and out of my sight, she'll kick over the traces and run wild. She and her friends will be noisy and boisterous all the time. It will be bad for her if I don't give her some work to do, to hold her in check and instill some discipline in her."

So, the day I went back to school, she got up and came into the living room. She sat in one of the high-backed chairs and had Xiao Lazi bring in a soft cloth bundle. She pointed to it and told me, "Here are a dozen skeins of yarn and four knitting needles. "You won't have much to do at school and if you have any free time, you'll just waste it playing. Knitting is easy and doesn't take up any room. You can even knit during classes. I don't ask for much—but every Saturday when you come home, I want you to have finished at least one pair of gloves. Start by making a few pairs for the grownups, and tell me when you've used up all the yarn ... Well? Do you understand me?" She peered at me.

"Yes, Mother."

I picked up the bundle. My throat and nose hurt and I knew that my voice did not sound natural. I turned away and put the bundle next to my rattan box because I wanted to avoid her sharp, searching eyes.

After everything was ready and Mrs. Shao had told Mrs. Zhang to call a rickshaw, she warned me, "Remember, no matter what kinds of meetings there are at the school, you are not to attend them. Even less are you to go out on any demonstration. I'm saying all this for your own good. I want you to remember all this and not let it go in one ear and out the other as soon as you're out of the house and out of my sight. Let me tell you, don't think that just because I'm here at home I won't know every single thing you do at school!"

"Mistress," Mrs. Zhang called from the courtyard, "the rick-shaw is here."

"All right. Take our eldest daughter to the school. You can go now. I'll have Mrs. Zhang come for you on Saturday."

This was how my mother-in-law sent me to school, with those four knitting needles and those countless skeins of wool as my constant companions. At first, I was afraid my fellow students would laugh at me, so tried to hide my knitting. Sometimes when my friends saw it they would say, "Baowen, why don't you come and play with us? Why are you always so busy?" or, "Winter's almost over, but you're still knitting woolen things? You certainly are far-sighted!" And they would all laugh.

I could say nothing, so I would put down my needles and force myself to laugh with them, and as soon as they were gone I would start in again.

As time passed I stopped caring whether the other students laughed at me or not. I knitted not only outside class and during the ten-minute rest periods between classes but sometimes even during classes. My eyes would be on my books and I would be listening to the teachers' lectures, but my hands never stopped moving under the desk. Before long, there were two deep, black marks imprinted on my hands, between the thumb and first finger. They were the marks of the needles, and I could not wash them away. I kept hoping that if I was able to knit the gloves quickly enough, Mrs. Shao would not be angry. I knew it did not matter to her if I did my lessons well or not—but I also knew that if I did not have a finished pair of gloves to hand over to her at the end of the week, she would create a scene and my two days at the house would be very unpleasant.

But no one can do two things at once and do them well. It was hard to knit and concentrate on what the teacher was saying. At the beginning of class I would make a great effort to under-stand, but gradually the teacher's voice would fade into a monot-onous, meaningless hum and my mother-in-law's harsh voice would take its place, just as her glare would take the place of the teacher's gentle, gracious face. It was as if there were a murky black shadow in front of my eyes that covered everything and kept out all the light. If I was unfortunate enough to be called on, it was like being awakened from a dream. I would stand at my desk like a wooden statue, unable to get out a word. Everyone would look at me until the teacher finally called on someone else. Then, awkwardly, I would sit down again. I felt so humiliated that I wanted the earth to open up and swallow me. And for the rest of the class I would keep my head down, not daring to look at the teacher or my classmates.

Those knitting needles and balls of yarn weighed on me more heavily than any scale could ever tell. Mother-in-law, to this day I cannot but admire you—you were so clever, and you knew so well how to gain the advantage. You thought of everything—not only was I so ground down that I could not lift my head while in your home, even when I went to school you did not loosen your grip. It did not matter whether you were there or not —neither my body nor my mind could escape your grasp.

Youth and adolescence should be years of gaiety and lighthearted-ness. I had imagined that school would be a place where I would study and increase my knowledge. Ever since upper pri-mary school, I had longed for the day when I would start middle school. But when that day finally came, there was only indescrib-able pain and disappointment. I would see the other girls my age laughing and playing in the school garden. They looked like spring flowers, and the little breezes would blow their loose, wide, short skirts when they walked so the fabric floated and swirled around their plump, solid legs. I would hear their sweet voices competing with the songs of the birds as they sang, in the clear, cool air of early spring. My heavy heart would become lighter for a moment, and I too wanted to open my mouth and sing, and to let my feet go running and jumping, but my mother-in-law's invisible, unfeeling iron hands would pull me back.

Every time my schoolmates came to get me to play with them, or take a walk and chat, or go to a meeting, I wished that they would leave me alone, because I could not always come up with an excuse for refusing. But when they realized I was reluctant to join them and stopping coming for me, and when even my seven roommates began thinking I was eccentric, and stopped talking with me, I felt very lonely. Xiao Ming sometimes came to see me, but because she was a day pupil we seldom met. When the weekend came, the other students could not wait to leave for home, but I felt as if I was being sent back to jail. I would wrap up the gloves I had knitted in a kerchief and sit silently in the dormitory until Mrs. Zhang came. Then I would follow her out the gate, wishing that Long Street would suddenly become fifty or a hundred *li* long, so that even if I walked forever I would never reach the Shaos' home.

Mrs. Shao no longer treated me as she had in the past, when she would make an effort to pretend to give me some respect. The idea of the money my father had lost choked her. It preyed on her constantly, and she vented all her feelings about it on me. She now went out of her way to humiliate and harass me, especially when Zhongyao was present. She would shout and scold and berate me for the least little thing. Because her voice was naturally so deep and flat, when she got angry and raised it, it became grating and sounded like a man's. It made me tremble, and I trembled all the more if Zhongyao was present because I had no way to preserve my self-respect and felt my humiliation even more deeply.

Zhongyao seemed unhappy too. Whenever he saw his mother scowling at me, a shadow would come over his face even if he had been smiling. When she scolded me he would hang his head and listen silently looking very distressed, and when his mother saw this it made her even angrier. The weekends were almost as difficult for him as they were for me because she would constantly find fault with both of us. It was as if she were determined to crush us both. I no longer saw the gleam of happiness that used to shine so often from his eyes. I knew it was all because of me, and I worried about him. I felt happy when his mother treated him well and my heart sank when she treated him badly, and how she treated me, well or ill, was secondary.

Now, whenever I came back for weekends or holidays, the happiness he and I used to feel when we saw each other again would change immediately to a feeling of defeat and misery.

After I had made five or six pairs of gloves I thought there would be no more knitting. I never expected that Mrs. Shao would wrap up another big bundle of yarn for me and tell me sternly, "Knit a few pairs of children-sized gloves. If my own children don't wear them, we can sell them in the shop." After a while, as if to make herself feel better, she smiled and murmured to herself, "Even if the capital is gone for good maybe we can salvage a bit of interest." Soon, the gloves I knitted, pair by pair, were hanging in the glass display cases in the shop.

In front of other people, especially people from the church, Mrs. Shao treated me differently, and acted as if she did not care about the lost money at all. When she spoke of this—and she brought it up constantly—she would quote Mr. Shao's words about how people in business must expect to lose sometimes. She would also add, "We do not blame Baowen. We've treated her like our own daughter ever since she came to live with us. We've even let her go to school, just like our own Rolan."

When outsiders heard this, they would nod and praise her and tell her she was benevolent and liberal-minded. After showering her with compliments and flattery, they would turn and congratulate me on my good fortune, saying I must have led a virtuous life in my previous cycle of existence to have been rewarded with so estimable a pair of in-laws.

No matter how strong my will, how could I have been a match for what I experienced every day? Even if my body had been made of iron, I do not think it could have stood my mother-in-law's relentless ill-treatment. As time went on, I lost not only my ambition but all my youthful energy. Even my mind was affected —I often felt confused and could not concentrate. And in addition, though the chilblains on my hands and feet—which I had gotten sitting in that cold, drafty hallway all winter long —had healed, I had also caught scabies from Xiao Lao Si and Xiao Lao Wu. They had caught it at school, and I had caught it from them because I had to dress and undress Xiao Lao Wu and wash his hands and face and wait on him day and night when I came home on weekends. I started feeling so ill that I could barely put one foot in front of the other. Mrs. Shao kept complaining, "The longer you're here, the clumsier you get. The longer you're here, the lazier and more stubborn you get."

She neither knew nor cared that for months I had not been able to keep up my physical energy and that my spirits were ever lower.

Chapter 25

I went on feeling ill for most of the spring. I felt weak, my chest often felt congested, and I had no appetite. I had no interest in anything and felt everything was too much trouble to do. Spring lost all its color for me; the red flowers and green willows, the birds' chatter and the insects' songs in the garden, my school-mates' laughter and singing, all seemed to mock me. The beautiful golden sunshine was like a warm, bright net that covered the whole earth. All the flowers and plants and living things were caught in this net, and nourished themselves on the brightness and thrived. Everything seemed to be laughing in the soft spring breeze. But I alone was trapped in a dark, damp corner. The sunshine might cover the whole earth, but it could not shine in my heart.

At first I forced myself to keep going because I was afraid that if I fell behind I would have to leave school and go back to living with the Shaos. My life at school was not happy, but returning to their home would be even worse. The teachers seemed to notice the change in me. In the music and physical education classes, Miss Hai asked me more than once, "Zhou Baowen, are you all right? You aren't looking well. Didn't you get enough sleep last night? Why are you always sad and depressed?" If only we had been alone, if only we had been in a quiet, secluded spot where no one else could have overheard! I think that then I would have been able to open my heart and tell my beloved teacher about all my hidden pain and humiliation, about the injustice and the impositions, hard though that would have been. But with so many people around, on the noisy exercise field or in the classroom, I could not get out a word, no matter how much I wanted to. I could only shake my head and let her take that as my answer.

I always paid attention and never knitted in Mr. Wei's classes, because I knew that he had considered me the most promising student in that year's entering class. He often asked my opinion and obviously thought highly of me. I was grateful and did not want to disappoint him. But for reasons I did not understand, neither my comprehension nor my memory were as good as they had been. My essays, for instance, which I had always enjoyed writing, had deteriorated. It was as if my path of thought were blocked by pebbles that made me stumble, so that I could not think or write. Sometimes Mr. Wei would come over to my desk and ask gently, "Zhou Baowen, is there something you don't understand? Do you have a question?" I would shake my head and keep my eyes on my desk because I was afraid to look at him. He would stay there for a while as if he wanted to ask me something but he would hesitate and then leave. Once, after Qing Ming Festival (Pure Brightness Day)* he assigned us the topic, "Sweeping the Graves at Qing Ming Time," in our writing class. I started remembering the graveyard near our house in Nanjing when I was small, and how people would come to the graves every Qing Ming Festival to burn paper money. I remembered the people—men and women, old and young—coming and going, and the many tiny triangular white paper flags relatives would place on every grave and the black smoke rising above the graves as the imitation money burned. And I remembered how the sad sounds of mourning mingled with the gay laughter of the children. I picked up my pen and wrote more than five hundred words without stopping. When Mr. Wei gave my essay back to me, I saw that he had written two sentences on it in red ink. I will always remember them: "You write so well—why have you not written more?" When I saw this I was mortified, but there was nothing I could do to do better.

I now had even less time and less inclination to write to Zhongyao. He was the same as ever and still wrote often, but if I answered at all it was only with a few words. One afternoon when classes were over and most of the other students were on the exercise ground or out playing in the garden, I was alone in the dormitory knitting a glove. Suddenly I heard the gatekeeper calling to me from outside the window, telling me I had a visitor. I thought Grandfather or Grandmother had come to see me, so I dropped my knitting and ran to the reception room. But when I lifted the blue wool door curtain I was astonished to see Zhongyao standing near the long table. My heart started pound-

*"Qing Ming Festival" occurs around the beginning of April each year. People offer sacrifices to their ancestors and burn imitation money to be used in the afterlife.

213

ing with joy. Without a word, I went and stood across the table from him. It was the first time he and I had ever been alone, face to face. We both kept our eyes lowered. The silence between us seemed to last forever. Finally he looked up. "You ... are you feeling well?" he asked gently.

"Yes." I could not help looking up at him. He smiled at me and my eyes fell again.

After several seconds he said, "You haven't written for so long ... it made me uneasy."

"I ... I've been very busy. I haven't had time to write." Again I looked at him. "You ... Today isn't a holiday. How were you able to leave school?"

"I asked for three hours of leave just so I could come and see you." He again smiled at me and again I dropped my eyes. We did not know what to say next.

After a while he spoke again. "You're much thinner."

"I ... I hadn't noticed."

"Your chilblains, have they healed completely?"

I had been clutching the edge of the table, but when he asked this I quickly put my hands behind me and said, "They're almost well."

After another silence he handed me a small parcel. "I brought you some embroidered handkerchiefs and a package of imported stationery and envelopes." He smiled again.

Hesitantly, I put out one hand to take it.

"Don't worry ..." he said in that same soft, gentle voice. "You know I still feel—"

My classmates' clear, high laughter interrupted him. We both wheeled around—out in the courtyard we saw three of my fellow students, their arms around each other, passing the reception room window. They were smiling at us in amusement. After they were gone, Zhongyao went on, "No matter what my family—no matter how they treat you, I'll always be faithful to you."

How tender his voice was, and how loving and intimate his words were! They warmed my heart, but also made me feel a little sad, because there were so many things I wanted to say to him, but I did not know where to start. We gazed at each other for a long moment, then, suddenly, his handsome young face, sunburned and a bit too long, blurred before my eyes and my throat tightened. I quickly gulped back my tears, but it was a long time before I could speak, and when I did my words were not at all what I wanted to say and had nothing to do with what I was really feeling. "You ... won't you be late getting back to your school?" I said.

He looked up at the clock on the wall and picked up his woolen hat but did not move. It was as if there was much he still wanted to say, but after a long time he said only, "If you have time, be sure to write to me."

I nodded.

He put on his hat. "I'd better go."

"Yes."

Still his feet did not move. He went on standing there hesitantly for quite a long time. Then he turned and almost ran out of the reception room.

I rushed over to the window that looked out onto the lane and pulled on the lattices until I managed to open half of it. I leaned out. His tall figure moved along the grey brick city wall and then disappeared. I picked up the parcel he had brought me and ran back to my dormitory, where I pulled down my bed curtains. I lay on my bed and suddenly the tears came, hot tears that gushed from my eyes, like water from a mountain spring. I covered my face with my handkerchief. My heart ached with a sweet sadness. His smiles, his words, his tender voice stayed in my mind and in my ears for a long, long time.

Finally my body and mind both gave way. After I could not get out of bed for two days, the school got in touch with the Shaos. Mrs. Shao sent Mrs. Zhang to bring me back. When I came into the living room, my mother-in-law's first words were, "What's wrong with you? I know you've been eating too much and the food has clogged in your body. Also, you haven't been dressing warmly enough and have caught a chill. It's nothing serious. Stay home and fast for a couple of days and I guarantee you'll soon be well."

It was easy for her to offer that guarantee, but my illness did not listen to her. I spent the next two weeks in a high fever. I lay delirious in Zhongyao's grandmother's big bed. I could swallow nothing except water and was constantly thirsty. Except for his grandmother, who came in to feel my forehead two or three times a day, and Xiao Lazi, who brought me some tea from time to time, no one came to see me.

After two weeks had gone by, Zhongyao's grandmother brought Mrs. Shao to my bedside and said, "Feel her forehead and her palms—she's burning up. She's been running this fever night and day for two weeks now, and hasn't eaten a single thing in all that time. I think she's very, very ill. I think you'd better hurry and call a doctor so we can find out what's wrong with her. That way we can stop worrying." Mrs. Shao felt my forehead and immediately snatched her hand away. She retreated to the long narrow table and stood there thinking for a while. Then she left.

The next day she sent for a physician who was trained in traditional Chinese medicine. Grandmother brought him into the room. He sat down next to the bed and felt my pulses* for quite a while. Then he asked her about my symptoms and how long I had had them. He looked at my tongue and stood up. "It's a very serious case of typhoid," he said. As they were leaving the room I heard her ask, "Doctor, do you think it's really serious?"

"If I'd seen her right at the start, it would have been much easier," he replied. "You waited much too long. I'll give you a prescription—give her two courses of the medicine and we'll see how she does. If it brings her fever down gradually, there's not much danger. But if it doesn't go down, I'm afraid it may be very dangerous."

My fever did not go down. I could not taste anything and my chest was as congested as ever. I could not keep down any food. Twice a day, early in the morning and late at night, I had to force myself to swallow a big bowl of warm, bitter, brown medicine soup. Sometimes Zhongyao's grandmother would try to slip a piece of rock candy into my mouth to take away the bitterness. She would also urge me to drink a little thin gruel, but if I did I would immediately vomit it and the medicine. When my fever was at its worst, I would struggle over towards the side of the bed and touch the frame, trying to find a cool surface to relieve the burning. Most of the time I was delirious, half-awake and half-asleep. Sometimes when I opened my eyes, Zhongyao's grandmother would be standing by the bed. But sometimes a whole day would go by without my seeing or talking with anyone. But no matter how sick I was I always remembered one thing —not to groan, not even once. I did not want to give Mrs. Shao any excuse to say what she had said about Da Biao Sao once when she was ill, "She's young and only has a bit of fever. So why is she groaning like an old woman? Doesn't she realize how much

---

*"Felt my pulses." In traditional Chinese medicine, pulse-taking is a highly sophisticated diagnostic method. Chinese doctors are trained to discriminate as many as thirty types of pulses, each indicating a different condition. Pulses are judged according to depth, speed, width, strength, rhythm, length and other factors.

trouble she's causing?"

Ten more days went by, but I was no better. Zhongyao's grandmother got very worried and even Mrs. Shao finally started feeling a bit concerned. One day after lunch, they both came into the room. Grandmother told her daughter, "She has taken the medicine but the fever has not gone down at all. I think that maybe we should try to give her a bit of opium. Maybe it will help."

"All right. Prepare a pipe and let her try it."

Grandmother took out her opium tray and heated a pipe. She handed it to me, but I was so weak and it was so long and heavy that I could barely hold it up. Grandmother helped me to hold it and pushed the pipe into my mouth. I do not know whether it was because I did not want the opium or because I was not used to it, but at first I could not make the pipe draw. They both urged me, "Draw hard! Draw the smoke back into your throat." So I did, but when I tasted the smoke, my stomach turned over and I started vomiting and could not stop.

Mrs. Shao hastily covered her mouth and nose with her hand and retreated to the table to watch. After a while, she told her mother, "Her fever won't break, and she's delirious and sleeps all the time.... If we don't do something, I hate to say it, but maybe she'll fall asleep and never wake up."

"It could happen. I'm worried about that too."

"I think that Mrs. Zhang and Xiao Lazi should sit her up in the living room for a while every day after lunch. Let's get her to walk a few steps, slowly, and see. Maybe it will stimulate her system. Who knows? Even healthy people could sleep themselves into an illness, sleeping from morning to night like that."

Grandmother agreed.

"All right, we'll help her sit up and get some air, and see what happens."

The next day, she helped me sit up in bed and wrapped some clothes around me. Then she had the two servants hold onto my arms and help me stand up. My slippered feet seemed to be floating on a cloud or in a mist that felt as empty as the wind. My clothes hung on my body, which was no more than a skeleton. Suddenly, as they were helping me into the living room, countless red and black stars exploded in front of my eyes. They flew and danced everywhere and the cloud under my feet turned into the rolling waves of the sea. The whole house, and heaven and earth itself, began spinning around me. There was a roaring in my ears and everything turned black. As I reached the table, I fell forward, but Mrs. Zhang and Xiao Lazi caught me. I was still conscious enough to hear Grandmother say, "Hurry, take her back to bed and heat up a bowl of ginger soup for her."

For ten more days I lay semi-conscious in bed. The weather turned warmer, but because I was on the inside of the bed and behind the curtain, I could not get any fresh air. Grandmother had Mrs. Zhang bring in a small bamboo bed for me. Sometimes my fever would remain high for a whole day and I would sleep it away in a daze, but at other times, especially in the mornings or at twilight, it would drop and my mind would clear somewhat. As I lay alone in bed in that dim room, I would look at the two skylights and the blue-stenciled white curtain, which had now turned yellow, on the big bed, at the thick layer of dust on the bed frame, and at the spiderwebs that hung from the beams. I could hear Mrs. Shao's harsh voice coming from the living room as she scolded the servants and Xiao Lazi, and hear Rolan and her little brothers shouting. And I would feel troubled and depressed.

My thoughts, however, flowed turbulently and without ceasing, like water bubbling from a mountain spring. I remembered how Mother used to sit by my bed and watch over me when I was a child and had a fever, how she used to bring me tea and feed me and would not leave me even for a moment, and how she would think of ways to comfort me and make me happy. Then I would think of my present illness and how empty and chilly the room was. No one paid any attention to me or came to comfort me. I began to think that if I were to die, as Mrs. Shao had said, it might not be so terrible and might spare me much misery. I would have no regrets and the only person I would miss would be Zhongyao. I felt he was the only person I cared about, the only person I could not entirely let go of. Sometimes I could hear him come home. I heard him talking in the living room and heard his leather-soled shoes in the hallway. They would stop at my door and he would pace back and forth. I hoped so much that he would come in to see me and say a few words to comfort me, but perhaps he had been forbidden to come in to see me, and of course there was no longer any way we could write to each other. It seemed he and I were now to be kept even further apart.

Sometimes I wondered why my grandparents did not come to see me. I wondered whether they even knew that I was ill. I was so sick that I could not quite remember, but it seemed I had heard either Mrs. Shao's mother or Mr. Shao telling me that my third uncle had died. How sad my grandparents must be, I thought, and how much their lives must have changed.

Sometimes Mrs. Shao would take the children and go out visiting. The house would be quiet and I would feel very lonely and wish that someone, Zhongyao's grandmother or Xiao Lazi, would come in to see me.

My illness dragged on for more than two months. None of the medicines helped. One afternoon when I was in my usual feverish daze, I felt a hand touch my forehead. I seemed to hear a soft voice calling my name. "Baogu, Baogu, dear ... wake up. It's your grandfather." I opened my eyes and closed them again—it seemed as if Grandfather was standing at my bedside, but I thought I was dreaming.

"Baogu, how are you? Do you recognize me?"

It took all my energy to raise my eyelids. I rubbed my eyes and saw Grandfather's thin, wrinkled face bending over mine. He was still lightly feeling my forehead. "How are you, dear?"

"Grandfather, you've come!" I started crying and tears trickled down my cheeks and onto my neck.

"How are you, dear?"

"Grandmother! Where's Grandmother?"

"Grandmother ... isn't very well. In a few days, when she's better, she'll come to see you."

Why was she ill? I wanted to ask, but I was crying too much. I could not stop the gush of tears, even though my throat and nose ached.

"Don't worry, dear. We want you to hurry up and get well. What would you like to eat? I'll buy it for you."

"She can't swallow anything. All she ever says is that she's thirsty and wants water," said Zhongyao's grandmother, who was at the foot of my bed.

Grandfather wiped away my tears with the sleeve of his gown. He stood by my bedside for a long time, and then gave two deep sighs and left the room with her. Their voices were very soft and I could not make out their words. After a while I got drowsy and confused again and went back to sleep.

When I woke, the room was already dark. The lamp had not been lit. My throat and mouth were parched. I was going to sit up and pour myself some water when suddenly I smelled the fragrance of fresh pears. There was a parcel wrapped in a kerchief on the round stool at the head of the bed. I opened it and found about ten tiny fresh pears. I took one to quench my thirst—I never realize pear juice could be so fragrantly sweet and good. I ate three or four, and felt much cooler and more comfortable. After a while, Xiao Lazi came in to light the lamp. She brought a small bowl of broth and I drank several mouthfuls.

The next morning Zhongyao's grandmother came in to see me after breakfast. She remembered the pears and when she saw that I had eaten all but two or three she got very worried because the doctor had warned that cold and raw foods were bad for fevers. She felt my forehead and palms and then went out to the hallway to call Mrs. Shao. "Daughter, guess what—Baowen ate seven or eight of the pears her grandfather brought yesterday and, strangely enough, she seems better, not worse! I think she has some life left in her after all. Since she likes the pears, let's buy another catty or two and let her have all she wants. Maybe if she gets her appetite back, she'll get well."

"All right. Buy some and let her eat them, and we'll see."

After lunch, Zhongyao's grandmother brought in a little basket of pears and put it on the stool. She told me to eat as many as I wanted and that after I had finished them all she would have Mrs. Zhang buy more.

Chapter 26

I cannot say whether my illness turned the corner just then or whether the pears had some effect, but from that day on my fever started dropping.

When Mrs. Shao saw this, every day after lunch she would tell me to get out of bed and walk around the house. "Move around. Exercise your muscles and bones. Don't let them get paralyzed from too much sleep."

But I was still very weak and had no strength in my legs. My heart would pound and I would be dizzy and short of breath before I walked around the house twice. I would have to hold onto the backs of the chairs with both hands, or prop my hands against the walls and try to catch my breath. I looked like a ghost. Every morning when I combed my hair, it came out in handfuls. Though I had regained a little of my sense of taste, I still had almost no appetite. When I saw Xiao Lazi or the wet nurse sitting in the courtyard eating big bowls of food, I would feel the urge to eat, but once the bowl was in my hands I would find I could not get any food down.

But it seemed the crisis was over. Every afternoon, I could feel my fever rise a little after my walk, but the rest of the time it was normal. Illness and health seemed to be at war in my body. If Mrs. Shao had not forced me to get up and walk around once the fever broke, but had let me rest for a few more days, I think I would have recovered more quickly, but I dared not suggest it. Even when I was exhausted I would clench my teeth and force myself out of bed. Perhaps it was because I still had a teenager's stamina that I was able, in spite of everything, to conquer my illness and recover gradually. Suddenly, my appetite became enormous, two or three times bigger than before my illness. I could eat several bowls of food, even if it was only salted vegetables scrambled with red peppers to flavor rice, and still felt unsatisfied and hungry. Nevertheless, I did not gain back any weight and still felt weak. My hair continued to fall out and my face was dry, yellow and haggard.

As soon as I started eating again and got strong enough to hold my own rice bowl, Mrs. Shao brought me my old rattan sewing basket. She said nothing about my going back to school or about any special care for me while I convalesced. Then Grandmother suffered a recurrence of her heart trouble. I was given the tasks of serving her food and tea, bringing her hot water, and preparing all her medications. I also had to help Rolan and her brothers. I was busy all day long, but my work was never done. It was late spring and the weather was warm, but Zhongyao's grandmother's room was rather stuffy. So every day after lunch she would go out to the back gate and open it. She would rest on a long rattan chaise, facing the river nearby, and smoke her water pipe. The green trees on the river bank offered a pleasing, restful view. I would bring the portable stove on which I cooked her gruel and medicines out onto the steps outside the gate, and would keep her company while I sewed and cooked. If no one called me to do anything else and if Rolan and her brothers were in school, it would be quiet and calm out there.

One day after lunch, when Zhongyao's grandmother and I were in her room, I suddenly heard Mr. and Mrs. Shao's voices erupt. They were shouting. I listened carefully, but they did not sound the same as when they scolded me or the servants. At first I did not know what was wrong, but I soon learned that there was trouble in Mr. Shao's family in the countryside and that his first cousin had come in haste into the city to bring the news. The widow of Mr. Shao's younger brother wanted to remarry less than a year after her husband's death. She would not stop demanding that her family let her marry again. The relatives could not persuade her to change her mind and had sent the cousin to get the advice of Mr. Shao, the eldest son in the family, before making a final decision.

Mr. Shao's own family had been poor, and so were all his country relatives. The Shaos ordinarily avoided going to the country and the relatives seldom came into the city. When they did, they would stay in the store out in front and rarely came into the house. This time, probably because the matter was so serious, Mrs. Shao not only spoke with the relative herself but also had him eat dinner with the family. All during dinner, the Shaos continued discussing how they could keep the widow from marrying again. The country relative remained silent and ate politely. Keeping his eyes on his food he said, "Cousin, Cousin-in-law, if you heard the things she's been saying! You have no idea how fierce she is! She doesn't have the slightest sense of shame—the other day I actually heard her say, 'The world is more civilized today. I'm free to remarry if I wish!'"

"Free!" the Shaos chorused, as if they could not believe their ears. Mr. Shao shook his chopsticks at his cousin. "Go and ask her, ask her what kind of freedom she thinks she's talking about?"

"She thinks she has the right to talk about freedom!" Mrs. Shao frowned and picked up a tasty morsel of food, depositing it forcefully in Rolan's bowl. "Has there been a revolution? Are there no more rules? Go and tell her that in our family she can do anything except remarry. She must not rebel and talk about freedom."

"Cousin-in-law, you're always so perceptive. Cousin-in-law—"

"I've never detested anything so much as remarriage. Such shameful behavior!" Mrs. Shao interrupted him. "I think ..." She broke off, considering, and then turned to her husband. "I don't think you should leave the stores. I'm the only one who can handle this, so I'll go.... I want to see just how much courage that woman has. Even if she can't be talked out of her folly, I'll certainly give her a hard time. I won't let it be said of us that the Shao family name can be put on and taken off like a suit of clothes!"

"That would certainly be the best thing, for you to go," said Mr. Shao, smiling. "I'm just afraid that it's too hot and too far and that you cannot go and come back the same day. Besides, the countryside is dirty. You love cleanliness so much—how could you stand to spend a night there?"

"It doesn't matter. I'll take Mrs. Zhang with me. Now that the weather's warm, I'll need to take only two thin quilts. Anyway, it'll only be one night, I'll manage."

"Then there's nothing more to be said. I appreciate your doing this for me. In a while, I'll send someone out to hire two sedan chairs. You should start at daybreak tomorrow to avoid the heat, so you should go to bed early tonight."

Mrs. Shao nodded and ordered Mrs. Zhang to pack up the quilts and pillows, and some towels, wooden combs and scented soap. That night, the Shaos went to bed earlier than usual.

The next morning, before the red face of the sun had even fully risen, one of the shop apprentices came to say that the chairs had arrived. Mrs. Shao was still in bed. Xiao Lazi and I hurried into her room with hot and cold water, basins, and bath towels to serve her as she rose. Mrs. Zhang brought in fresh jasmine tea and a little bowl of fine noodles in chicken soup with chopped green scallions and two soft-poached eggs. Mrs. Shao said she could not eat anything because she had gotten up so early, and drank only two mouthfuls of soup and a small cup of tea. Then, dressed and ready, she went out to the store gate with Mrs. Zhang. Mr. Shao, in his slippers, followed, yawning and giving Mrs. Zhang instructions. "Take good care of your mistress ... (yawn) ... Don't let her get too warm." Xiao Lazi and I stood at the shop gate and watched Mrs. Zhang help Mrs. Shao into the front chair. She then seated herself in the second one. The cousin walked behind them. They went around the corner and disappeared from view.

The day passed as usual, but because, as the saying goes, "When the cat's away, the mice will play," it seemed shorter. Mr. Shao and Zhongyao's grandmother both thought that she would return by noon the next day, but it was almost sundown before we heard Mr. Shao shout down the hallway from the shop, "Rolan, boys! Come quickly—your mother's back! Baowen! Xiao Lazi! Hurry up and bring her some wash water and some tea!"

Amid much shouting and running about, I led Zhongyao's grandmother slowly into the living room. Mrs. Shao had already settled herself on the chair near the long table. Mr. Shao was sitting opposite, smiling and praising and comforting her. Rolan and her brothers were not paying any attention to them but were crowded over in a corner looking at something. I went over and saw they were looking at a little boy. He was six or seven, and thin and dark. He was wearing a coarse, blue cotton coat and trousers, so ragged that they hung in torn strips. His unkempt hair stood out in every direction and his feet were bare. His huge black eyes darted about in astonishment at the new things he was seeing. He looked terrified, like a little wild animal that had just been caged. He was clutching his ragged coat around him in his filthy fists.

Mrs. Shao wiped her face with a towel, sipped some hot tea, unbuttoned the collar of her jacket and started telling Mr. Shao about her experiences. "As soon as our chairs rounded the hill, even before we reached the village, the people all came out to see us—everyone, the grownups and children alike. They said, 'The honorable sister-in-law from the city has come! We think there's going to be a quarrel.' As soon as I went inside the house, your two youngest brothers' wives dragged the widow in to see me and told her to kneel down and kowtow. She wouldn't stop talking!

Complaining about 'bullying a lone widow' and saying she'd 'rather die.' When I heard her, I got angry. I got up and told her to shut up and then, pam, pam, I slapped her face. And then I said, 'Don't you realize who I am? Or is it that you really don't know how to behave decently? Shut up! I've travelled a long way —you have no business saying anything!' But that one slap struck her dumb! She buried her face in her hands and crouched on the floor like a funeral mourner and wailed for a long time."

"Pam, pam! I slapped her face!" Xiao Lao Si and Xiao Lao Wu suddenly picked up on their mother's words and began clapping their hands, facing each other, as if slapping each other's faces.

"Hey, you two, be quiet! Your mother is talking seriously. Listen carefully and don't interrupt." Mr. Shao, a half-smoked cigarette in his mouth, smiled at the children and waved them away. Then he turned his smile on his wife and nodded to show how much he admired her courage and her way of managing things.

"The other women said, 'Honorable sister-in-law, she always was worthless. Don't hurt your hand hitting her.' I said, 'What does she think she's saying? The whole family is here and I've come all the way from the city. None of the rest of you have opened your mouths. She's been doing all the talking!'"

Mrs. Shao laughed, and the more she talked the more pleased with herself she became. "No one dared speak. Again I spoke to her. You can do one of two things. Choose one of them. If you decide to listen to me and come to your senses and do your duty, it's not too late to save your reputation. But if you don't change and really want to ruin yourself, we know how to deal with you. Our family name is not one you can take on and toss away whenever you please!"

"'That's telling her!' Everyone around us agreed. I nodded and told them to take her out to the back and told my other sisters-in-law to take turns guarding her and not to leave her alone because she might do something foolish. Then I talked it all over with both families and your mother's brother and all the other relatives there. First I asked them what they had already tried. They said that in the beginning they had thought they could hush it up and not wash dirty linen in public, that they could beat up that scabby-headed peddler and run him out the village, shut her up in the house, and be done with it. But she let it be known everywhere that she wanted to remarry and she wouldn't be intimidated. So, since the scandal couldn't be suppressed and since she kept threatening to kill herself unless she was allowed to remarry, they came up with another solution. After all, the situation could have dragged on for a long time, and something might really happen. Then the family would not only lose her and the bride-price but would also be out the price of the coffin. That would be even worse. So they decided to let her marry the old rattle-shaker and move away—if he'd pay a hundred yuan in silver for her. But it turned out that he was so poor that he could only pay twenty yuan! So they were still in trouble."

"That does make things difficult," said Mr. Shao, shaking his head doubtfully.

"Difficult?" Mrs. Shao gave him a triumphant glance. "I think that if you'd been me, you wouldn't have been able to work things out."

"That goes without saying!" Mr. Shao nodded humbly and smiled again.

Mrs. Shao looked even more pleased with herself, and went on, "I thought out a compromise—make him hand over fifty yuan." She dropped her hand lightly on the table. "And if he couldn't come up with it all at once, make him sign a promissory note. With the promissory note, we have nothing to fear even if he tries to run away. He's in our power. Also they must be made to leave the village, and she shouldn't be allowed to take any of your late brother's few ragged belongings except the clothes on her back. All that remained to be dealt with was the three children. That presented some difficulty. The two little girls were easy—no one wanted them, so the widow and her peddler were allowed to take them with them. But Da Huantuan (Big Dumpling) was after all a son, and a Shao—and a Shao is a Shao no matter what. So I told them, 'None of you wants him. I want him. Tomorrow morning let me take him back with me. I'll raise him. He can go with my two boys when they go to school. And a few hours later they did what I told them and an agreement was reached."

"Very good! Wonderful!"

"This little brat ..." Mrs. Shao pointed to Da Huantuan. "This morning, when we got into the chairs, you never heard such yelling and squealing. He screamed like a stuck pig. No matter what we said, he refused to get into the chair. It finally took several people and many threats to shove him into it."

"It's true," said Mrs. Zhang, who walked in shaking out a suit of Xiao Lao Si's. "I don't know where he got all that strength. I couldn't hold him—my arms were so twisted that they still ache. Everybody there said he was the luckiest of the three of them. Strange! Having a chance to come to the city to live with his uncle and aunt, to eat good food, to wear good clothes—he must have been very virtuous in his past incarnations to be so fortunate—and still he wept. Mistress, shall I dress him in this old suit of the fourth young master's?"

Mrs. Shao nodded. "Take him out to the courtyard and scrub him from head to toe with soap and warm water. And shave his head—for all we know, he has lice. And throw out that suit. I'm afraid it's also full of lice."

Mrs. Zhang frowned. "Da Huantuan, come with me."

"What?" Xiao Lao Si's eyes bugged out. He pointed to Da Huantuan, who was cowering in the corner, and bellowed, "He's called Da Huantuan? Pooh! That dirty thing! He's six inches shorter than me, and called Da Huantuan? What about me then? What should I be called?"

"He—he—is he called Da—Da Huantuan?" Xiao Lao Wu, stammering and stuttering, copied his brother. "I—I—I'm called—"

His brother interrupted. "Shut up, you stammerer! Let me do the talking! I say he's black and dirty and has lice! Pooh! I know what we should call him! We should call him Heitan (Charcoal)!"

Mr. and Mrs. Shao threw back their heads and laughed.

"Yes, how clever he is!" Mrs. Zhang laughed too. Then, immediately picking up on the new name, she said, "Well, Heitan, when are you going to start moving? What's the matter? Have you forgotten how to walk?"

Mrs. Shao stretched and yawned several times, "The countryside is certainly primitive!" She laughed and said, "They all tried to be so hospitable. When they saw me coming, they swept out the room and began cooking. They tried so hard, but I couldn't stand to eat any of it. We talked until after two in the morning before we went to bed. But, oh, the bed bugs! They were like ants. There must have been armies and platoons of them! I couldn't shut my eyes all night, not even once!"

"Wife, you're all tired out. Go to our room and rest. I'll prepare a pipe of opium for you to smoke. Rest first, and then we'll have dinner."

Mrs. Shao drank some more tea, inquired about her mother's health, and then went with Mr. Shao into their room.

Suddenly we heard loud yells coming from the courtyard. "I want my mother! I want to go home! I want ..."

Then came Mrs. Zhang's sharp, scolding voice. "What are you yelling about? I haven't even touched your head with my razor and you're screaming. I'm not going to kill you! Look, Madam, he won't let me shave his head!"

"Mrs. Zhang, all you have to do is wallop him on the head a few times. I'm sure that'll make him let you," Mrs. Shao yelled from her room. "He's too used to running wild. The worst thing we could do is be too easy on him now, right at the start. He's got to learn how to behave! In a few days I want him to accompany the boys to school."

Mrs. Zhang grumbled, "I've worn myself out, I'm covered in sweat, and you're wailing about wanting your mother! Your mother! She's long since run away with that old rag-picker. You're dreaming! You could shout your throat raw and she wouldn't hear you! Now behave yourself! And don't move—if you move again I'll cut your scalp open and it'll be your own fault!"

Da Huantuan's sobs lessened slowly and finally stopped. When dinner was ready, Mrs. Zhang pushed him into the living room. His head was completely shaved and he was clean all over but there were still tear stains on his face. He crouched in the corner and clutched the cast-off coat around him. Xiao Lazi filled a bowl with rice and took it over to him, but he refused to look at it or take it.

"Ignore him," said Mrs. Shao. "Put the rice on the counter near the kitchen stove. He hasn't eaten all day. Just wait and I guarantee he'll go and eat."

When darkness fell, I went out to the kitchen to fill Grandmother's thermos bottle with boiling water. Mrs. Zhang and Xiao Lazi were in the courtyard peering through the latticed window into the kitchen. When they saw me, they smiled and motioned to me to be quiet. I crept over to them and saw Da Huantuan at the counter near the stove. He was alone. He had the rice bowl in one hand and chopsticks in the other. He was still gulping back sobs, but was also shovelling the rice into his mouth.

Chapter 27

TWO days later, Heitan, as he had now been dubbed, accompanied Xiao Lao Si and Xiao Lao Wu to school.

Mrs. Shao was uneasy because she was afraid the two little boys would be asked questions about him. The night before, she had summoned them and spent some time giving them detailed instructions in a low voice. Then, speaking more loudly, she said, "If the teachers or your schoolmates ask you who he is, what will you tell them? Do you remember?"

"I remember." Xiao Lao Si answered as if it were of no consequence. "It's not so hard—even Xiao Lao Wu could tell them, and he stammers!"

"I ... I could ... I could say them."

After giving her sons the instructions, she had Heitan come in. "Tomorrow morning you'll go to school with them. I want you to behave and do what they tell you and play with Xiao Lao Wu. Don't be stubborn. I brought you here mainly because of them. They're both very well behaved and you're used to running wild in the country. You mustn't be wild with them when I'm not around. I'll find out and punish you. Are you listening? I'm talking to you."

"Uh," Heitan muttered, his head drooping.

"'Uh?' He has no manners at all," snapped Mrs. Zhang, who was nearby. "When your aunt speaks to you, you must say, 'Aunt, I hear.' Say it! Are you a deaf-mute?"

"Aunt, I ... I hear."

"That's better!" Mrs. Shao smiled and waved him away. "Go on now, what're you standing here for? Be sure to get up early tomorrow morning."

The next morning, Rolan and her brothers ran gaily out the gate as usual. Behind them came Xiao Lazi, with Rolan's book-bag hanging from her shoulder, and Heitan, with the boys' book-bags hanging from his thin shoulders. Rolan, neatly dressed and looking like a newly opening flower bud, led the way. Behind her, Xiao Lazi, dry and yellow and thin, looked like a parched little weed. Xiao Lao Si and Xiao Lao Wu, both fat and round and empty-handed, jumped and leaped about mischievously, and looked like two fat little poodles. And Heitan, his shoulders sagging and wearing Xiao Lao Si's cast-off cloth shoes, which were too big and kept falling off his feet, waddled along like an ugly, long-necked, undernourished duckling.

When Xiao Lazi returned, Mrs. Shao asked her, "Did anything happen with Heitan on the way to school?"

"Nothing, Mistress."

Mrs. Shao asked nothing else. Ever since she had returned from the countryside, her ears had been filled with praise for her ability to endure hardships and handle difficult situations. She probably thought that, since she had been able to solve such a big problem so easily, no one would say anything about something as trivial as having Heitan go to school with the boys, especially since she had given them such careful instructions and had planned everything out. But it turned into an unexpected problem that caused many headaches. That very afternoon, as soon as the boys came into the living room, Xiao Lao Si shouted, "Mother, the teacher questioned me today!"

"What did he say?" Mrs. Shao called from her room.

"He asked, 'Who is that?' I said, 'He's Heitan. He's a poor relation. His mother and father are both dead. My mother felt sorry for him and brought him home to live with us.'"

"That's right. That's exactly what I told you to say."

"Teacher said, 'Since he's a relative, your family should send him to school. Why leave him waiting outside, if you two are sitting in the classroom?'"

"Oh, really! That teacher of yours certainly knows how to mind other people's business! He should stick to teaching. What business is it of his? What did you say then?"

"I said ... I said ..." Xiao Lao Si scratched his head and thought and then said brightly, "You ... last night you didn't tell us what to say."

"Really!" Mrs. Shao came out of her room. "We give him food to eat and clothes to wear. It should be like being in heaven for him! I tell you, next time that teacher of yours says anything, you tell him, 'My mother says it'll soon be summer vacation. She wants him to come with us and be a companion for Xiao Lao Wu so he has someone to play with. We'll deal with his going to school later.' Do you understand?"

"I uh—uh—understand."

"Mother, they ... they ... asked me ..."

"That's right." As usual, Xiao Lao Si snatched the words away from his younger brother. "Our schoolmates ..."

"You ... you let me ... let me tell."

"You stammer too much! He's right. Our schoolmates asked questions too. They said, 'You two are wearing nice clothes and he's wearing old clothes. You have new shoes on and he's wearing old ones.'"

"Really! I've never heard anything like it. What's wrong with them? They're just like the teachers! They have nothing better to do than spend all their time meddling in other people's business." Mrs. Shao frowned and flounced over to a chair. "Why didn't you say, 'If it weren't for us he wouldn't even have old clothes to wear, or anything to eat?'"

"I did! I told them he was barefoot and in rags and that his whole body and his head were full of lice! And that Mrs. Zhang shaved his head and washed him, and that afterwards the water was black!"

"So it was," put in Mrs. Zhang loudly. She was washing clothes in the courtyard. "It was blacker than the water in the drain. Mistress, look at how clever the little master is! He can outthink any grownup. And he's not afraid of anything or anyone!"

"All right! You two, have the servants draw some water for you, and wash your hands and faces. Then ask Baowen to get you something to eat. But what about Heitan? Did he obey you?"

"Obey us? If he ever dared to be stubborn with us ..." Xiao Lao Si puffed out his chest and patted it. "Look, I'm ten times as strong as he is!"

"You little hellion!" Mrs. Shao's frown softened into a fond smile. " All right, run outside and wash and rest ... Oh, why do I have to get upset and angry all because of that little devil?"

The next afternoon, the moment the two boys set foot in the house, Mrs. Shao demanded, "How was it? Did any of those busybodies ask you anything today?"

"No. Nobody."

"Good! Maybe they know how to behave after all."

Nothing happened for the next two days, so Mrs. Shao got more confident. But then, on the fourth afternoon, the two brothers came back from school pouting and muttering to each other. When their mother overheard them, she asked, "What are you muttering about?"

"The teacher scolded us again today."

"Scolded you again? What's the matter that he should scold you?"

"After school, just when we were going out the main gate, Mr. Luo came along. He told us to stop, so we stopped. Then he asked us, 'Why don't you two carry your own bags? Why do you have someone else carry them for you?' He also said ... he also said, 'You two, as big as you are, wouldn't you be ashamed to have somebody feed you?'"

"They really are a plague!"

"Mr. Luo also said," added Rolan, "'It's a shame, when your family belongs to the church.'"

"How strange that Mr. Luo must be! Hasn't he scolded you enough? Such meddling! Well, that's enough of that—I can't be bothered. I think we'll stop having Heitan go to school with you. I have better things to do than bother with teachers and students who like to mind other people's business!"

And so Heitan stopped following them to school. During the day, he ran errands and did odd jobs in the store in front. In the late afternoons, after school, he had to play with Xiao Lao Si and Xiao Lao Wu. But it was not easy to "play" with them. No matter how much trouble her own children managed to create, Mrs. Shao seemed to be wearing blinders and to have cotton wool in her ears. She could neither see nor hear what her children were doing, but should Heitan mutter the slightest complaint, or should one of the sons roar, "Mother, look. Heitan won't listen to us!" and she would immediately start scolding him. "Heitan, you're asking for a whipping! I'll skin you alive if you provoke them into calling me again!"

"Don't you hear us? Hurry up and bend over? We want you to be our horse. Bend over! Bend over!"

"You ... you ... bend over ... I ... I'll shout for ... Mo—Mo—" Xiao Lao Wu could not stammer out the last syllable before Heitan would hurriedly bend over so Xiao Lao Wu could ride him. Xiao Lao Si would chase him around the courtyard, urging him on with a small bamboo stick and shouting, "Watch out for the horse!"

Before long, Heitan lost all the natural, childish spirits he had brought with him from the countryside. Whenever he saw his aunt, he was like a mouse seeing a cat or like someone who had just met the devil. He would shrink into a corner, not daring to move. When he saw the two little masters, he would hang his head and, no matter what they thought up to torment him with, would submit to them. Gradually he even stopped whimpering. Sometimes they would push him too far and it would seem he was about to resist, but all it took was for one of the two brothers to shout that ominous phrase, "Mother, look at Heitan!" and he would give in.

Strangely enough, whenever Heitan was scolded or victimized, he would turn his big black eyes on me, though I had scarcely spoken with him and certainly could not protect him. It was as if he wanted to tell me his wrongs or as if he hoped that I could come to his defense. Whenever he could, he would edge over towards me. Did he perhaps see my sympathy for him in my eyes? Or did he realize that, like him, I too had to endure Mrs. Shao's scoldings, and did he feel I was thus not to be feared but someone stay near to? I was not sure, but I thought he probably realized I was his friend. The wet nurse also treated him well. When Mrs. Shao and Mrs. Zhang were not around, she would secretly mend his clothes, socks, and shoes for him.

Some afternoons, before the boys came home and while Mrs. Shao was taking her nap, Heitan would creep out to the back gate and sit on the steps. He would hunch over and rest his cheeks in his hands, and would not move or make a sound for a long, long time, as if lost in his own thoughts and feelings. I would look up from my sewing and see his thin little back, and I could not help thinking, "Poor little Heitan, you're so very young! What are you thinking about? Do you miss your mother and sisters? Or are you thinking about how your life has suddenly changed? How strange, how confusing, and how cruel life must seem to you! Everyone tells you how fortunate you are to be living in the city with your uncle and aunt, but what do they know of the pain and sadness you suffer every day? It isn't just you. I'm exactly ten years older than you, and sometimes I can't understand my own life. I too was brought here against my will, and my life isn't much easier than yours...."

Thinking about Heitan's situation naturally led me to think about my own. Ever since my illness, I had been feeling as if something were gripping my heart. It would not let go. I was constantly trying to draw a deep breath, but I never could. And the last time Mrs. Liang called to hold a Bible study and prayer session, Mrs. Shao told her that since I did not know how to manage a household, she was planning to keep me to home from then on so I could concentrate on learning to sew and keep house. Although my days in the school had not been easy, my hopes dimmed even more now that I knew they had ended.

Sometimes when I was sitting at the gate I would see the students, boys and girls alike, walking in laughing groups along the street. Their faces were flushed and healthy and they looked incomparably cheerful. Sometimes I would see them walking in procession, all wearing little white sailcloth hats against the sun, while the bands blew and beat bright, merry marches as they marched off to the summer-session athletic meets. I could not help thinking that that part of my life was over forever and that I would never again have happy times. But though I knew this, whenever I saw newspaper advertisements for summer schools for students who wanted to make up their lessons, or notices for autumn classes in Wuhu and elsewhere, I could not keep from going off by myself and reading them over and over again. I would not bring them back until I had read them so many times I had memorized them. But why I did this, I could not have said.

Ever since my illness, I had become afraid to look in the mirror. Not only had I lost that natural young woman's desire to be beautiful and to look my best, but even finding a time when my hands, face, and hair were not covered with ashes and soot was difficult. My fingers were dotted with tiny white needle marks and my clothes, shoes, and socks were covered with bits of thread and ashes from the portable stove. I could never get rid of them all. I had grown to resemble Xiao Lazi and Da Biao Sao. My hands were always busy with the sewing because after Da Biao Sao left, I was alone and of course could never get through it all. Cloth shoes were not durable in the first place, and Rolan and her younger brothers were at an age when they were very active and wore them out quickly. They would go through a new pair every ten days or two weeks. In addition, all of them—Mrs. Shao, Rolan, and the boys shared one trait. They could not tolerate anyone else having any leisure. If they saw any of us stop working for a minute, even if there was nothing they wanted, they would come up with something for us to do. "Bring me some tea!" "Bring a basin of water!" "Bring the matches!" "Bring the water-pipe!" Then, while I was still serving in one place, someone else would shout at me from somewhere else, "My garter is loose! Hurry up and fasten it for me!" "Xiao Lao Wu's nose is running again. Run and get a piece of paper and help him blow it!" They never seemed satisfied until they had turned Xiao Lazi and me around so much that we were completely confused.

Every morning when I went to the mirror to comb my hair, I

saw a thin, pointed, sad face without a trace of color. My eyes were sunken. My hair, which was still falling out, got thinner by the day. My forehead was puckered. I would look and wonder how it had happened that I had become so plain. I would hurriedly throw the cloth over the mirror so I would not have to look at myself. But even if I did not want to face that mirror, there were people in the Shao family who inevitably reminded me. Mrs. Shao's eyes and mouth were sharper and quicker than the mirror. They were also more unfeeling, and reflected everything, down to the last detail. When she saw me bringing my rice bowl to the dining table she would let the breath whistle out through her white teeth and sigh. "Well! I can't understand why someone her age she should care so little about looking good. So unkempt, from morning to night! And if she doesn't care enough to be embarrassed, everyone around her who has to look at her is certainly embarrassed for her."

She never looked at me directly as she talked. It was as if she were talking to her bowl and chopsticks, but the eyes of everyone at the table except Zhongyao's would swivel around and look at me.

"When I was her age ..." Mrs. Shao, not having harped enough on my appearance, would continue, "when I was even younger, the age of my Rolan here, I knew enough to want the best. I can't tell you how fastidious I was. Take my clothes as just one example. If there was the tiniest spot, the tiniest crease, I wouldn't wear it. My braid, my hair, was always combed until it shone and was smooth. Not a hair could be out of place. The least disorder, and I'd undo the whole thing, comb it again, and rebraid it. I could never have stood to be as slovenly as she is!"

"Even now, you're still so fastidious! Would we ever see you wearing wrinkled clothes?" Mr. Shao smiled at his wife and then looked at me, shook his head and sighed. "Oh, well, people are as they are and it's no use trying to change them."

"That's true. That's so true! What the master says is completely true. In my more than ten years, I've never worked for a family that had anyone like the mistress, any one so particular about her clothes. When have we ever seen the mistress without a shining head of hair and a clean, glowing face?" Mrs. Zhang was dancing attendance on Mrs. Shao, serving her and filling her rice bowl. "Just look at her hair, how it shines every morning after the hairdresser comes and combs it! It really is shinier and smoother than a mirror! You could really say 'A fly that tried to climb it would fall and break its legs. A mosquito that tried to jump on it would break its back'! I could sit and stare at it all day long!"

"Whenever Mrs. Zhang gets an idea, she turns it into a bouquet of flowers," Zhongyao, sitting next to his father, observed with a frown.

"But the important thing is that she's right." His father jabbed at the air with his chopsticks and reiterated, "She's right."

"Oh, well, now I'm just an old woman and no longer pay much attention to such things." Mrs. Shao seemed to be holding back a self-satisfied smile and gave an exaggerated, theatrical sigh. "Just wait a few years until they're married and start having a family. I'll be a grandmother, and then no one will be able to call me fastidious anymore ..." She paused, sighed again, and turned towards Zhongyao and me. "I'm more worried about *them*. They're not married yet and Zhongyao is so much in love, that of course he's on her side. He can't see clearly. But later, when the honeymoon is over his eyes will be opened. He has always been fastidious, too—how will he be able to stand it if his wife is slovenly? What will he do, close his eyes and spend the rest of his life pretending he's blind?"

For her to say *I* knew nothing about how things should be! For her to call me slovenly! Anger surged up in me and I wanted to shout, "Every day, from morning to night, you treat me as if I were less than human, you grind me down until I don't even look human, and yet you can talk that way! If I slept enough every night like you do and sat around everyday with my legs crossed the way you do—the tea comes and you put out your hand, the food comes and you open your mouth—you're waited on hand and foot—and if I had nothing to do but make myself beautiful, I'd be smooth and shining too!"

But I swallowed my rage with two mouthfuls of rice and gulped back my words as if they were the vegetables I had to force myself to eat.

Chapter 28

THE weather grew warmer and warmer. The honeysuckle in the back courtyard put forth white blossoms that looked like white jade and light yellow ones that looked like gold sprinkled among the lush green leaves. The fragrance of the blossoms was as thick and sweet as honey. In another corner of the courtyard, rows of green and red pepper plants now bore tiny red peppers, as big as one's little finger. The early summer sun rose higher each day in the heavens. Early every morning the shrill voices of the women flower sellers cut through the morning breeze from along the lane next to the house. "Gardenias and white orchids!" "Jasmine blossoms and pearl orchids!" The height of summer arrived almost overnight.

School had closed recently, and Zhongyao had come home for the summer. But I had began asking myself questions I never had before. "Is he treating me the way he used to?" I wondered. "Can he listen to what his mother says about me and not be influenced by her? And even if he doesn't change now, is there any guarantee that he won't change in the future?" The more I wondered, the more lost and uncertain I felt. I wanted to hide from him because I hated him to see how unattractive and haggard I had become, but since we were living under the same roof there was no way I could avoid him completely. Whenever I ran into him, I would stare at my feet, afraid to look up at him. If he was around, I felt uncomfortable, no matter what I was doing, and I never knew where to put my hands and feet. Sometimes I would steal a glance at him, but this always made me feel that his attitude was not as warm and gentle as it had been in the past.

The back gate had turned into my refuge. The further I got from the people in the house, the more peaceful I felt. Mrs. Shao could no longer stand to have me around. Whenever she set eyes on me, even if she was in a good mood, her expression would turn as cold as ice, a layer of ice that would never melt. Whenever she got angry about anything or anyone, she would scold and scold and then she would remember the money my father had lost and would turn her anger on me, and I would become the subject of the postlude of the melodrama.

I became the sponge to suck the flood of her anger, and I knew that if that lost money were not returned, I would never have one day of peace as long as I lived in their house.

One morning I had just finished cooking Zhongyao's grandmother's medicine and was in the kitchen, getting ready to wash some rice for her gruel when I suddenly heard loud voices quarrelling in the front living room. It was Zhongyao and his next-oldest brother. At first I could only hear his brother, who was weeping and cursing at him. "Damn you! So hit me! Hit me again! Damn you! I won't be quiet! Your father-in-law has lost money for our family!"

"If you don't shut up ..."

"I revile your ancestors! I do, I tell you! He has lost money for all of us! Damn you! When we come to divide the family property in the future you'll have to make it up to us! It will come out of your share!"

"What's all this about?" Their mother stepped in to stop them. "You know you're not allowed to fight! Zhongyao, you're the oldest, you should know better!"

"He was swearing at me!"

"Damn you! Your father-in-law ..."

"Lao Er (Old Second), don't say another word! Go out in front to the shop. Zhongyao, go out to the backyard!"

I saw Zhongyao, bursting with anger, come out into the courtyard. The collar and both sides of his short, white lined jacket were torn. He stood silently facing the corner of the courtyard wall with his hands on his hips for a long time. Then he went back into the living room. I hurried to the back living room with the small iron cooking pot. Zhongyao's grandmother asked me, "What were they quarrelling about?" I replied, "I don't know."

After a while Rolan stamped into the room. She frowned and glared at me as if I were the one who had just beaten up her second brother and she wanted to pick a fight with me to avenge him.

"Where is your eldest brother?" Grandmother asked.

"Who cares about him? He's gone upstairs to his room to sleep."

"What were they fighting about?"

"What were they fighting about? About another person's family, who has lost money for our family!"

Zhongyao's grandmother groaned a couple of times, shut her eyes, and said nothing more. Rolan, still bubbling with anger, stood there muttering for a while. Then, seeing that no one was paying any attention to her, she stamped back to the front living room.

Zhongyao did not come down for lunch and no one asked about him. When he did not appear for dinner, Mr. Shao told Xiao Lazi to go upstairs and invite him to come down. She returned and said, "The eldest young master says he is not hungry."

"Not hungry? He missed lunch and dinner—how can he not be hungry? There must be something the matter with him. I'll go upstairs and see...."

"No, you won't! Leave him alone!" Mrs. Shao slammed her chopsticks down on the table. "I know what he's doing. He's angry at me. He wants to see who can hold out longer. None of you are to pay any attention to him! Mother, that holds for you as well! Good! I want to see how long he can hold out. If he acts this way now when he's so young, what will happen when I want to depend on him in my old age?"

No one spoke for a long time. Eventually Mr. Shao said, "I'm worried that he might be sick. Why else would he defy you this way?" But when he saw his wife's expression, he did not dare get up and go upstairs.

The next morning, Zhongyao's grandmother got up and smoked several pipes of opium. She was very uneasy because Zhongyao had not yet come out of his room. So, groaning and holding tightly onto the wooden railing, she made her way up the stairs. After a while, still groaning, she came down. I went to help her. I wanted to ask how he was, but felt it would be improper to ask. I restrained my impatience and waited until after lunch, but when he still did not come down, I became worried. Finally I could not stand it any longer. I went over to where his grandmother was resting on her long rattan chaise. I stood there a long time and then whispered, "Grandmother ... He ... what do you think? He hasn't come down for two days. We must think of some way to get him to come down and eat something. It gets so hot up there in weather like this, and he hasn't had any tea or water to drink. If this goes on much longer, I'm afraid he'll get sick."

"I don't know what to do. He and his mother are angry at each other. When I went up this morning, he turned his face to the wall, and covered his head with the sheet. On such a hot day! They're so much alike, both impatient and violent. I tried to talk to him but he wouldn't listen. He said, 'You're one of *them!*' I can't do anything. When I'm dead and gone, they can quarrel all they want. It won't matter to me."

Her words made me even more uneasy. I thought about him all day. My hands were busy sewing but my ears were always listening for the sound of his footsteps. I kept hoping to see him coming downstairs. I cared about him more than ever. All I wanted was to put down my sewing and go up those stairs so I could see him, suffer the heat with him, and starve with him. But I could not. I had to pretend nothing was wrong. I was so worried that my stomach was tied up in knots and I could not eat. At mealtimes I edged over to the corner of the table, sat down, and picked up my rice bowl as usual, but I had to force myself to eat.

In the year since I had been engaged to Zhongyao, and ever since I had come to live in his home, he had treated me with a great deal of affection and I owed him my gratitude. During all this time in his home, only he had sympathized with me and been concerned about me. For my sake, he had faced his mother's glares and angry words more times than I could count. But he had not heeded them, and had not retreated or withdrawn. He had continued to stand by my side, to share my pain and help me bear her mistreatment. Because he treated me this way, it gave me more courage to face my life. This present trouble seemed to show clearly that he had not changed, that he still felt the same and would stand by my side—and that my recent doubts and worries had all been unfounded.

At this moment I worried about more than that he might get sick. My unhappiness was heightened because, although he had always been able to show his concern for me when I was mistreated, now, when he was suffering on my account, I could not only not express my concern for him but had to pretend nothing was wrong. I had to conceal all my anxiety. The courtyard and living room stood between us, and I could only look at that long staircase, worry silently, and sigh.

As I tried to ride out this storm, not only did my doubts about him disappear but my own feelings towards him seemed to become clearer. When I had been unsure about what he felt for me, I had also been unsure about my own heart. These two days, however, made me feel certain that I had not only always been grateful to him but also that I had always loved him. And I felt that my love would never change, that this was the first time I had ever loved and that it would be the last.

Mrs. Shao had not said one word to me during the two days. If I greeted her, she acted as if she had not heard. I did not take it too seriously, I only wanted her to be a little concerned about her son. But she seemed totally unconcerned by his refusal to come downstairs. At lunch that day, she said in a deliberately loud voice, "Fortunately I have many sons. Even if one or two should starve themselves to death, I would still have others. So he's still fighting with me, setting his anger against mine! Well, I want to see whose will is stronger, his or mine. I want to see how long he'll hold out and go on being stubborn before he gives in."

"He's young and confused. Otherwise, why would he ever dare defy you?" Mr. Shao tried to calm her and comfort her. It seemed as if he was trying to talk her around and help Zhongyao. "What do you think? Let me just go upstairs in a little while and talk it over with him. I guarantee that he'll come downstairs very obediently and apologise to you. He's our own son, and we know him better than anyone else can."

"You understand! And you think I don't understand? I tell you, I forbid you to go upstairs. He was conceived in me and carried by me for ten months and borne by me! I know him and his ways much better than you do! Can we allow family discipline to be ignored? No authority, no respect for the elders by the younger? That is rebellion!"

And she slammed her bowl on the table to emphasize the word "rebellion." Mrs. Zhang hurriedly poured her a cup of tea and handed it to her respectfully. No one said a word. We just kept on eating.

Mrs. Shao's view of the situation was correct. She knew her son. Late that afternoon, at tea-time, Zhongyao finally came downstairs of his own accord. He came into the living room, went over to his mother, smiled apologetically and greeted her, "Mother."

"Oh, I thought we were going to be at daggers drawn for the rest of our lives."

"How could that be? I was ... I did not feel well—I felt ill." He was standing across the table from his mother. His face was pale and his eyelids a little puffy, perhaps because he had not eaten and had slept so much.

"How do you feel now?" Mrs. Shao was looking at him as if her anger had suddenly disappeared. Her voice was soft and motherly-love seemed to radiate from her eyes. "Quickly, get Xiao Lazi to draw some water so you can wash your face. The afternoon refreshments are ready and there is some freshly-brewed tea. Have some tea, and then eat something."

I was sitting at another tea table, keeping an eye on Xiao Lao Wu as he ate.

Zhongyao soon returned, after washing his face in the court-yard, and sat down across from his mother. He picked up his teacup with one hand and propped his cheek on the other. The two of them, mother and son, sat across from each other for a long time without speaking a word. Then Zhongyao suddenly put down his cup and said in a quiet, deliberate voice, "Yesterday, I was angry only because my brother said things he should never have said. If I have the ability to support myself, why should I depend on getting a share of the family property in the future?"

I was startled. It was the first time I had ever heard Zhongyao speak to his mother like one adult to another, with dignity. Mrs. Shao not only was not annoyed but seemed to want to placate him and said, "That'll do, it's all right. Lao Er sometimes speaks without thinking, but he doesn't mean anything by it. Fighting is no way to solve problems. He has learned his lesson and will never talk that way again."

Zhongyao picked up his teacup and said nothing more. At dinner that night everyone seemed more cheerful than usual. The anger between Mrs. Shao and Zhongyao had dissipated like the clouds after a storm. Mr. Shao talked and laughed and from time to time gave everyone else, including his wife and Zhongyao, food with his chopsticks. He kept urging everyone, "Eat, eat! It tastes good." The children, seeing that their parents were in a good mood, chattered more than usual, and the chill that had hung over the table for the past two days was gone. I watched from my place in the corner and felt I could stop worrying, even though Mrs. Shao's attitude towards me had not changed—she still refused to look me in the eye and still kept ignoring me.

The sun set after dinner but it was still very hot outside. Xiao Lazi and I carried out two big pails of cold water and splashed it all over the backyard to drive away the remaining heat. Bamboo cots, rattan chairs, and bamboo stools were brought out, and the whole family, old and young, bathed, and, wearing fresh, clean clothes, came outside as usual to rest and cool off. Slowly waving their fans and drinking tea, they ate melons and fruit and chatted idly. This was the only time all day that Xiao Lazi and the servants and I had a little time to ourselves—to take care of our own needs, to wash our sweat-soaked bodies, to comb and arrange our messy hair that had become loosened and disordered, to change into clean clothes, and to seize the opportunity to wash our dirty ones and hang them up to dry. If the conversation among the family was lively, they would forget for a while to call us and order us around. I would take a little bamboo stool and sit by the back gate to catch the cool breeze.

The moon, a curved thread, rose slowly and tangled itself in the strands of the weeping willows on the stream banks. The moonlight was as clear and cool as water. That night, on the other side of the stream, someone was playing the *erhu* and people were singing ballads. Their poignant, charming voices floated across the water. They were singing the ballad of Meng Jiangnü, who travelled a thousand *li* to look for her husband, who died building the Great Wall. I listened carefully:

> Spring is warm and swallows fly in pairs to the south
> Their new nests are carefully built
> And they perch on the beams two by two
> But Meng Jiangnü's husband is building the Great Wall
>
> In summer the heat is hard to bear
> Mosquitos sing their song of heartbreak
> Bite me and take a thousand drops of blood
> But do not bite my husband, Wan Xiliang
>
> In autumn we go to the rice fields
> Turn the wheel and polish our rice for taxes
> Others have plenty of grain for taxes
> The husband of Meng Jiangnü was taken for taxes
>
> In winter the snowflakes fly
> Meng Jiangnü carries her husband's clothes a thousand *li*
> The crow flies in front to lead her
> "Xiliang, it is cold and desolate at the Great Wall."

I do not know whether the sound of the *erhu*, or my heart, was more than usually sad, but as I sat there alone with my hands clasped around my knees, and listened to that beautiful old ballad, and looked at the moon and the distant Milky Way with its river of stars, I felt sad. And without my realizing it, my tears fell, fell in streams on coat and my hands, until even my knees were wet.

Chapter 29

EVERY morning when I opened my eyes to the thread of grey light coming through the two tiny glass skylights in my room, I could not help wondering how I would manage to get through the day. The life that lay before me seemed to hold out no hope and no expectation of change. These feelings of tedium and hopelessness had become stronger since my illness.

"Water flows toward the lower places;
Mankind chooses the weak to oppress."

These words are completely true, as is the saying that misfortunes never come alone. In the next two days, Mrs. Shao turned around and began blaming me for her fight with Zhongyao. Ordinarily when she noticed me, it made me almost too nervous to eat. But when she ignored me, it was even harder to bear. I never expected that another crisis, the final one, would erupt on the third day.

It began almost as soon as I got up that morning. Heitan went out to the kitchen to get a bowl of gruel for himself. I do not know how it happened, but he was careless and knocked over Grandmother's jar of medicine, which had been sitting by the food cupboard. The pottery jar crashed into powder. Mrs. Shao heard it from her room. When she learned what had happened she first called Heitan to her bedside and scolded him. Then she called me and scolded me for my carelessness in not having put things away as I should. My heart filled with suppressed anger.

Then, when Rolan got up and I went in to comb her hair, I saw she did not look sharp, sour, and impatient, as she usually did. Instead, when she saw me walk up behind her, a sly smirk appeared on her face. She gave me a sidelong glance in the mirror and began idly stirring the jar of resin with a brush, as if to amuse herself. I immediately thought, "Watch out—who knows what new mischief she's planning?" I was right. I picked up the red bone hairpin and went to untie her braid, but before I could touch her, she tossed her head to one side as if to avoid something evil. "Mother says your hands are dirty. Every morning, when you come to comb my hair, I must inspect your hands first to make sure they're clean. So put out your hands and let me see them," she said.

I made no reply, nor did I move. I was still holding the hairpin.

"I told you to let me see your hands!" She glanced at me as if she wasn't sure whether to treat it as a joke or as a real order.

I felt as if I had caught on fire inside. The flames surged up to my head, but I clenched my teeth and stood there silent and unmoving.

"Are you deaf? I'm talking to you! Do you hear me?" She almost shouted. The self-satisfied smirk had disappeared, and she glared at me.

Suddenly, all my patient submissiveness evaporated, and I glared back at her. It was the first time I had ever met her glares with one of my own. But though Rolan had used her glare to discountenance others ever since the day she was born, no one had ever dared glare back at her. Now I had. She could not bear it. The unthinkable had happened! The sky had fallen! She jumped up and ran into her mother's room shouting, "Mother, Mother, look, look!"

"What's the matter? My own, my precious. What's the matter?"

"She's acting angry at me!" When she said the word "angry," she suddenly burst into loud sobs as if she had been grievously wronged.

I ran into my own room, unaware that I was still holding the red bone hairpin. The weeping, consoling and scolding outside blended into a big, confused chorus.

"Don't be afraid, my precious! Mother's here! Zhongyao! Zhongyao, come here! I have something to say to you!"

"Wife, wife, it's too early for you to be so angry! She is a clumsy fool. If she's done something wrong, give her a scolding and let it go at that. Your own health is too important for you to get so angry with such an idiot!" said Mr. Shao.

"I've never heard of such a thing! How can she dare try to treat Rolan that way? Zhongyao, things have gone too far! I can't tell you how much of my heart's blood I've used this year, hoping she would learn to become a responsible adult so you wouldn't suffer in the future. How could we have known that she'd turn out to be such an idiot, and incorrigible, besides? Just look at how dirty she is!" Her voice rose even more. "It's unbelievable how dirty she is! She had scabies—well, all right, all the children had it. But

none of them had it the way she did, all the way up to her neck. And it was because she scratched herself with her dirty hands!"

"Mistress, have some tea and calm yourself! Mistress, your health is too precious to risk!"

"Mrs. Zhang, you know what I'm saying—could anyone have been a better mother-in-law? Really, she's been spoiled by too much luxury. The longer she's here the more aggressive she gets. Now she's even persecuting Rolan! Rolan is my life—I will allow no one to touch her!" She stopped, and when she spoke again, her voice was controlled and distinct, as if telling the others something very important. "If she had any sense at all, she'd realize she has no right to put on airs!" Then I heard her voice come at me through the walls. "Your father lost our family's money! What right do you have to say anything?"

"Zhongyao, you're my son. Don't worry. If she refuses to mend her ways, I'll get you another wife, a good one. Since you're also a member of my mother's family, you should have two wives. It's common for one son to be the heir of two families. All we need is money, so we'll have no trouble finding you a beautiful, accomplished bride."

As I went on sitting on the edge of my bed, I felt as if a herd of wild horses was stampeding over me. I wished I could tear my heart out of my body and throw it through the skylight so I would never again have to feel anything.

"Oh, heaven, when will my sufferings ever end?" I asked myself.

I do not know how long it was before the chorus outside died down. At some point, I lay down and let my eyes close.

It seemed I could hear people talking in the hall. I could smell the fragrance of flowers, so I knew that the women flower-sellers had brought jasmine blossoms for Mrs. Shao and Rolan. Xiao Lao Si and Xiao Lao Wu were laughing and shouting in the courtyard. In the living room, the hairdresser told Mrs. Shao, "See you tomorrow." So I knew that it was almost noon. It might have been just another day, but everything seemed heightened. I felt sadder and lonelier than usual.

Two slanting rays of bright sunlight streamed through the skylights. The room was now oppressively hot. My blue cotton coat and trousers were soaked with sweat. I wanted to get up, straighten my hair, wash my face, and then go out to the living room, but as soon as I sat up I felt dizzy and the room started spinning around. The difference between today and all those other days was that today my anger lingered and I could no longer push it away from me.

What would happen if I did not get up, if I just went on sleeping? When I could stand the depression no longer, I began to think that perhaps the events of this morning had not happened, that they had been a dream. Even though I knew this was a fantasy, I continued to hope....

I closed my eyes again. The heat was suffocating. I seemed to hear Grandmother calling me, telling me to cook her medicine. Then I seemed to hear Xiao Lao Wu calling me to dress him. Once again, I seemed to feel his hands, covered with scabies and smeared with yellow ointment, clasped around my neck. Then it seemed as if someone was pushing me out into the living room. I reached the dining table and was reaching for a bowl and chopsticks when suddenly I felt someone standing beside me. I could hear his breath. He sighed loudly. I turned and saw Zhongyao standing beside me. His face was full of loathing and disgust. My heart stopped. Was it the smell of medicine on my neck that disgusted him? Then I thought, but the scabies on my neck had healed long ago. Involuntarily, I moved my hand and the bowl fell to the ground, where it spun around and around without stopping, and as it turned I heard it clanging. Startled, I opened my eyes. The sound was still in my ears, but as I listened I realized it was Rolan and her younger brothers. They were in the living room striking their bowls and plates to call Mrs. Zhang so she would cut watermelon for them. I turned over. My body was covered with cold sweat. The pillow was wet with sweat, too.

It must have been four or five o'clock in the afternoon. The sunshine had already reached the wooden partition at the head of Zhongyao's grandmother's bed. I slept again and awoke again. Although I did not sleep soundly, the dreams kept coming. I turned over and sat up. I pushed back my hair, thinking I would change my clothes and leave the room. But when my feet touched the ground, my tears gushed forth again.

Go out there? I was terrified of the cold, angry faces I knew I would see in the living room. This time I had really offended Rolan. This time a lowered voice, a conciliatory attitude, and a smile of apology would not be enough. I could not go out, but how long could I stay in this hot, oppressive room? I had to get up. But I felt like a kite whose string had broken, floating and turning aimlessly. I did not know what to do.

The whole family was in the living room, laughing and talking, and enjoying the color and sweet taste of the watermelon. Why was it that they should have such happy lives and I such a sad one? I was a human being, too—why should they be so proud while I should have to endure such humiliation? We both breathed the same air. Why should they be set above me, and why must I not show even a trace of my anger?

I could not sleep any more. My mind was like a reel of silk thread, winding and turning, faster and faster, but the more I thought the more confused I got. I felt that everything turned to darkness and ashes around me, and that I had exhausted all my courage. I no longer wanted to struggle with the life that lay before me.

At this moment the door opened softly and Xiao Lazi came in. She tiptoed over to Grandmother's bed and glanced at me but did not dare greet me. She lit the opium lamp and left. I lay down again, knowing that Grandmother would soon come in.

She came in a short time later and slowly smoked several pipes of opium. Then she got up to leave. As she passed me she bent over and felt my head and body. She whispered, "You're covered with sweat! Get up and wash your face and body. Then go to the back gate to cool off. If you stay in here much longer, you'll get a heat rash."

I nodded but did not get up. An idea had suddenly come to me and I wanted to think it out carefully and alone. I knew I could not continue to live like this. I *had* to think out a plan.

When people feel they have reached the end of the road and have no way out, they must turn and find another road. When they are so oppressed that they can no longer live, they find the courage to act. Some people take advantage of this courage and walk an active road; others let themselves drift. Although the roads are different, the reasons for walking them are the same. Both roads are walked in search of freedom.

While Zhongyao's grandmother was smoking her opium an idea seemed to emerge from the cloud of smoke and slowly enter my mind. It was not the first time I had had this idea—it had come often during the height of my illness, but then it had been like lightning and had passed in a flash. This time it lingered and would not leave me. It was "Death." Death seemed to be the only way I could escape the pain of the life I was facing. All day the idea had been lurking at the back of my troubled mind.

Grandmother went away and I was once more alone. The opium lamp's malevolent gleam was like a will-o'-the-wisp. It seemed to be blinking at me. I turned over and sat up. I looked and saw that the double doors were closed. I knew that no one would come in until much later that night. I slipped on my shoes and went over to Grandmother's bed. I sat on the edge and looked at the small cooper box. It was half-full of thick brown opium paste. My mind was blank....

I felt it would be so easy to pick up the box, raise it to my mouth, throw back my head, and swallow the paste. Then all my troubles would be over. I tried several times to reach for it, but my hand refused to obey me. I still felt there were things I could not relinquish, that even a life as bitter as mine had its beautiful, sweet, wonderful, and lovable aspects. But what were they? I had tasted so few of them that they were not as familiar to me as pain, suffering and cruelty. I was only vaguely aware of the good things of life, but I still felt I could not leave them.

"I am only in my teens," I thought. "I want to live. No matter how difficult my life is, I want to live." The strength of my will to live was even greater than at ordinary times. If anyone in that house had been willing, at that moment, to say one warm, gentle word to me or to show me the slightest sympathy, or even to smile at me, I would have been able to flee that hot room, and the demonic glare of the lamp, and my terrifying thoughts. But I knew there was no place in that house for me. I knew what awaited me if I went into the Shaos' living room.

I went back to my own bed and sat there for a while. My heart felt as empty as a cave. Then I got up again and went back towards the big bed. I started to step on the bench-step but stopped, and went over to the long wall table. I stood there aimlessly. Then I caught sight of the little hand-mirror on the table. I picked it up. That—that face in the mirror! How frightening it was, how eerie! My eyelids were swollen, red and bruised-looking like over-ripe peaches. There were tiny purple spots all over my face. My forehead was furrowed and my mouth contorted. Beads of sweat mixed with my tears and dripped down my cheeks. I dropped the mirror and went back over to the bench and sat down again. It was as if my body were enshrouded in a blinding mist. All I could see was the sinister glow of the opium lamp blinking at me. I picked up the box of opium paste. Then I put it down again. I picked up the iron rod, dipped it into the paste, and put it in my mouth. Immediately, my whole body shivered and the strong, bitter taste pierced like a poisonous thorn through every cell in my body.

Suddenly, an old, long-buried memory rose up in my mind. It had happened eight or nine years earlier, when we were still living in Nanjing. I must have been only six or seven, but the memory was clear and distinct. It was a sunny afternoon in early spring. Mother and I were sitting and talking in the living room, when suddenly many people started running past our front gate. A neighbor came running in. She struck her hands together and told Mother, "It's unbelievable! Unbelievable! Only yesterday, the third daughter of the Zuo family was so lively and beautiful. But she managed to get away from them—she swallowed gold and killed herself!"

The Zuo family lived next door to us. The next day they laid their daughter out on door-boards in their living room. When it was time for her to be placed in the coffin, I stole into the courtyard and squeezed through the crowd to see. Later, I heard people say that her wedding day had almost arrived and that her mother-in-law's family would soon have come with the red sedan chair to take her to their home. But it turned out that she loved someone else. So she had taken the only road open to her, and ended her life. It was the first time I had ever heard of suicide. It frightened me, but I did not understand. After a while, people stopped talking about it and I forgot. But that sad vision, which had been buried in my memory all those years, had suddenly come to life again just when I too was about to walk the only road open to me.

Swallowing gold? No, no! Swallowing raw opium is easier. "All I need to do is pick up the box, take a deep breath, and swallow the paste, and my sufferings will be over...." The words kept ringing in my ears and mind. Involuntarily I leaned forward. My hands were shaking so violently that I had to wait for a while. I steeled myself, picked up the box with both hands, and raised it to my lips. I threw back my head and let the paste flow slowly, slowly, into my mouth.

"What are you doing?" It was a sharp, harsh shout. I could not tell whose voice it was. Someone snatched the box from my hands. "Daughter! Son-in-law! Trouble! Come quickly. Hurry! Hurry!" It was Zhongyao's grandmother.

"What's wrong?"

"Trouble, trouble ..."

"Mother, what's frightened you? What's going on?"

I heard running footsteps, shouting, and people rushing into the room in confusion.

I had fallen onto the bed next to the opium lamp. People were climbing onto the bench and crowding around me. Grandmother stopped shouting. "I was a little worried about her and came back to see her. Who would have thought ... that she'd swallow raw opium paste?"

"How much did she swallow?"

"I don't know—I haven't looked."

"Calm yourself, Mother. Give me the opium box." It was Mr. Shao. "Not so bad. There's still more than half a boxful left. If she swallowed any at all, it wasn't much. It'll be all right. It doesn't matter. What a girl! Why would you want to do something so stupid? You have everything you want here—enough to eat, enough to drink, enough to wear. What more do you want? So what if your mother scolds you once in a while? It's for your own good! But if this is how you're going to behave, it's hopeless."

Mrs. Shao let out a harsh bark of laughter.

A hand lifted my eyelids, then my lips. "Mistress, it's all right. The insides of her eyelids and her gums haven't turned black. It doesn't look as if there's any danger." It was Mrs. Zhang.

"Her heart is black though! She tried to kill herself to frighten us! She thought she could damage us with a lawsuit!"

"If I had been one second later, it would've been too late!"

"This little girl is even stupider than I realized! I never thought she would try something like this!"

"Husband, Mother, enough talking! I dare not keep her here any longer. My family's reputation is spotless—I don't intend to have it damaged by a lawsuit! Mrs. Zhang, bundle up her clothes! Xiao Lazi, run out to the back gate and call two rickshaws. Husband, get dressed and take her back to her grandparents immediately. And ask those Zhous if they have any family pride or ethics!"

When I was young, I had often heard my grandmother and her friends talking idly when they had nothing to do. They said that the worst thing a young girl could do was ruin her reputation while she was still living with her parents. If her loss of virginity was to be discovered by the bridegroom on the wedding night, she would immediately be sent back to her mother's home in a small blue cloth sedan chair and from the back gate. She would never redeem her reputation, not for the rest of her life.

Although Mrs. Shao was sending me back to my grandparents for an entirely different reason, I was facing a similar disgrace, and my situation was almost as pitiful and cruel.

The rickshaws were at the back gate. Many willing hands lifted me off the bed and dragged and carried me from the room, out to the gate. They shoved me into a rickshaw and threw bundle of clothes in after me. I could still hear Mrs. Shao's harsh, angry voice saying, "Take her away quickly! Get her away from here!"

The lingering taste of raw opium made my stomach turn. The weather was still hot and oppressive and I had not had anything to eat or drink, not even a drop of water, since breakfast. As the rickshaw bounced over the cobblestones it shook me until it made me sick. I began to vomit. My head felt heavy and dizzy. I felt both sad and angry. There was a bitter taste in my mouth. My heart ached with hopelessness and complete desperation. My thoughts were in a jumble. They spun around until they could spin no faster, and then stopped—until gradually they coalesced into one clear, distinct thought: "I've borne all I can bear. Do your worst—I'm no longer afraid of anything."

Gradually this thought calmed me and made me feel I had nothing to worry about. The rickshaw reached my grandparents' front gate. I got out and, summoning up all my courage, hurried through the gate and into the living room. I could not worry about what Grandfather and Grandmother would think, seeing me suddenly come back in this helpless way, nor wonder how they would receive me. Even less could I worry about what Mr. Shao would say. He followed me and sat down in one of the high-backed chairs and, like a judge of the high court reading out an accusation, counted out all my crimes. He lit a cigarette and drank tea to moisten his throat, and the familiar complaints, which I had heard so many times, were outlined for my grandparents. How they had done their best and given me every opportunity, how they had treated me like their own daughter, hoping that I would strive to become responsible adult. How when I was ill they had called in doctors and bought me medicine, and spent no little money on me. How I had had servants to wait on me. How stupid and intractable I was ... I was not surprised. I did not care. Let him say what he liked. But then —I never expected that after all that, after he had recited the entire litany of complaints and he was about to take his leave, that he would say the unthinkable:

"We must depend on the two of you to teach her how to behave. Keep her for us for a while. Discipline her. And in two weeks or so, after her mother's anger has subsided and she has reformed, bring her back to us," he said.

His words swept away all my calm and all the clear, fearless thoughts I had just had, and threw me back into fear and confusion.

Chapter 30

I slept away the next five or six days in my grandmother's room. For the past year my body had been like the string of a bow that had been strung too tightly. Now, suddenly, it had snapped. My arms and legs were so weak I could hardly lift them, my eyelids were so heavy I could hardly raise them, and my heart and soul were filled with fear. Each time I opened my eyes, I had trouble believing that I was back in my own home and that Grandmother was sitting beside me. I kept asking, "Grandmother, is it really you?"

"How do you feel? Are you hungry? What would you like to eat? I'll get it for you."

I would shake my head, close my eyes, and go to sleep again, but my heart was more peaceful.

Sometimes, right after I had eaten, my mind would feel clearer and more awake, and I would feel like talking everything over with Grandmother. But as soon as I called for her, my nose would ache with tears and I would not be able to go on. Grandmother would hush me and comfort me gently. "First, we must get your health back again. Then we will talk. You're young. You must try not to worry. Put it all out of your mind."

"Grandmother, you don't know ... I feel ... so much suffering ..."

"Why don't I know?" She would fan me gently, leaning close as if to comfort and advise me. "You're like the sun that has just come up from behind the mountains, or like a tender bamboo shoot that has just come up out of the ground. You've tasted so little of life—the good and the bad, the bitter and the sweet. I'm old; I've seen much. If you listen to me, everything will be fine. But first you must get well again. Then we'll decide what to do."

I turned over and remained silent, hiding my face in my arms so she could not see my tears.

Was it only one summer ago that she had taken me to live with the Shaos? Then, I had been like any other teenager—my body and mind had been vigorous and I had been full of optimism. But in only one year, the Shao family had ground me down and torn me apart. It was obvious that I was thin and weak, but the damage they had inflicted on my heart and mind was not so visible. Grandfather and Grandmother must have been upset when the Shaos sent me back in such a weak, helpless condition. I knew they were trying to act calm and to hide their pain from me.

After several days of rest and careful nursing, I began to recover my strength. Before long I was able to sit up and walk around a little. I began to realize that there was a place for me in the tiny, three-room, upstairs apartment that was my grandparents' new home. I could stand and sit, move and walk around as I pleased, without feeling constrained. Every time we ate, Grandmother would say, "Baogu, eat more meat and vegetables. I cooked this dish especially for you." Though there were only a few dishes and the rice was coarse, these meals tasted better and more flavorful to me than anything else I had ever eaten. I felt that my grandparents' home was really lovable and dear to me. But my year of oppression at the Shaos' had left me fearful, and I could not get rid of my feelings of humility and inferiority. I constantly feared that people would dislike me and was timid and careful in everything I did.

The first day I got up, I was sitting at the dressing table when Grandmother came over. She picked up the comb and began combing my hair. I felt very uncomfortable—there was someone to comb my hair. I sat stiffly on the stool, not daring to move for fear that Grandmother would be displeased. I felt that she was being too kind to me. She waited until I had gotten strong enough to move around and even smile again before bringing up what I had done. She said that people my age had many years ahead of them and that they could be forgiven anything—except thoughts of suicide. She told me to consider the ants—tiny though they were, they had a strong will to live. So, how much stronger should our human will be? She also said, "Ever since time began, daughters-in-law have led difficult lives and have had to endure the anger of their fathers- and mothers-in-law. If everyone thought the way you did, there wouldn't be any marriages, or any people on earth!" She told me that a responsible adult must be like the pine or the cypress, able to brave the cold and endure the heat and not be beaten down by driving rains or raging winds.

Whenever I talked about how the Shao woman had treated me, Grandmother would first comfort me and tell me about her own experiences as my great-grandmother's daughter-in-law. "I can't tell you how much she ground us down, first your real grandmother and then me!"

"And you let her? Didn't you ever think of resisting her or getting away?"

"How could I? She was in authority over us. Besides, 'Daughters sent out the gate are like water poured through the gate.' That means they are both gone. There's nothing to be done except perhaps if a daughter has been driven to suicide or been injured by beatings. That, of course, opens the way to a lawsuit. Listen to me—get a little better first, and then write to your father and stepmother in Shanghai. Tell them it's important that they come up with a way to return that money to the Shaos, and quickly." She sighed. "These past few years have been full of painful events we would have preferred not to suffer. If your third uncle were still alive, he'd be able to help us and you'd be better off."

When Grandmother gave me advice her voice was always as calm as if she were discussing ordinary household affairs. It was only when she spoke of my third uncle that she would show any emotion. Her calm would return when she smoked her waterpipe. She urged me to learn to endure anger with patience. "To endure one day of anger with patience is to avoid a hundred days of sorrow," she would say.

The more advice she gave me, the more I realized that I was on my own. There was nothing anyone else could or would do for me. Grandmother was speaking to me out of a tradition that was thousands of years old—how could I fight it all by myself? If the Shaos had treated me worse than they had, my grandparents would have been even more unhappy. But that would not stop them from returning me to them. It was too important a matter for them to even consider questioning, much less breaking with, tradition. If the Shaos had beaten and injured me, or driven me to suicide, my grandparents might have said something. But by then it would have been too late. I thought of what Grandfather had said to Grandmother after Mr. Shao had left that night. "I wanted to question Shao Anling, but I was afraid it might mean they'd make Baogu suffer even more once she goes back there."

I knew it was no use to write to my father. I had written

257

before, telling him about how cruel the Shaos were, but he had never answered. Now my father and stepmother's circumstances were too hard for them to be concerned about me. After much thought, I decided that the only person I could expect to defend me was Zhongyao. But I wonder why I had not heard a word from him since I had left his home two weeks earlier. Did it mean he had started believing what his mother said and had stopped loving me? I wanted to write to him, but I was afraid that the letter would fall into his father's or mother's hands. I was especially afraid of his mother.

Time pays no attention to human wishes, but passes inexorably and unceasingly. Each day I grew more afraid that my grandparents would soon take me back to the Shaos or that the Shaos would send someone to force me to go back. Sometimes I thought I should ask Grandmother about it, but then I would think—foolishly—that I should keep my mouth shut: "If I bring it up, it'll just remind them, and then maybe they'll send me back sooner."

But I knew that sooner or later I would have to return to the Shaos' home. And so it was. One night after dinner, when Grandmother and I were cooling off on the sun porch, she told me that Mr. Shao had sent a message to Grandfather through an intermediary. Zhongyao's grandmother had taken a sudden turn for the worse and they wanted me to come back soon. Grandmother said she and Grandfather would probably take me back within two or three days.

When I heard this, I said nothing. I knew it would be no use to beg for a delay. My only hope was to see Zhongyao as soon as possible and to talk it over with him. But what did I have to talk over? I had no plan worked out, and I knew there was nothing he could do either. But I felt that when I went back there my life would be even more difficult, and that in my extremity of fear and anxiety I had to have someone who could stand beside me and give me courage. I wanted even more to know the truth, to know whether he still felt the same towards me or whether he had changed. But how could I bring up his name with Grandmother? Then again, how could I not speak, since time was so short? I hesitated for a long time and decided I could no longer afford to be modest. I told Grandmother that before I went back to the Shaos I wanted to write to Zhongyao and ask him to come and talk things over with me face to face.

She smoked her water-pipe silently, considering, and then

said, "I'm afraid it would not be suitable. What if he tells his mother?"

"He wouldn't. I know he wouldn't. I must talk with him before I go back there."

Grandmother went on smoking. She shook her head. "But suppose your letter gets into your mother-in-law's hands."

"Grandmother!" I could not stop myself from interrupting her. In desperation I begged her, "*Please* let me do this! I promise that once I've talked with him face to face, I'll return to his home."

She sighed and blew on her paper spill but did not smoke her pipe. She held the spill and gazed at me for a long time. Then, her voice full of compassion, she said, "Child, let me think about it some more. I think there's only one way—write the letter this evening and tomorrow morning ask your youngest uncle to ask one of his schoolmates to look for Zhongyao and hand him the letter in person. That would be the safest way."

I got up and went into the bedroom. I turned up the oil lamp on the table and took out some notepaper. When I had been talking with Grandmother, I had felt very sure of myself but now that I had to pick up my pen, doubts filled my mind. It was as if I had a premonition that something might be wrong. What if his feelings had changed? It was very hard for me to write the letter. First I wrote a short note. I read it over several times and made several changes but still felt it was not satisfactory and tore it up. Then I tried again. Finally I wrote:

"Zhongyao,
Grandmother will bring me back to your home in a few days. I have some things to talk over with you. After you receive this letter, I hope that you will come to my home to see me. It is very, very important.

Baowen"

I thought for a while longer and then decided to leave the note unsigned. I copied it again, put it in an envelope and sealed it. I felt peaceful and satisfied. Then I turned down the lamp, got undressed, and went to bed, but tossed and turned all night. The next morning, I gave the letter to Grandmother, and after breakfast my youngest uncle took it away with him.

I felt anxious all day. Every time I heard a knock at front gate or footsteps in the courtyard, I would tense up thinking he had come. I would hurry to the window and look out through the lattice, but then I would see that it was only one of the neighbors in the courtyard and would feel disappointed. After a while, however, my disappointment would again turn into hope. I roamed back and forth between the living room and the bedroom all day. I could not keep still. I waited until after dinner, and then until long after dark. I would not even go onto the porch to cool off because I was afraid that when he came I would not hear him. I waited until the living room clock struck ten before I stopped hoping he would come that evening.

The second day seemed even longer and I felt even more uncertain. I could not even pretend to be calm. I could not sit, I could not stand, I could not walk, and I could not sleep. I began doubting that the letter had ever reached him. Grandmother kept telling me, "Perhaps Zhongyao will come today." I remained silent, as if I did not care, but deep down I hoped she would be proven right.

I waited until lunch and then throughout the afternoon, until Grandmother went downstairs carrying the finely-woven rice basket to cook dinner. My hope began to dissipate. Then, suddenly, I heard an unfamiliar voice out in the courtyard asking, "Is this the Zhou family's home?" I peeped out of the window and recognized one of the apprentices from the Shaos' store. My heart was thumping. A few moments later, Grandmother walked into the room with a little envelope in her hand. "See," she said, smiling. "I said he'd certainly answer your letter today."

I took the envelope. My hand was trembling. My feeling of premonition grew even stronger. I waited until Grandmother had left. Then I closed the door, went over to the window and tore open the envelope. I read the letter at one glance—it was a few lines of carelessly-written big characters, in his calligraphy, on one sheet of paper:

"Grandmother is very ill. I can not be in two places at once. If you want to talk to me, why not come here and talk with me here? People have told me you have said publicly that you dislike me and that I am unattractive and not a good match for you. Since this concerns both of us and is so important, why did you not make your feelings known to me a long time ago? And what is more, look in the mirror and then tell me what right you have to call me unattractive."

I had to hold onto the back of the chair. Slowly, I sat down.

I felt as if I had been hit by a hammer. My heart contracted. A shiver shook my entire body. I felt cold all over.

Once again, I stood at the end of the road—alone. The pain of being hurt by a loved one is sharper, deeper, and more severe than any other pain. I felt that everything I had endured in his home, all the humiliations and oppressions, were as nothing compared to this. But now I felt as if my eyes had been opened. I could see everything I was facing and had no illusions left. I was now determined that I would never return to the Shaos' home. I had to find a way to escape, and quickly. In a day or two Grandmother would take me back. I had to think of a way to escape.

Escape? Where to? I suddenly remembered Miss Hai and my schoolmates in the student association at the school. They were all against arranged marriages. They were all progressive and would certainly sympathize with me. But then I remembered that it was now summer vacation and that Miss Hai no doubt was away from the city. And I wondered whether, even if she and my fellow students had been in the city, they would dare take me in. After all I would be running away from my family. And even if my fellow students were willing, their parents would not dare have anything to do with me. Should I go to Father in Shanghai? That was even less possible. No sooner would I reach their home than my father and stepmother would drive me away, back to the Shaos.

Where could I go? Where could I go? It seemed as if there were no place anywhere in the world where I could hide. Every door seemed closed to me.

"Baogu, dinner is ready. Come and eat." Grandmother opened the door softly and came in.

"Grandmother, you eat. I'm not hungry."

"Not hungry?" She came over to me and cocked her head at me. She asked quietly, "Was there something unpleasant in Zhongyao's letter?"

"No. Go and eat. I have a headache. Let me rest alone for a while and I'll be all right."

Grandmother stood there silently for a while. "All right, I'll save some rice and vegetables for you and you can eat them when you're hungry." She tiptoed out of the room.

I was alone. The dusk deepened slowly outside and twilight settled over the earth. Wuhu's dark-grey tiled roofs looked like ocean waves rising and falling. A few patches of leafy branches dotted the dark-grey waves with green. The leaves stirred in the evening breeze. The smoke from kitchen fires coiled up into the sky, thinned, and finally disappeared. I heard the call of the bugle from the military encampment atop the hill. It sounded softer and more mournful than usual. I—what am I thinking about? Oh, yes. I am wondering how I to escape.

Time is short. I must hurry and think of a way to escape.

BOOK III

I Reach the End of the Road and
Determine to Make Another Life for Myself

Chapter 31

The moon hangs high over the wooden bridge.
The bridge is narrow,
The bridge is high,
And the waters are rough below.
The waters are rough below,
How can I escape?

The waves are high yet boats still sail,
The bridge is narrow yet people cross.
If the heart is set and courage great,
The bridge can be safely crossed.

SUDDENLY, it seemed as if the sun had broken through the clouds and as if a way out had been revealed to me. I had remembered my mother's only two living relatives, her mother and her sister-in-law, my aunt.

Neither of them had had anything to do with my family since my mother's death. And for about two years after her death, Father had occasionally exchanged letters with my aunt, but they no longer wrote. And though my grandmother still lived near Wuhu, my grandparents were very prejudiced against her because she had remarried after my mother's father died. When Mother was still alive, they would occasionally see each other to make Mother happy, but after she died they broke off all contact and became strangers to one another. My grandparents would never speak of her unless they had to, and she had too much pride and self-respect to ever come to their home uninvited. Two years earlier, she had learned that I was studying at Fengjia Hill, and had quietly come to see me a few times with her younger sister, my great-aunt. Each time, when she left, she would always warn me repeatedly never to let my grandfather know.

I had visited her home when I was very small, with Mother. I had forgotten where it was, but remembered that she lived on the south bank of the river near a mill that polished rice and ground

265

wheat. A year ago, I had learned that her second husband had also died. She was living with her step-son and his wife and helping them manage a small teahouse on the river bank.

"She and my aunt are the only people I can turn to. Even if they do not care about me for myself, they'll take me in and help me for my mother's sake." I put my head in my hands and forced myself to calm down and plan. "I won't be able to stay long with my grandmother, I'm afraid. It's not far enough away. It would be too easy for the Shaos to find me. My aunt's home is the best place to go. It's in another province. Also she's educated, experienced and knowledgeable. But I don't know if she still has the school."

I remembered my cousin, Biying, whom I loved so much. "She's now more than twenty years old," I thought. "If I can only escape and reach my aunt, I know everything will be all right. She won't mind feeding an extra mouth and if she'll only take me in, I'll do anything. I'll use all my strength, do all the heavy work—I'd even be a servant." When I got this far in my thinking, the road ahead of me seemed clearer and my hope grew stronger.

"Now, how can I get there? The only way is by water, along the river by steamboat from here to Hankou, and I'm afraid it will take three or four days. The steamer doesn't run every day. I can't go and inquire about the boat. And it will be dangerous to have to wait for it. Then there's the problem of money. Even a third-class ticket will cost many yuan. I think I'd have to buy my own food. I don't have enough money." I went over to my bed and took out my little cross-stitched purse, which I kept under the mattress near the pillow end. I emptied it out onto the straw mat. I had a total of one yuan and twenty-four coppers. This was, of course, not nearly enough to buy even a third-class ticket.

"There has to be a way. I won't give up. There has to be a way. I won't give up." I kept repeating these words to encourage myself. "The only way is to get to my grandmother's first. I don't know the address, but it doesn't matter. I can get across the river and find the mill. Then I'll know where she is. Once I've found her and talked it over with her, we'll come up with a way to get me to my aunt. But I must get to my aunt, and quickly. Tonight, after everyone's asleep ... No, tonight isn't good. What if someone sees me? It's better to wait until the middle of the night when everyone is asleep. No, that's not good either. If I go out in the middle of the night, the dogs would bark, and a young woman out all alone would make the police suspicious. It's better to wait until early morning, until it's just starting to get light but before anyone else is awake. I can tiptoe downstairs and out the front gate. Once I get to the street, I can hire a rickshaw and get away."

Once I developed this plan, I felt very tense and excited. I wanted it to be dawn right then so I could put it into action immediately. I had to keep telling myself to remain calm, because my grandparents could not suspect I was planning to leave.

After the lamps were lit, Grandmother returned and asked me if my headache was better. She told me to go and eat something. Though I had no appetite I forced myself to act normal and to sit at the dining table. Grandmother, smoking her pipe, sat across from me to keep me company. Though my eyes were on my bowl of rice, my mind was rehearsing what I would do the next morning. Grandmother was talking, but I did not hear her.

"Baogu, Baogu."

"What?"

"What are you thinking about?" she asked, peering at me.

"What am I thinking about? Nothing. I'm not thinking about anything."

"I've been talking to you, but you haven't been paying any attention." She went on peering into my face.

I made no answer, but lowered my head, shoved two or three mouthfuls of food into my mouth, gulped them down, put down my bowl and chopsticks, and ran back into my room. After a while I heard Grandmother go downstairs to the kitchen and, knowing that there was no one in the living room, I hurriedly bundled my clothes into a big kerchief and put it under my bed, which was behind Grandmother's big one. Then I took off my clothes and got into bed. When Grandmother came in to go to bed, she came over to look at me and to tuck in the bed curtain for me. I pretended to be asleep because I was afraid she would ask me more questions.

But I stayed awake all night. From time to time I would sit up very quietly and then lie back down. I dozed off around two o'clock but soon woke up again. The room was quiet—there was no sound from Grandmother's bed. I heard Grandfather coughing in his room, on the other side of the living room. Then there was nothing but the ticking of the clock in the living room.

I dared not shut my eyes again. I was afraid I would oversleep. I sat with my arms around my knees and my cheek resting on my knees and waited for daybreak. I do not know how long I waited before I at last heard the sounds of cocks crowing in the distance. A little later I heard the peasants who had come into the city to empty out the latrines. A faint grey light came through the window and skylight. "Good, the time has come!" I eased myself off the bed and got dressed. I reached under the bed, carefully drew out my bundle of clothes, and hung it over my left arm. In my right hand I carried my cloth shoes. Holding my breath, I tiptoed past Grandmother's bed. "Good, I've passed the head of Grandmother's bed!" I stopped for a moment and took a deep breath, and then tiptoed towards the door. When I got to the door, I looked back and saw that the white linen curtain on Grandmother's bed was motionless. The door was bolted as usual. I transferred my shoes to my left hand and tugged softly at the big wooden bolt with my right. "Heaven, let there be no noise! If there's no noise, it'll be all right." The bolt moved silently. Then, still very cautiously, I pulled open one leaf of the door. It swished slightly. Quickly I stopped and looked back at Grandmother's bed. All was still. I pulled the door open about a foot, just enough to let me sidle out, and was just putting my foot over the threshold—

"Baogu! Where are you going? Don't be foolish!" Grandmother's voice was as soft, low, and calm as usual, but to me it sounded like a thunderclap. She pushed her curtain aside and swung her feet out of bed. "Did you think I was sleeping? I knew last night that you were upset and that something was wrong. I haven't closed my eyes all night. Come here. I must have a serious talk with you."

My back was against the edge of the half-opened door and my feet were straddling the threshold. I felt as if I were glued to the door frame. For a long time, I could not move.

My attempt to run away only hastened my return to the Shaos' home. That same day, after lunch, Grandmother changed into the suit she wore on formal occasions, and hurriedly took me back to my in-laws.

We shared a rickshaw and all the way there she repeated the advice she had given me that morning. "You mustn't be so reckless and foolish! One wrong step can ruin your entire life." She told me I had to be patient and act like a responsible adult. "And then, someday, the time will come when you can hold your head high and lead a happy life." I said nothing, nor did I pay much attention to what she was saying. I was too busy considering my situation and planning how I could escape from the Shaos' home.

The rickshaw stopped at their back gate. It was open and there was no one in the back wing of the house. Zhongyao's grandmother was not on her rattan chaise. Mrs. Zhang was hanging out clothes in the courtyard. When she saw us come in, she hurried to lead Grandmother to the front living room and usher her to a seat. Then she went into Mrs. Shao's room to announce us. I heard Mrs. Shao reply coldly, "I have heard." Mrs. Zhang then went away without even pouring a cup of tea for Grandmother.

Grandmother and I sat alone in the living room. She sat on a chair next to the little tea table and I stood beside her. We waited silently until we had had enough time to drink three cups of tea but did not hear one sound from Mrs. Shao's room. Grandmother began looking uncomfortable. She kept looking at the door to Mrs. Shao's room. It was half-open and the bamboo curtain, which had a green design on it, was half rolled up. Then she would look at me, and from time to time she would tug at her black gauze skirt. We went on waiting, long enough to have drunk two more cups of tea, but still no one came. Then Grandmother suddenly stood up, took my hand, and went to Mrs. Shao's door. We saw her standing at her clothes cupboard sorting out her clothes. She did not even glance at us.

Grandmother shoved me forward and said, "In-law, I have brought Baogu back to apologize." She gave me a strong push in the back and my knees sank to the floor. "Baogu, kowtow to your mother."

"Oh, I am not worthy of such an honor," Mrs. Shao uttered the polite expression in a level, cool, ironic voice. Her face was as cold and hard as steel. I could see her rage in her frown and in the look in her eyes. Though she had finally deigned to answer my grandmother, she gave us only one quick glance from under her lowered brows before going back to sorting and folding her clothes.

Grandmother's voice sounded less calm than usual and trembled a little as she said to me, "Baogu, my child, listen to me and remember what I say. You must behave and listen to what your mother says. You must never cause her problems again. And you must do your duty and serve your grandmother in her illness."

"I'm afraid my mother has been too ill to wait for her services. She has not been so fortunate!" Mrs. Shao spoke but still refused to look at us.

Grandmother waited a little, as if she did not know what to say next. She hesitated again and then pulled me to my feet. In an even lower voice, she said, "In-law, she is still so very young. She was foolish. We look to you to guide her in everything. Find it in your hearts to forgive her. Teach her and make allowances for her. Baogu, you must remember to behave ..." Grandmother turned away from me. "In-law, I'm going." She turned to leave.

Mrs. Shao did not move. "Go in good health. I will not accompany you to the gate," she replied in an icy voice.

I watched Grandmother cross the courtyard. It had seemed to me that in the few months since my third uncle's death her back had become bent. Today, she was stooping even more and her head was drooping, but her footsteps were much quicker than usual, as if she wanted nothing more than to flee through the Shaos' back gate.

"Poor Grandmother! I understand. Though your whole life has been filled with pain and suffering, you have never before been willing to bow your head to anyone. You always kept your self-respect, your self-esteem. You always refused to enter the Shao's home because they were rich and we were poor. In all your fifty years, this is the first time you've ever been subjected to such coldness and disdain. It's all because of me that you've had to stand at the Shao woman's door and speak so humbly to her."

After Grandmother left, I picked up my bundle of clothes and went down the hallway to Zhongyao's grandmother's room. It had been changed around. The tall clothes cupboard which had been against the wall had been moved to behind her bed and the two small latticed windows it had hidden were now open. Even though they opened onto the outside wall and a drain they let more air into the room. Grandmother was propped up against the head of the bed. Her eyes were closed and she was breathing with difficulty. Not having seen her in almost three weeks, I could see how much she had changed. Her cheeks and her eyes were sunken and her face was as deep a yellow as coarse paper.

"Grandmother, I'm back." I stepped up onto the bench to greet her. She opened her eyes and looked at me and nodded slightly, then closed her eyes again.

I spent the whole afternoon sitting on my bed, but not a soul came in to speak to me except the children, when they came in from playing outside. The two little boys and Heitan stuck their heads in the door and when they saw me. They said, "Big sister Baowen, you're back!" I sat there and thought about my plans.

When it was almost dark Xiao Lazi came in to give Zhongyao's grandmother her medicine and gruel. The table in the living room was being set for dinner. Zhongyao's grandmother told me, "Baowen, go and eat."

"Grandmother, I'm not hungry."

She said nothing more.

Out in the living room, the Shaos were all laughing and talking as usual. I could hear Zhongyao's voice above the rest. He was talking and laughing as if he was feeling especially gay. But all their voices, even his, no longer had their old power over me. I felt that none of them meant anything to or were of any concern to me. Whether those people said good things or bad things, were happy or angry, praised or scolded, none of them could affect me. I was myself; they were themselves. I had my own road to walk, and no matter how difficult or dangerous it was, I had to walk it. I must leave this place, this place where I was treated as less than human, and the sooner the better. Early tomorrow morning ...

"Big brother, Big—big brother—" Suddenly I heard Xiao Lao Wu's stutter, "Big sister Bao—Baowen—has come home." There was a silence. The laughing and talking stopped for a few seconds. Then the noise started again as if nothing had been said.

Zhongyao's grandmother's illness was always worse at night. She could not stop moaning and she vomited constantly. I went to her bedside and poured her some tea and handed her hot towels to wipe her mouth, and massaged her legs and back. Zhongyao's grandmother had always treated me well, and it made me sad to see her sick and in pain. But she became quieter after midnight and I could go back to my own bamboo bed to sleep.

But that evening I had lost my calm confidence of the night before. I felt tense and uncertain. It is said that we learn through experience, and it is certainly true. My failure to escape from my grandparents' home had made me look more closely and cautiously at every aspect of the problem of escaping. I knew I had to plan much more carefully. I was now able to foresee and think about eventualities I had not considered the previous night.

First, if I tried to get away and was again stopped, the Shaos would take it much more seriously than my grandmother had. I could not even imagine what they would do to me. Second, even if I did get away, they would never willingly let me go. If they guessed my destination they would bring me back, and my only recourse would be suicide. I remembered how Mrs. Shao had

271

warned Da Biao Sao that she would pursue her to the ends of the earth. "If I do not try, that's that—but if I do try, I must get clear away. I must escape from her hands."

"How can I keep them from guessing where I've gone, when there are so few places I can go?" I thought and thought and then an idea stirred in me. I could lie and say I had gone to my father in Shanghai. I could leave a note for Zhongyao. They would expect me to do exactly that. As I was leaving, I could give the note to the wet nurse. She was usually friendly to me and was a reliable person. I would ask her to wait until Zhongyao got up and then give it to him.

I had to plan to leave neither too early nor too late. The crucial thing was not to let Mrs. Zhang see me. I would have to wait until she had gone to the market to buy vegetables. No one else would be up yet, and if the wet nurse or Xiao Lazi or Heitan saw me it would not matter. I would tell them I was going out to see a schoolmate and would soon return. Even if they were suspicious, they would not try to stop me. I wanted to jump out of bed and write the note, but I was afraid I might wake Zhongyao's grandmother. I felt a hundred times more frightened than I had the night before. I felt as if there were monsters crouching in the corners eyeing me. The oil lamp, which had been turned down very low, cast a faint circle of pale-yellow shadows on the dark-grey partition. I crossed my arms over my forehead, not daring to take a deep breath or close my eyes.

I waited anxiously all night long. When the oil lamp finally burned out, I closed my eyes for a while. I did not actually sleep, but I kept dreaming nonetheless. The dreams were only fragments, strange and frightening. It was as if my mind was wide awake but a thousand catties of stone were weighing down my body so I could not move. Just before daybreak, Zhongyao's grandmother vomited again. She called me, "Baowen, Baowen! Wake up! Get up! Pour me some water so I can rinse my mouth!" I forced my eyes open and sat up. My heart was racing. I regained my composure and went to the table, where I poured out half a cup of hot water from the thermos and added cold tea to it. I gave it to her. My own throat was dry, so I drank half a cup of cold tea. Then I helped her sit up comfortably against the head of the bed and handed her her water-pipe. I lit the paper spill and waited until she had smoked her pipe twice before going back to my own bed.

The skylight turned pale with the coming of dawn. Before

long, Grandmother began snoring a little. I found a little pencil in my cross-stitched purse, but I had no paper, and I dared not open the drawer to look for any. All I could do was to take a few sheets of the coarse toilet paper that lay at the foot of my bed. I bent over the paper and wrote:

"Zhongyao,
I am going to Shanghai to see my father. If I find him at the end of my journey, I'll be satisfied. If I do not, the broad ocean and its great waves will receive me.

Baowen"

When I wrote about the ocean and its great waves, even though I only meant to deceive him, I felt sad and could not hold back my tears. Was I sad because our past affection was no more? Or because of my own troubles? I could not tell.

Soon I heard the sound of sweeping in the courtyard and the sound of someone dipping water out of the great jar. I knew that Xiao Lazi and the other servants had gotten up. Very quietly I put on my clothes and shoes, washed my face, and combed my hair. Suddenly I thought that if they saw me carrying a bundle of clothes when I was supposed to be going to see a classmate, it would make them suspicious. It would be better to take my rattan school box. Noiselessly, I took the box out from the storage space behind the door. Inside, still in order, were my school books and writing materials. They were covered with a thick layer of dust. I emptied out the box and opened my bundle of clothes. I selected a suit of underwear, a coat and skirt, a lined coat, a few handkerchiefs, and a few pairs of cotton stockings. I wanted to add a lined sleeveless jacket, but could not get it in. The only other thing I could squeeze in was a wooden comb.

I sat down on my bed and waited.

Chapter 32

AT last the living-room clock struck seven.

I heard Mrs. Zhang ask Mrs. Shao, "Mistress, is this all you want me to buy? Then I'll leave now." When I could no longer hear her footsteps, I picked up my rattan box and went to the door. I stood there listening for a while and then went out into the hallway clutching the note in my hand. I could see the wet nurse sitting on a stool out in the courtyard. She had a big bowl in her hands and was eating her breakfast. Xiao Liuzi (Little Six), the Shaos' youngest son, was in a sling on her back. I leaned into the living room and beckoned to her. I had to beckon four or five times before she saw me. Then she tiptoed into the hallway.

"Good morning, eldest young mistress. You've come back." She smiled as she greeted me.

"Wet nurse," I whispered, "I'm going out to see a schoolmate and will be right back. In a little while, when the eldest young master gets up, I'd like you to please give him this note."

Because the wet nurse had just come from the sunny courtyard into the dark hallway, it took her a moment to realize that I was wearing a linen suit and carrying the rattan box, ready to go out. She looked at me, then at the note I was holding. She almost put out her hand to take it, but then seemed to reconsider. She hesitated for several seconds and then suddenly backed away from me and raised her hands as if fending me off. "No, miss, you had better ask someone else to give it to him."

I was going to try to persuade her, but at that moment one of the apprentices, carrying a teapot, passed us on his way to the kitchen to make tea. The wet nurse and I sprang apart—she hurried back out to the courtyard and I returned to my bedroom. I knew I could delay no longer. I tucked the note under the oil lamp and began to creep out of the room. Just as I reached the door, Zhongyao's grandmother asked, "Who is it?"

"I," I said, and stopped still. "Grandmother, are you awake?"

"Mmm."

I waited near the door, but she said nothing more. A few more steps and I was in the hallway. When I reached the iving room, I saw that Mrs. Shao's door was open two or three inches. Involuntarily I stepped back. I heard her call for Xiao Lazi, who answered and went into the room. Without even stopping to take a breath, I ran across the living room and through the courtyard as if I were flying. The wet nurse stared at me. Her mouth was open, as if she were startled or wanted to say something to me. My heart burned with impatience. I could not stop and listen to her. I ran out the back gate and down the stone steps. Then, suddenly, I heard a loud voice, "Young miss! Going out so early in the morning? Where are you going?"

I looked over and saw that it was the wife of the owner of the rice shop across the way. She was sitting next to the big braided-straw rice bin and was feeding one of the younger children. She smiled and waved the chopsticks at me. I murmured something indistinct. I knew she liked to talk and was afraid she would delay me. I kept my head down and hurried towards the entrance of the lane. When I got there I hesitated, not sure whether to turn right or left. Just then I saw an empty rickshaw on the side of the road. I stepped into it. "Across the river to the south bank, to the mill. Hurry, please hurry!"

The rickshaw puller stood up, tightened his belt, lifted the poles and headed off towards the south end of Long Street. Apprentices were busy taking down the shutters and opening the shops. People carrying goods swinging from poles on their shoulders or piled in their arms were on their way to the early market. The rickshaw moved slowly through the crowd. I was frightened that we might meet someone I knew. I tried several times to pull up the top of the rickshaw but it was too heavy for me. Although the sky had clouded over, it was not raining, so I could not ask the rickshaw puller to put up the top and hang the curtains. Also, I did not want any delays. So I kept pretending to be wiping something from my eyes or arranging my hair to hide my face.

It took quite a while for the rickshaw to get through Long Street. Then we bumped and shook along several small cobble-stone lanes and twisted down several long, narrow dirt roads until we reached the old city wall with its broken crenellations. We followed the foot of the wall to the east gate. Once outside the gate, we were on a wide, level dirt road bordered with trees. There were very few houses and not many people walking on the road, so I started to feel less frightened. But the rickshaw puller was old and slow, and my impatience made me feel he was much too slow. I kept urging him to go faster by promising I would pay more. He would grunt agreement, but his feet could move no faster.

I could not stop worrying. I did not know how far from the mill my grandmother lived, or the name of their teahouse or whether it would be easy to find. I estimated that I had left the Shaos' home about half an hour earlier. I was afraid they had already discovered that I was gone. Perhaps they had already sent out people to look for me ... I kept asking the rickshaw puller, "Why can't we see the river bank yet? How much further is it to the old pontoon bridge? When can we cross it?"

Each time he would answer, "It's not far. It's just up ahead."

I wanted to turn around to see if anyone was coming after us, but I did not have the courage.

A little later, the rickshaw puller suddenly pointed forward. Panting a little, he said, "There, right ahead of us. It's the bridge. After cross it we'll be on the south bank. The machine mill is a few li further on." I looked where he was pointing and saw the bridge and the long lines of irregularly-spaced weeping willows that lined both banks of the turbulent river. I sighed with relief but still dared not turn my head. I did glance fearfully from side to side, but saw only a few peasants balancing shoulder poles and walking rapidly along the road.

When we reached the bridge, the rickshaw puller stopped. Wiping the sweat from his forehead, he said, "Young lady, you will have to walk across the bridge. Once we're across you can ride again." I had no choice but to get out and follow him onto the bridge. It was long and narrow and in poor repair—some of the boards were broken, as were the wooden railings on either side. The whole bridge shook as we stepped onto it. The cracks under our feet were two or three inches wide. It seemed as if the slightest misstep could result in disaster. Step by step, keeping my eyes on my feet, I went forward. The muddy yellow water of the river rolled and surged beneath me. If the pursuers sent by the Shaos were to catch up with me at this moment, I thought, I would let myself fall into the river and be carried on the current. I wanted to look behind me but I still lacked the courage.

On the south bank of the river, a small group of women were squatting on the stones washing their clothes. Many little children were running back and forth the bank, splashing and skipping stones on the water, and picking through the garbage for bits of coal. The sky had grown even darker and thick black clouds were building up. The river and the weeping willows looked darker. The wind, coming from behind us, blew my blue-and-white-striped skirt until it billowed and I felt big cold drops of rain on my face. I held my jacket close with one hand and tried to push back the loose hair that had blown into my eyes with the other. The words "It's raining" escaped me but my weak, feeble voice did not sound like my own.

The rickshaw puller stuck out his hand and said, "A shower is coming." Then he again bent forward and struggled on. Although his words were so few and so commonplace, they made me feel warmer and a little more comfortable. I felt that he was beside me and on my side at this dangerous and difficult time.

The rain became heavier after we crossed the bridge. The rickshaw puller stopped and got out the oilcloth curtains and his own straw raincoat and hat from under the seat. He waited until I had sat down again and then raised the top and hung the oilcloth across the front. I shrank back until I was entirely hidden and we continued along the river bank. The rain started coming down in sheets and the wind picked up. Lightning flashed and thunder rolled. I thought the worn-out top of the rickshaw was going to be blown away. I leaned forward and grabbed onto the iron frame. My legs were wrapped in the cold, wet oilcloth and the rain was beating in between the oilcloth and the top of the rickshaw. In minutes my hair, clothes and entire body were soaked. It seemed that the rickshaw was only crawling along, like a snail. The cold rain, the sad wind, and the angry black sky all seemed to symbolize what lay before me. My fears and uneasiness increased. I was sure someone was following us but the rickshaw puller could not go any faster. he had already reached the limits of his strength.

I do not know how long the storm lasted, but finally the wind and rain lessened. I looked out and saw that there were green fields and plow oxen on either side of the road, and very few people. Suddenly, a flock of black crows flew across the lowering sky. Their harsh cawing hurt my ears like curses. I sat back and began a desperate, silent prayer. "Oh, Mother, if you have any power, let this flock of crows lead me in peace to your mother's home. Oh, Mother, if you have any power—" When people are in the extremity of fear and helplessness, they hope for miracles. I hoped that the legend that crows could lead the way for one was true. I hoped that my mother really did have the power to protect me from danger and to help me escape from the Shao woman's grasp.

The dirt road seemed endless. We rode and rode, but there was no sign of the little market town. The rain finally stopped and the rickshaw was able to travel more quickly. Then suddenly the stillness of the countryside was broken by the cries of people hawking their wares, the squeak of wheelbarrows, the sounds of women laughing and children shouting, and the barking of dogs. I peered out through the space between the oilcloth and the sides of the rickshaw and saw that we were passing low wooden gates, some with stands in front of them where rice, other grains, vegetables, fish, shrimp, and other goods were being sold. We had reached the town. I rolled down the oilcloth halfway and looked all around. I did not want to miss the mill or the teahouse.

We had passed three or four gates when suddenly I heard a woman calling her chickens. The voice seemed familiar but I knew it was not my grandmother's. I looked in the direction of the voice and saw a middle-aged woman wearing a light-blue cotton coat and trousers scattering the feed she held in the corner of her jacket to a flock of chicks and chickens at her feet. She was talking with another woman. I recognized her at once. I immediately pushed down the oilcloth the rest of the way and stomped several times on the bottom of the rickshaw. The rickshaw puller looked around and I gestured to him with both hands to put down the shafts. "Stop, stop!" I cried, and jumped out and ran towards the middle-aged woman. "Great-aunt! Great-aunt!"

My great-aunt turned and stared at me silently for several moments. She was so surprised that she let go of the corner of her jacket and the bran and grain scattered all over the ground. She clasped my hands and shouted joyously, "It's Baogu! Child, it's been so many years since I saw you. You're so tall! But so thin! How did you manage to make it through that terrible storm? Look at you—you're soaking wet!" She turned and looked out at the street. "Did you come alone? Just wait until your grandmother sees you—I can't tell you how happy she'll be!" She took my hand as she talked and led me towards her brick house.

As we went inside before she spoke again, I tugged at her sleeve and whispered, "Where does my grandmother live? Is it far? I must see her right away. It's urgent. Please, take me to her right away."

My great-aunt nodded and said, "It's not far. I'll take you there. But won't you stay here at my house for a bit and drink a cup of

tea to warm yourself?"

"I don't want anything right now—let's go quickly!"

She dusted off her clothes and came back outside with me. I saw the rickshaw puller sitting and waiting at the side of the road and remembered I had not yet paid him. I had also left my rattan box in the rickshaw. I hurried over and picked up the box. I shook out all my money from my purse and gave it to him. Then my great-aunt and I walked towards the end of the village. The whole time, she kept asking me about my trip. When had I left? Did my grandparents know I had come? Why was I there alone? And she said that she and my grandmother had never dreamed I would come that day. Then she laughed and said that I was like a precious jewel that had fallen from heaven.

Perhaps it was the cut of my coat and skirt, which were obviously those of a student from the city or perhaps it was my great-aunt's loud, excited voice, but people began coming out of their houses and eyeing me curiously. I could not ask her to lower her voice. All I could do was answer her quietly. Fortunately, we had not walked far when I saw a big building of red-painted sheet metal in the distance. I knew by the chugging sounds coming from it that it had to be the mill. At that moment my great-aunt pointed at a wooden house on the right side of the road near the water and said, "There—that's the teahouse of your step-grandfather's family. Your grandmother lives opposite."

As we approached the teahouse, I saw a thin-faced man of about thirty sitting inside at the counter working with his abacus. His hair was cropped and he was wearing a short coat of grey cotton. He nodded when he saw my great-aunt, and greeted her. The teahouse was surrounded by water on three sides. It had latticed windows on all sides. They had been pushed up and were wide open. The busiest time of the morning was over and most of the benches were empty, but a few customers, holding teacups with covers, were sitting at the windows looking at the water and chatting. My great-aunt took my hand and said, "Daya (Big Sprout), this is your stepmother's granddaughter. She has come out from the city today to see her and me." Then she told me, "This is your uncle." I knew that he was my grandmother's stepson and nodded to him.

"Where is your mother?"

"I saw her at the gate just now. I think she's gone back into the house. Mother, Mother!"

"Don't shout." My great-aunt made a hushing gesture and led

me to a low brick house across the street. Before she crossed the threshold she herself began shouting.

"Elder sister! Elder sister! Come out and see who's here! You'll never guess what special guest has come!"

"Who is it? I'm busy. I'll be right out!" It was my grandmother's voice. How dear it sounded to me! And how important!

We waited in the small, narrow, windowless living room. The floor was of packed earth and smelled damp after the rain. From behind the blue cloth curtain that hung in the doorway to the left came the sound of a door being opened. Then my grandmother came in, wiping her hands on her apron as if she had just washed them. She laughed and asked, "Who is this special guest?"

My face twisted. I did not know whether I wanted to laugh or cry. My great-aunt patted my shoulder and said, "There, look! Is she not a gift from heaven?"

My grandmother looked as if she could not believe her eyes. She came forward and seized my hands and gazed at me intently. "My child, I never dreamed you'd come here!" Her voice was trembling. Then she turned and looked towards the street. "Are you alone? Didn't anyone come with you? Your grandfather and grandmother—do they know you're here?"

I shook my head and, holding her hand, went towards her bedroom. My great-aunt followed us, saying, "Elder sister, Baogu's clothes are wet through. I'll go and get some hot water. You must help her get her damp clothes off. We don't want her to catch cold." Before I could stop her, she left. Immediately I asked my grandmother to shut and bolt the bedroom door.

Grandmother dried my head, hair, and arms with a piece of cloth. I opened my rattan box, but found that all my clothes had gotten wet. Grandmother rummaged through her wooden chest and brought out one of her own suits, a coat and trousers, and told me to change right away. At that moment, my great-aunt tapped at the door. My grandmother opened it and let her in. My great-aunt was carrying big white metal pot of hot water in one hand and a little pottery teapot in the other. The two sisters divided up the tasks of pouring me some tea, pouring out the hot water for me to wash my face and feet. They asked me if I could stay for a few days and what I had had for breakfast and whether I was hungry and then chatted to each other about what to make me for lunch. I tried to stop them and asked them to sit down and listen to what I had to say because it was important, but they would not. At last I said, "Grandmother, Great-aunt, when I came out this morning, I was running away. My grandfather and grandmother—no one at home knows I'm here. And I'm not going back." This silenced them. They were startled, and as they began to realize this was not an ordinary visit, their smiles disappeared. I sat on the edge of my grandmother's bed holding my bowl of hot tea in both hands. They sat on either side of me and their eyes did not leave my face as they waited in silence for me to explain.

I looked around the room uneasily, again afraid that someone might have caught up with me and gone to the teahouse to make inquiries and that my grandmother's stepson, not knowing any better, would tell them where I was. Then it would all be over! So I told my grandmother, "Please, go and warn my uncle that if anyone comes looking for me, he must not tell them I'm here. Not even if it's my grandfather."

When my grandmother and great-aunt heard this, they looked uneasy. They exchanged glances but said nothing. Then my grandmother got up, dusted off her clothes, coughed twice, and went out the door.

Chapter 33

FOR a long time I did not even know where to start. Several times I opened my mouth, only to be stopped by my own sobs.

When my grandmother and great-aunt saw me in this state they could not help remembering my mother and they started crying too. The three of us wept together silently until at last, haltingly, I told them how Father and his wife had sent me to the Shao family as a child bride and how the Shao woman had treated me. I told them about my illness and how I had tried to kill myself and then been taken back to my grandparents, and how Grandmother had returned me to the Shaos the previous day. As I talked, my heart ached and all the wounds I had suffered seemed to open up again, one after the other.

My great-aunt and grandmother shook their heads and sighed as they listened and condemned my own family as well as the Shaos, saying they were all heartless and inhuman. They kept patting me on the back and putting their arms around me, and called me a "pitiful unfortunate child." After I finished, I clung to their hands and begged them to keep me and help me escape to my aunt's home. "If you don't help me, if I'm forced to go back to them, I'll kill myself."

"Oh, it's pathetic! My Xiao Baogu's destiny is so bitter!" Grandmother wept as she gathered me into her arms. "You're bone of my bone, flesh of my flesh. If I don't help you, who will? If your mother had not died so young, you never would have had to undergo such sufferings." She could not hide the pain she was feeling.

"It's impossible to predict what people will do," sighed my great-aunt. "Who would have thought that your father and your grandparents could be so cold and heartless? When your mother was alive, everyone treated you like a treasure. But once she died and left you alone, they showed their true colors and got rid of you. It was like taking a little lamb and giving it to a tiger."

They sighed and criticized both families for a while longer, and then began discussing what to do. They decided to let me stay with my grandmother for a few days while they consulted with my late second great-aunt's widowed husband and my great-aunt's oldest son, Laoda (Old First) about how to get me to my aunt's home. Grandmother felt my back and arms and said I was pathetically thin, only skin and bones. She repeated that the way my father had treated me made her angry enough to burst and that if she had known about my sufferings she would have confronted my grandparents' hostility, no matter how great, and come to see me. My great-aunt began worrying again. She was afraid I would get sick because I had left on an empty stomach, gotten wet through in the rain, and been so anxious and frightened that my hands were still trembling. She told Grandmother to get me some more hot tea and some food from the teahouse. Then she piled up the pillows on the bed and told me to get in and lie down. She told me not to be afraid. She then said she was afraid that some of the neighbors might have seen us arrive. She decided to go and tell them to say nothing if any strangers should show up and start asking questions. As she left, she cautioned Grandmother, "Elder sister, if her father's father comes looking for her you must not let yourself be nervous. As long as he finds no trace of her, we're safe."

"Her grandfather? Would he dare come here looking for her?" Grandmother exploded with anger. "If he comes here asking where she is, I'll tell him, 'You're the ones she ran away from! Have I been questioning you about how you've treated her? How dare you come and question me?' I'd like to see what he says then!"

My great-aunt nodded, sighed, and went out. Grandmother gave me a cup of tea and left, taking the metal pot with her. Soon she returned with a bowl and chopsticks. Behind her came a young woman, about twenty years old, wearing a coat and trousers of blue homespun stencilled with white flowers. She was carrying a round wooden tray with two big steaming bowls. One had salty fried cakes and the other, steamed sweet pastries. She put the tray on the tea table near the bed. Grandmother said I was to call her Aunt. Aunt told me cordially, "Niece, the food in the countryside is not very good. All we have are these plain refreshments. Eat as much as you like." She left, and Grandmother asked her to close the door behind her.

By now, I was feeling much calmer. My grandmother put the tray on the bed mat and urged me to eat. She said she would soon prepare more for me. I had not eaten at all the day before and had had only a few sips of tea before leaving the Shaos', so when I smelled the food it made me feel very hungry. I picked out a steamed dumpling filled with white sugar and sugared cassia blossoms and had just taken my first bite when I heard my grandfather's voice. It came from the living room. "Hello, in-law, are you at home?"

Only yesterday, his voice had been familiar and loved, but now, after just one night, how much I feared it and how threatening it was! I clutched my grandmother's waist and she held me close.

His voice came again. "Hello! Are you at home?"

Grandmother coughed several times before she was able to reply, "I'm at home." Then she whispered in my ear, "Child, don't be afraid, don't be afraid."

"In-law, how are you? Are you still in bed?"

"No, no, I've been up since dawn. Oh—it's you! Please sit down out there. I have one little thing to finish, and then I'll be right with you."

"There's no hurry. Take your time. I'll sit down."

"Please do." As she spoke, Grandmother loosened my arms, stood up, went to the door, and silently drew the bolt. Then she came back and let down the bed curtains. She drew them together and tucked them under the matting. Quickly I rolled over to the farthest edge of the bed and drew the thin quilt over my head so I was completely covered, but a few moments later, I felt Grandmother tug my shoulder. I poked my head out—she was gesturing to me to get up. I jumped out of the bed. She pointed at the back of the clothes cupboard—I went over and was just about to squeeze in behind it when she shook her head. She thought for a moment, scanned the room and, suddenly, as if she had discovered buried treasure, squatted down and began to pull the bench-step away from the bed. Immediately I understood that she wanted me to hide under the bed. I helped her to move the bench. We did not make a sound. Then I crawled under the bed. The space was crowded with bundles and boxes. I did not know how I was going to fit. It took all the strength of my poor old grandmother to kneel and push the bundles, and me, under the bed. She kept whispering to me not to be afraid. Then she would raise her voice and call to Grandfather, "I must ask your pardon. I'll be right out!"

She waited until I finally managed to creep far under the bed. It smelled damp and moldy. Then she pushed back the bench.

The whole thing had taken a little more than ten minutes. I heard her dust off her clothes, wash her hands, and cough a couple of times. Then she went over and opened the door.

"I must ask your forgiveness. I've kept you waiting too long."

"That's all right. It's I who have inconvenienced you."

"Please sit down. It's been a long time since we met."

"That's true. We seldom meet."

There was silence for a while. Then I heard Grandmother say, "In-law, you've never before paid us a visit. What brings you here today?" Although she had been so nervous with me when he first arrived, now that she was talking with him, she seemed to have regained her calm. But she also sounded sarcastic, as if she were harboring some resentment. "Is your wife well?" she asked.

"We are both well, thanks to heaven. And you, have you been well all this time?" Grandfather's voice was cold.

"We mere peasants can't afford to hope for much. If heaven protects us and we do not have any disasters or illnesses, and have only a little tea to drink and rice to eat, we're satisfied. But you've been sitting here all this time without even a cup of tea. Daya, quickly—prepare a pot of the best tea and bring it here for my in-law."

"No, no—don't bother. In-law, I would not have dared disturb you if I did not have a problem to talk over with you. The only reason I'm here today is because of Baogu." Grandfather's voice became more serious now that he had revealed the reason for his visit. "I have come to ask you whether Baogu has come here." He said these last words very distinctly.

I could hear my own heart pounding as I crouched on the dirt floor.

"Who? Baogu?" Grandmother sounded startled.

"Yes," Grandfather's voice was emphatic.

"She has never been here. Baogu ... where has she gone?"

"Where? We don't know where ... that's why I'm here. Perhaps you know that a year ago she was betrothed to the Shao family and went to live with them."

"Betrothed! I didn't know! Imagine—my own daughter's daughter, my own little granddaughter, and no one took the trouble to come and tell me! If ..."

"Yes," Grandfather interrupted. "Yes, well, things were all right for the whole year. They treated her well and there was no trouble between them. But a few weeks ago, because of a little quarrel—maybe her mother-in-law scolded her—they brought her back to us. But her grandmother and I feel that, although it will never be as pleasant for her there as in our own home, that for better or worse she's now part of their family. There are bound to be disagreements, but we felt that if she stayed with us for a few days there wouldn't be any more trouble. So her grandmother took her back yesterday afternoon. But this morning when we were talking in the living room, Mr. Shao suddenly came running in. He looked furious. 'Has Baowen come here?' he demanded. We said no. He said, 'That's odd! I don't know who's been telling her things and leading her astray, but for no reason she ran off this morning, secretly, all by herself!'

"We were so stunned that we could not say a word.

"Mr. Shao said that no one realized she was gone until Mrs. Shao's mother called for her and she was not there. Then the whole family got up and started looking for her. They found a note on the table saying that she was going to Shanghai to look for her father."

"Really? I can't believe it!"

"He said that everyone had always treated her well ... And when their eldest son, her betrothed, saw the note, he went into his room, closed the door, and lay on the bed and wept! Mr. Shao told us, 'He has loved her ever since he's known her. He loves her very much. What's wrong with her? What did she have to complain about? She's made such a fool of herself she'll never live it down!' He also said that she had left with only the clothes she was wearing and had no money, so he did not think that she could have gotten very far. The Shaos have already sent people to all the piers to keep watch. He asked me whether I knew of any place in the area where she might go. I told him about you —"

"About me?" my grandmother broke in loudly. "From the time when I got up this morning until now, I've seen no one but you. And I'll tell you something else—ever since her mother died, all those years ago, Baogu has never been here. Do you realize that, in-law? Perhaps you have forgotten! Did you tell the Shaos that?" She sounded angry.

"In-law, please!" Grandfather's voice was firm and serious. "I'm here solely for Baogu's sake. I'm worried about her future. I'm here because I want to be sure that she'll be able to hold up her head with pride and self-respect and to keep her position in society in the future! I'm afraid that she's too young to understand right from wrong and how to behave, and that she may have come under bad influences. If she loses her honor, her life will be ruined." He sighed. "She's fifteen. She's not a baby. It's dangerous for her to be out on her own! Is it any wonder we're upset? I've come here to tell you that if she's here, it's a good thing, because I can take her back with me right away and that'll be the end of it. If she isn't here now, but comes here later, I beg you to send us word immediately. It's for her own good. Otherwise, not only will her life be a disaster, but also I'm afraid that the Shaos will pursue her until they find her. And if there is a scandal, it will be too late."

I heard Grandmother sigh deeply but she made no reply.

There was a long silence. Then Grandfather cleared his throat and said, "I must leave now and go to look for her. If I don't find her in the next day or so, I'll have no choice but to come back and trouble you again." I heard him stand up and go out.

Although at first Grandmother had treated him with courage and defiance, his talk about my future and my whole life seemed to worry her, and she was not able to respond to him as quickly as before. It was several moments before I heard her call after him, "If you find out where she is, please come and tell us!"

In my hiding place under the bed, with only a thin wood partition between me and my grandfather and grandmother, I was shaking uncontrollably. My teeth were chattering with fear. Grandfather's voice sounded not like his own, but like the voice of respectability and authority. In everything he had said, especially his warning that I would not be able to hold up my head in the world, he seemed to be expressing not only his own beliefs but also those of the Shaos, all my relatives and friends, and all of society. I understood. I also realized that though my father's parents could not bear to see me suffer at the hands of the Shaos, they could bear even less to see me reject that life, and run away, because it meant I would in turn be rejected and deserted by everyone. They would rather see me driven to suicide by the Shaos—even though they and others would bemoan my "bitter destiny"—than see me turn into something as dangerous as a rebel, because it would disgrace our family name.

My mother's mother had braved so much social disapproval, that she understood my grandfather's warning only too well. Perhaps his words had reopened her old wounds and made her so worried about my future that she could not help losing her earlier firmness.

Grandmother stayed in the living room until she was sure that

Grandfather was not going to return before she was able to calm herself and come back into her room. She pulled the bench away and said, "Child, don't be afraid. He's gone. Hurry and come out."

"Mother! Mother!" The voice at the door was unfamiliar and I dared not move.

"Daya, come in. I must talk with you."

"Mother, your sister came here a while ago, but when she heard that Baogu's grandfather was here she did not come in. She has told me a little of Baogu's story. But, Mother, you shouldn't have stayed in your room so long—it must have made him suspicious."

"Oh, you're right. But Baogu was so frightened that I got worried and confused and kept him waiting too long. Little one, don't be afraid. It's only your uncle."

"Where is she?" He came into the room.

"I made her hide under the bed."

"Mother, Mother—you're usually so clearheaded. How could you be so muddled today? Mr. Zhou would never have come into your room! Besides, your door was shut. But even if it had been standing wide open, and even if he had suspected that Baogu was there, he would never have dared enter a woman's bedroom. No wonder it took you so long! He must have been suspicious!"

This seemed to worry Grandmother very much. She helped me up onto the bed. She closed the window that looked out on the river and shut the lattice. She asked Daya to ask his wife to heat a bowl of brown-sugar-and-ginger water because my lips were pale and my hands and feet were cold, and she was afraid I would be ill.

Then she told him, "You must be on guard, both of you, and watch the gate. I think that Mr. Zhou will come back. Tonight, when you're free, we must sit down with my sister and talk this all over very carefully and come up with a good, safe plan."

Chapter 34

EVERY day I stayed at Grandmother's, my danger grew. I had to get farther away.

The day after Grandfather's visit, two suspicious-looking young men, strangers, were seen near the mill. They wandered around and looked around all day, and were still there the next day. On the third day they came into Daya's teahouse and sat down at a table that faced Grandmother's gate. They stayed there from the time the teahouse opened until it closed. Daya and his wife were very worried. They were sure that Grandfather had become suspicious and told the Shaos, and that the Shaos had sent the men to keep an eye out for me. Daya and his wife were afraid that if there were any trouble, they would not be able to survive it because their business was so small.

Grandmother was disturbed and worried too, but she reassured her stepson and his wife, telling them that they would surely come up with a plan and that even if there were trouble she would take the responsibility and not let them be involved. However, each time she looked out and saw the two strangers sitting across the street, she would get very worried. She could not keep the gate closed during the day because that would have looked suspicious. My great-aunt did not want to attract attention, so she did not come to Grandmother's house during the day. On the third day, after dinner, she told her little grandson to keep watch. When he saw the two strangers go away she hurried over. Grandmother immediately closed the gate behind her and the two talked in low voices. They were both anxious, because the situation was serious. They both said, "Clever people prepare for trouble before it comes along." The crucial thing now was to get me away from there until the pursuit died down. My great-aunt said that Grandmother's house was not a good place for me to stay, even if the two spies had not come. First, it was too close to the teahouse, which attracted many people who might talk. I was too old to be hidden away in the house for very long. Because "walls have ears," and there was no guarantee that news of my presence would not leak out. Second, Daya and his wife were not brave and were unwilling to run the risk of protecting me, and Great-aunt was afraid that my staying there would lead to quarrels. But where could I go? My great-aunt's home was not safe either, because it was right next to the market and too near Grandmother's. After much discussion, they concluded that the safest place for me would be the home of their middle sister's husband. He lived about eight *li* from town, in an out-of-the-way place. His family was small; my second great-aunt had died several years ago. Their three daughters were all married, and the only people living at the farm with my great-uncle were his youngest son and that son's fiancée. It would be a temporary refuge from the storm brought about by my escape.

"If we're going to go, we should leave right away," said my great-aunt. "It would be best to go tonight. Each day here is another day of danger."

Grandmother nodded and looked at me. She sighed as if asking me if I was willing to go. Immediately I nodded to show that I was willing.

My great-aunt asked my grandmother to go into the other room and call in Daya and his wife. Grandmother nodded and went out. She soon returned, followed by Daya and his wife. My great-aunt explained that they had decided to take me to my great-uncle's house because it would be safer. Daya and his wife seemed much relieved, and little smiles broke over their tense faces. They nodded and agreed. After some more talk, the family decided to wait until the market closed for the day. Daya and his wife would go to the edges of town and look around everywhere. Once they were sure no suspicious-looking people were around, Grandmother and my great-aunt would take me away.

As Daya and his wife were about to leave, Grandmother said to me, "Child, may heaven watch over you and protect you, that you may escape and reach your aunt's home safely. Always remember this uncle's and aunt's kindness in helping to save you —what your great-aunt and I have done is secondary." Although she was talking to me, she was looking at her stepson and stepdaughter-in-law. I understood. I knew that her words were meant both to express her gratitude to them and to keep the door open so that they would stand by her and not turn against her as she got older.

"You shouldn't say that—we've done only what we should have done," Daya and his wife protested when they heard her. They were both smiling again.

"Besides, Baogu is our own relative," Daya continued. "If we met a stranger in trouble on the road, we'd help him. It's too bad that Baogu can't stay with us longer and that we haven't been able to entertain her properly. If things were different, we'd welcome her to stay for a couple of weeks and would feed her and put her up without a second thought."

Daya and his wife left and I packed my little rattan box. Shortly after midnight they returned and reported that there were no strangers in town, that the market had closed down, and that the coast was clear. If we were going, we should leave immediately. Great-aunt picked up my rattan box and went out the front gate. Grandmother took me by the hand and we followed her. We did not carry a lantern because we did not want to attract any attention, but Great-aunt had a box of matches in her pocket in case we needed them.

It was fortunate that Grandmother's house was near the edge of the town and that the townspeople were in the habit of going to bed early. All the house gates and shop fronts were closed up tight. The only lights we saw were the weak rays of a lamp that shone through the half-open doors and cracks of a wineshop and a grain shop at the edge of town. The river banks were dark and quiet. In the distance, the lights of several small boats anchored near the bank gleamed like bright beans. We could hear the murmur of the water. The crescent moon and a few scattered stars were covered from time to time by floating clouds. The evening mist dampened the air. With my great-aunt leading and Grandmother and me close behind, we hurried past the wineshop and the grain shop. A few more steps took us outside the town. We walked along the dike and then turned left, away from the river and the main road. We followed the winding little roads for quite a distance. The countryside grew quieter and quieter and the dirt roads dwindled into paths. There were no lights in the narrow streets of the villages we passed. The only lights came from the occasional flicker of a firefly. We could see only a few feet ahead of us and could not tell what direction we were headed in, but fortunately our eyes gradually adjusted to the darkness and both Great-aunt and Grandmother knew the road well. And because neither of them had bound feet they could help me over the rough places when I needed it.

We met no one. Once we saw the light of a lantern on the dike. It was making the dogs bark. My great-aunt pulled us into a field, where we waited until the swinging light of the lantern disappeared in the distance and the barking died down. Then we continued on. Sometimes when we passed a farmhouse, the dogs would bark, but when the sound of our footsteps died away the barking stopped too. We spoke very little and when we had to speak we whispered. The only other sounds we heard were the occasional croakings of the frogs, the lowings of a water buffalo, the sounds of our own breathing, and the patter of our cloth-soled shoes on the footpath. All three of us were tense and watchful. We had walked for about half an hour when my great-aunt suddenly drew a deep breath and said, "It's all right now. After we pass that long mound we'll be at our brother-in-law's house."

Grandmother coughed a bit and clasped my hand more tightly. She seemed relieved.

We passed the mound and suddenly the darkness was no longer open and empty. I could see high and low masses of dense blackness, but could not tell whether they were houses, haystacks, or trees. Great-aunt led us towards one of the dark patches. When we got closer, I saw it was a thatch-roofed house that stood in a clearing bordered by trees on all four sides. The house was dark. Great-aunt felt her way to a square wooden window and called softly, "Brother-in-law! Xiao Guizi (Little Cassia)!"

Grandmother joined her and called softly, "We've come. Open the gate!"

A dog started barking from inside the house. Then we heard a voice say, "It's the middle of the night! Who's there? Huazi (Flower), stop barking! Oh, it's my sisters-in-law. Xiao Guizi, get up!" A ray of light shone through the latticed window and the cracks in the door. The two leaves of the wooden gate opened and a big spotted dog bounded out and jumped up on Grandmother and Great-aunt wagging his tail. My great-uncle came out. He was more than fifty years old and was holding up a tin oil lamp. Behind him came a peasant girl of sixteen or seventeen, buttoning her coat. She greeted my grandmother and great-aunt and grabbed the dog's tail so we could go in.

The house was cave-like and sparsely furnished. There was a square table in the center and four or five long benches scattered around. Rice straw, hay chaff, grain, and farm tools were piled against one wall. A large clay stove stood against another wall. My great-uncle set the lamp on the table and gestured for us to sit down. Grandmother led me over to him and said, "Brother-in-law, this is Zhou Baogu. Her mother brought her here once when she was four or five, and you met her then. But you'd never recognize her now."

He looked at me, nodded and again indicated for us to sit down. Xiao Guizi went to light the stove to heat water for tea. Grandmother and Great-aunt gestured that they did not want any and said, "Don't go to all that trouble. We just wanted to talk with your father-in-law for a bit, and then we'll go." They pulled one of the benches against the wall. "Brother-in-law, come and sit down so we can talk."

But he first went to another room that was partitioned off by a mud-and-straw wall and brought out a long pipe of yellow bamboo with brown stripes. He took it over to the table and lit it at the lamp. Then he went and sat down between them. The two old sisters whispered to him for a long time. Xiao Guizi and I were sitting at the table and could not make out what they were saying. My great-uncle said nothing. He just puffed on his pipe and listened. Sometimes he looked over at me, but his face, as red as the earth and ringed with short, black whiskers, betrayed nothing.

Though I kept my head bent, my eyes never left his face. I was afraid that he would suddenly shake his head. If he did, where else could I go, on such a black night? But he did not shake his head. All he did was bend over and tap the bowl of his pipe on the ground several times to knock out the ashes. Then he looked up and, after thinking for a while, said, "Her aunt's home is far away. How do you plan to get her there? I'm afraid it will be an expensive journey."

Grandmother sighed. "That's true. We need a foolproof plan. If she hadn't run away, there'd be no problem, but since she has, we cannot possibly send her back. If she goes back, sooner or later they'll drive her to suicide or work her to death. That's the only thing that will satisfy them."

My great-aunt was frowning. "It seems to me that trying to get her on any ship at any dock around here would be impossible. But we don't know any other way she can go. We'll have to wait until things quiet down and until Laoda (Eldest Son) comes back." She sighed. "Luck isn't on our side right now. It would happen that he's away on his raft, shipping a load of wood. He knows the upper and lower reaches of the river—things will be clearer once we can talk with him."

My great-uncle thought for a while longer and then said, "All right. There's plenty of room here. Let her stay here a few nights."

I was overcome with relief.

Grandmother and Great-aunt both sighed their own relief and stood up. Grandmother came over to me. "Child, stay here a few days. We'll come to see you when it's safe." She turned to Xiao Guizi. "Child, take good care of her. Her life has been full of sorrows. She has no mother and has quarrelled with her family, so she has run away. You must not say anything about her to anyone, and don't let anyone see her."

Xiao Guizi nodded. She picked up the lamp and led me into another little partitioned-off room where she put my rattan box on a wooden chest at the head of a little board bed. Grandmother went to the bed, felt the blue homespun quilt, which was stencilled with white flowers, and gave her a few words of instruction. Then she and my great-aunt took leave of my great-uncle. He told Xiao Guizi to light a paper lantern, the color of rice hulls, for them to take with them. He and Xiao Guizi then walked with them to the edge of the yard. I stood at the gate and watched. The lantern and the two shadowy forms soon disappeared into the night. Great-uncle and Xiao Guizi came back into the house and I followed her into her room.

The bed was very small and narrow. She and I lay down on our sides, our heads at opposite ends of the bed. It was very quiet and lonely out in the country at night. The only sound was the wind blowing through the thatch and the leaves of the trees. Xiao Guizi turned over carefully and then did not move again, but though I was very tired, I could not get to sleep.

I was awakened the next morning by the smell of burning twigs and cooked rice. I opened my eyes and saw that it was still quite dark. I put out my hand and realized that Xiao Guizi was already up. I heard the sound of bowls and chopsticks in the next room, and then Great-uncle's voice and his footsteps as he went out to the fields. The darkness was turning to grey.

Xiao Guizi and I were alone in that big empty house all day long. She was never idle. She moved constantly—washing clothes, cooking, feeding the pigs, feeding the chickens, feeding the dog, carrying water from the river, going to the garden to water the vegetables, going to pick the vegetables, taking lunch out to the fields, coming back to thresh the grain, and grinding the rice into flour. I wanted to help her but did not even know where to start. Besides, I could not go outside with her. I could help her only in small ways inside the house or in the yard. She was polite to me but we did not have much to say to each other.

She was too busy and I was too worried. I wondered how the Shaos were planning to find me and if the two strangers had gone to Daya's teahouse again that day. I wondered whether my grandfather had come back to see my grandmother, and when I would be able to leave the farm, and whether my grandmother and great-aunt would come to see me. I kept looking across the enclosure to the mound, but the only living creatures there were the water buffalo and the farmers at work in the green and yellow fields. As the sun was setting behind the hills, Great-uncle came back. He was carrying a hoe on his shoulder and wearing a blue homespun short jacket. It was open and showed his suntanned chest and his trousers were rolled up high above his knees. Behind him came a dark thin boy of thirteen or fourteen. He had a long curved knife in his hands. They leaned the knife and the hoe in a corner against the wall and went out to wash their hands and feet before sitting down at the table to eat dinner.

I greeted my great-uncle when he came in, and he pointed to the boy and said he was his youngest son, Laoyao (Old Last).

In the middle of the dining table was a pottery bowl of newly brewed tea and two big red-painted bowls full of freshly-picked vegetables. One bowl contained scarlet and jade-green peppers flavored with coarse salt, peanut oil and fermented soybeans. The other contained young leafy vegetables and golden-brown fried bean curd. There was also a little plate of steamed salted fish, and the rice was unpolished. The colors, the smells and tastes were all delightful. No one spoke. The only sound was the clatter of chopsticks against the bowls. After the rice bowls had been brought out, my great-uncle picked up his chopsticks and told me not to stand on ceremony but to eat as much as I wanted. He told Xiao Guizi to cook some extra rice the next morning because one of his cousins was coming to help with the work. After dinner, he took his pipe and sat on the threshold looking out and smoking silently as he watched the colors of the hills, the earth, and the fields fade gradually in the twilight. Xiao Guizi poured a bowl of hot tea and placed it on the ground by his feet.

While she and I were washing up, I suddenly heard a voice outside the house. I could not hear the words, but my heart sank and my hands went still as I strained to listen. Xiao Guizi nodded reassuringly and said, "Don't worry. It's only Laoyao talking with the pigs. He loves the pigs and every evening he must talk with them for a while before he goes to sleep."

It was quite dark by the time we had finished washing up.

When Great-uncle had finished smoking his pipe and had drunk his tea, he shut the door and blew out the light, and we all went to bed.

Although I was consumed by my own problems, when Xiao Guizi and I were taking off our clothes and I saw her sturdy shoulders, full round breasts, and the heavy braid that hung down her back, I could not help feeling sorry for her. I thought, how can this strong, mature young girl mate with someone like Laoyao, who still seemed like a child. When they were together she looked like a chrysanthemum in an autumn field or like a plump lettuce-cabbage growing out of the rich earth, while he seemed like a furry little caterpillar that had just struggled out of its cocoon. She was truly like a flower growing in a dung-heap. Although she had no evil mother-in-law standing over her, her whole life would be buried in this meaningless way. It seemed to me that her situation was even sadder than mine. But, I thought, I cannot think through my own problems—what strength do I have left over to think about someone else's? And besides, there were so many, many girls like Xiao Guizi and me, who have been given away as child brides. No matter how sad it made me, sadness did not reveal any solution. I was there because I was trying to escape trouble. Out of his kindness, my great-uncle had taken me in for a few days. For that I had to be thankful. How soon would I be able to leave? I had no idea. How could I worry about anything or anyone else?

The problems I had worried about all through the day came back into my mind one by one.

Chapter 35

MY second, third, and fourth days at the farm passed without us seeing my grandmother or great-aunt. I grew more and more uneasy because I knew that something had to be wrong or they would have come.

When one is anxious, even the murmur of the wind and the rustling of the grass can make one uneasy. Whenever I saw the chickens being scattered by the dog or heard him bark, I was sure that one of the pursuers sent by the Shaos had arrived. It was as if I could see Mr. Shao leading a small army made up of the clerks from his stores, apprentices, and policemen. Each of them was carrying a cudgel and a length of coarse hemp rope to bind me. These visions haunted me. But sometimes they were replaced by pleasant fantasies. Once, a little white cloud and a flock of birds flew over my head, and I began to think about my coming journey. I wished I could sprout wings and fly away with that cloud, fly out of that county town with its grey tiled roofs, across the muddy yellow Yangtze River, where the Shaos could never touch me again.

I eventually learned that while I had been sitting in the farmhouse imagining all these things, my grandmother and great-aunt had been facing many real dangers on my account. It was on the fifth day, just after sunset, that my great-aunt arrived. She was alone and carrying a kerchief bundle. As soon as she came through the gate, she said, "Child, come with me," and went directly to Xiao Guizi's room. She sat down on the bed and gave a deep sigh. Although she tried to keep a smile on her face for my sake, her eyebrows were drawn together in a frown. She untied the kerchief. Inside were cakes and candy from my grandmother. My great-aunt urged me to eat and told me that Grandfather had come back almost every afternoon to inquire about me. He would always stay a long time and would tell her about all the terrible things that were happening, perhaps to frighten her. He said that the very day I left, the Shaos sent a special delivery letter to my father in Shanghai. They were expecting a reply in a day or two. They had decided that I had to be still in the neighborhood because I would not have been able to get away, so they had people watching all the piers day and night. Grandfather also said the Shaos had had the wet nurse arrested and put in jail.

"Put in jail? What did she have to do with it?" I asked startled. "Why should they put the wet nurse in jail?"

My great-aunt sighed again and hugged me. "Your grandfather said that one of the shop apprentices saw you whispering with her the morning you left. So they suspect her of conspiring with you. He said that if your father writes and says that you've reached his home, there will be no trouble for the wet nurse. But if they do not hear from him, the Shaos will continue questioning her. They might even try to beat a confession out of her."

"Oh, no! It's all my fault because I got her involved! I never thought of that—it makes me very unhappy."

"Child, it's no use to be sorry. The most important thing now is to get you away from here. I'm afraid there'll really be trouble if we wait any longer. We've decided that tonight, after dark, the whole family will come out here and talk over what to do. The sooner you go the better."

After dinner my great-aunt told Xiao Guizi to prepare a large pottery jug of tea and to clean and fill the two tin oil lamps. One lamp was placed on the stove and one on the table. Their bright, clean flames lit up the whole room.

Grandmother was the first to arrive. She looked thinner and more worried than the last time I had seen her. As soon as she saw me, she said, "Child, don't worry," and started crying. She took my hand and led me over to the bench near the stove and sat down. She wept a bit longer and then dried her eyes with her handkerchief and said, "The relatives have learned everything about the best way to go to your aunt's. Your great-aunt has agreed to take you herself. In a little while, when everyone gets here, we'll discuss how much money you'll need and what precautions to take when you are travelling and resting. You'll be able to leave tomorrow, or the next day at the latest."

This was better news than I had expected. I was excited and happy, but Grandmother began weeping again and said she did not know when or whether she would ever see me again. And the thought of her son's daughter, my cousin Biying, also made her sad. She said she would have liked to take me herself, so she could have seen her other granddaughter once again. I knew only too well why Grandmother could not go. I could not say anything to comfort her and could only hug her.

In a little while, everyone else arrived. My grandmother wiped away her tears. The door was bolted, and everyone sat down. Xiao Guizi poured out tea for them and then came over to sit next to me.

No one spoke for several minutes. It was as if everyone was waiting for everyone else, or as if they were all thinking things over. My great-uncle and Uncle Dong, with his white beard and hair, sat next to each other on the long bench against the wall and silently smoked their bamboo pipes. Daya sat with his elbow on the table, resting his cheek on his hand. He stared at the flame of the lamp and said nothing. Grandmother and Great-aunt sat next to him fidgeting with their teacups and watching the men. They all shook their heads and sighed but none of them opened their mouths to speak. Laoda, my great-aunt's oldest son, who was about twenty-five and was wearing a long blue homespun gown like a small merchant, finally told Grandmother that she should start the discussion.

Grandmother sighed and picked up her tea, but put it down again untasted. "I don't have much to say. Everyone here knows why we're here." She looked at Uncle Dong and said, "We invited you tonight because you are so experienced and have seen more than we have and can help us think out our problems. In your opinion, will Laoda's plan work? We'll go overland to Lugang, to Datong by small boat and then by steamboat to Hankou. Do you think it's safe? Oh, if only heaven will protect this little granddaughter of mine. Her life has been so hard! If she survives this trial and reaches her aunt's home in peace and safety, I'll be able to rest in peace. If she gets away, I don't care how many people the Shaos send after her. I won't be afraid. And Daya and his wife will also be at peace."

Uncle Dong nodded and grunted and put down his pipe. He stared at the flame of the lamp and pondered.

My great-aunt looked at him and said, "You know that there is no comparison between her aunt and us. She's much more intelligent and educated. If we can only get Baogu to her, then she can take the lead and make the decisions. No matter how much trouble there is, one word from her will carry more weight than a hundred of ours. Whatever happens, it'll be more easily resolved if she's in charge."

"Taking her to her aunt's is by far the best plan. Let me think a little ..." Uncle Dong thought out loud. "From Lugang to Datong is a safe road. The only question in my mind," he said to Laoda, "is whether you have any guarantee that, once they get to Datong there will be a steamboat they can take. Also, exactly how long will it take to get from here to Hankou? They are women and find it harder than men to travel. What will they do when it gets dark and they must find places to sleep? And besides—" he began counting on his fingers, "the cost of eating, drinking, staying at inns, buying boat tickets, not to mention miscellaneous expenses—it's all very expensive and prices keep going up. Have you done a careful, complete estimate? How much money will they need in all? Travel cannot be compared with living at home. If there isn't enough money, one is trapped. We must know what it will cost, down to the last penny."

Everyone sighed and nodded their admiration of Uncle Dong's foresight and wisdom. He looked complacently around the room at everyone and pulled out his little blue cloth tobacco pouch from his sash. He shook out some tobacco and refilled his pipe.

"Sir, you've thought of everything." Laoda edged his bench nearer Uncle Dong's. "I've made the estimate. If they start overland from here early in the morning and keep away from the main road to avoid meeting people but wind along the paths which my mother knows so well, they can be in Lugang by sunset. They can rest there and with any luck there will be a steamboat to Datong the next day. Things will be easier when they reach Datong. The big steamers go from there to Hankou every two or three days and they will have no trouble finding an inn. Every day the inns put up lists of all the steamers that are leaving to go up or down the Yangtze. It's very easy. As for how long it will take for them to reach Hankou, it will take at least ten days, but not more than two weeks. As for expenses, if we include staying at inns, food and drink, third-class tickets—since third-class tickets do not include bedding or food, buying food and renting bedding—and all the other unexpected little costs they will need at least—the smallest possible amount is ... well, I'm afraid they cannot do it without at least thirty or thirty-five silver dollars."

"Oh, dear! Will it really take that much?" Great-aunt asked in surprise.

"And you will have to be tight fisted to get by on that," said Laoda, nodding emphatically.

It was a large sum. For a while no one spoke.

I thought immediately of the two rings the Shaos had given

me for my betrothal. One was solid gold and the other was set with a ruby. Fortunately I was wearing both of them because I had been afraid that the Shao woman would be angry if I did not. I did not know what they were worth but guessed they could bring at least ten or fifteen dollars. I wanted to suggest this to Grandmother, but before I could open my mouth, she stood up and, without saying anything, went over to the other side of the stove. She turned around and crouched forward, lifting the corners of her jacket and rummaged inside her sash until she found her stomach-purse. It was shaped like the seed pod of the lotus and embroidered in many colors. Then she went back over to the table and, with hands that trembled slightly, unbuttoned, one by one, the twenty or thirty tiny, closely-set buttons that closed the bag. Then she turned it upside-down and bright, shining silver dollars tinkled onto the table. My great-aunt and Daya held their arms out around the table, afraid the coins might roll to the ground.

Great-aunt counted them twice. There were twenty-five—still not enough.

Grandmother looked at Daya beseechingly, but he turned his gaze away and fixed it on the light of the lamp.

I took off my rings, got up, and crept over to Grandmother. I put the rings in her hand and murmured. "Grandmother, ask whichever uncle you wish to go out and sell these for me."

"No need, no need, Baogu. Take them back." My great-uncle, who had not said a word all evening, suddenly took his pipe out of his mouth and shook it in a gesture not intended to repulse me but to indicate his good intentions. "Daya, I don't want to interfere, but since your stepmother has volunteered all her savings it would be appropriate for you to give something. Much or little, it doesn't matter, but you must give something. Laoda and I will make up whatever's still missing. Then there'll be enough. Why should we let Baogu sell her things?"

"I—" Daya stammered with embarrassment. "I—I don't have any more—I can only manage three dollars or so—I ..."

"All right," my great-uncle went on, "I think you should put in five dollars. Laoda and I will each put in five dollars. Three fives are fifteen." He counted on his fingers. "Fifteen and twenty-five make forty. It never does any harm to have a little extra." As he was speaking, he stood up and went into his room. A few moments later, he came out and laid five shiny silver dollars on the table. Then he went back to his bench and smoked his pipe.

Uncle Dong grunted and nodded his approval.

"When do you think they should start?" asked Grandmother with a smile, seeing that the money problem had been solved.

"The sooner the better." Great-aunt sorted the silver dollars into three little piles and pushed them over to Grandmother. "If we can get all the money tonight, I think it would be best to start early tomorrow morning."

"Can you be ready?" asked Grandmother.

"Of course. All I need to take is a couple of changes of clothes. I can go home right now and get them."

Laoda stood up as if preparing to leave. "If that's all you're taking, Mother, then you don't need to walk all the way back in the dark. Won't it be easier for me to bring them to you? I have to go anyway for the money."

"Wait a moment." Uncle Dong gestured for Laoda to sit down again and looked around at all of us. "I'm still worried about one thing—I think that anyone who sees this young lady will realize that she looks like a student from the city. And you," he turned to my great-aunt, "everyone will see at a glance that you come from the countryside. No matter what we do, we countryfolk seem to have a mark on us that tells people where we're from. When you and Baogu are together, you do not look like relatives. While you're travelling, someone might start asking questions, and if you don't give the right answers, they may think you've abducted her. That could lead to real trouble."

"I never thought of that!" groaned Great-aunt. She pounded her forehead with her fist in disappointment.

"I don't think it's important" said Laoda. "Uncle Dong has raised a good point, but if you and Baogu don't act nervous or confused and don't contradict each other, and tell the truth, which is, 'I'm taking my granddaughter to school,' if anyone does ask, you should be all right. Why shouldn't we countryfolks have a granddaughter from the city? Uncle Dong, what do you think?"

Uncle Dong merely grunted. He would not say it was all right and he would not say it was not all right.

"Of course! That's the perfect thing to say!" My great-aunt smiled and pointed to me. "If I say she's my granddaughter I won't be lying. In a way, she is."

"There's just one other detail." Laoda hesitated and then warned her, "Mother, you often talk a lot. But this time you must be very, very careful to keep your mouth shut. You mustn't talk too much."

"Really!" Great-aunt's face turned red and she seemed angry. "I'm no gossip! I speak only when I need to! When was the last time I spoke too much?"

"No, no! I'm just giving you a word of warning." Laoda hurriedly changed the subject. "Mother, do you have a better suit of clothes to wear on the journey?"

"I've been reluctant to wear that suit of light blue cotton broadcloth you had made for me last year because I thought it was too good to wear. I've had it on only two or three times, and it's only been washed once. There's another suit, of black cotton twill which is still quite new. They're both in the chest under my bed, but I'm afraid you won't be able to find them. It's better for me to go. It'll be safer. Now, is everything settled? All right." She rose and turned to my grandmother. "Elder sister, what about you? Are you coming with me?"

"I ... I want to stay with my little girl tonight."

"Then put the money away in a safe place. I'll be back before daybreak ... Oh, it's already after one in the morning!"

"Well after." Daya also stood up. "Step-aunt, will you get my five dollars from the teahouse as you go by?"

"All right."

Uncle Dong grunted again, knocked his bamboo pipe on the ground, and stuck it in his sash. Then he got to his feet and went over to the table. "Young lady," he told me, "may you have a favorable wind tomorrow and all the way. When you reach your aunt's, be sure to write us a letter so your grandmother and the rest of us need no longer worry."

I nodded, unable to speak. I felt so grateful to all of them, but I could not say a word.

Uncle Dong grunted once more and looked over at Laoda, who hurried to light the lantern and waited courteously near the door with Daya and my great-aunt to let Uncle Dong go out of gate first.

The lantern's light, their shadowy figures and the tapping of their cloth shoes on the path disappeared as they reached the other end of the long mound, and the countryside was once more wrapped in the silence of the dark night.

Chapter 36

MY great-aunt returned just before daybreak. She was carrying a bundle wrapped in a blue kerchief. Grandmother and I had slept on an improvised bed made up of several of the long benches pulled together, but had scarcely closed our eyes all night. Xiao Guizi cooked breakfast but we could swallow only a few mouthfuls of noodle soup. We put down our bowls and chopsticks and set off on our journey.

The morning breeze was gentle and, because summer was beginning to turn into autumn, it had a hint of cold in it. Fortunately, Great-aunt had been thoughtful enough to bring along one of her daughter-in-law's lined vests, which she loaned me. That and my lined coat were just right for keeping out the morning chill. The thatched roofs in the distance, the rice fields, and the mulberry trees all floated in the grey-white mist. We could hear the crowing of the cocks and the clear, crisp twittering of the birds as the day began to brighten.

Great-aunt and I reached the earthen mound. The pearls of heavy dew sparkled in the grass under our feet and soaked through our cloth shoes. When we reached the far end of the embankment, I turned around—Grandmother was still standing on a little pile of earth in front of Great-uncle's house. She was standing there all alone in those wide fields. I quickly turned away. My heart was filled with a sadness I could not express. I thought of all the fear and danger to which she had been subjected and how heavy a load she had carried for my sake. A person of merely ordinary courage could never have done it. But she had been firm and determined throughout. The night before, as we were going to bed she had told me that it would give me good luck on my long journey if there were no weeping when I left. But when I woke, I saw by the light of the oil lamp that her own eyelids were red and swollen. I knew that she had many reasons to grieve. I reminded her of her other granddaughter, Biying. If she had been able to take me to my aunt's she could have seen Biying again. It would have given her so much joy! But the past was too strong. My aunt would never forgive her for having remarried. So she had not seen Biying for twenty years, and now that I was leaving, she might never see me again either.

The night before, after everyone had left, I had given the Shaos' rings to her, so that if she were ever short of money she could sell them. I had thought, "She's so old, and has given me her life's savings. She has no son or daughter of her own to take care of her. If she has a little extra money it will make her more secure." But when my great-aunt had returned, Grandmother had put the rings into her stomach-purse along with the money for our journey and told her sister to fasten it carefully around her waist and to give me back the rings after we reached my aunt's home. No matter what I said, she would not keep them.

I stared down at my feet as I walked along and thought about Xiao Guizi. It seemed that the previous night was the first time she had clearly understood my situation. In the morning, she had crept over to me, slipped a little cloth bundle into my hand, and whispered, "I have nothing to give you but this red pinafore top. Mother made it for me several years ago at New Year's and I've never worn it. Please take it with you to remember me by." Then she sighed and said, "You are so fortunate. You're leaving misfortune behind you. Never in my whole life will I ever be able to think of being free."

I clasped her big work-roughened hand tightly. I knew that she meant every word and was speaking from her heart. I wished we could take her with us, but I knew it was impossible. After a long time I said only that I hoped she would never forget me, either, and she swore she never would.

The sun crept higher. Great-aunt and I trudged silently along the highways and winding lanes. About midday we saw a clump of thatched houses by the side of the road. Great-aunt said there was tea for sale there and suggested that we stop to rest our feet, wash our hands and drink a cup of tea before continuing our journey. She added that her daughter-in-law's mother lived in this area, but several *li* farther on. The sun was now beating down on our heads and I was perspiring. I wanted to change into lighter clothes so I immediately nodded my approval of Great-aunt's suggestion.

We stopped at the first house, a little country inn. An oblong wooden sign carved with big characters that read "Yong Xing Long" (Eternal and Abundant Prosperity) hung under the eaves. The red paper strips on the two leaves of the open gate were faded and tattered but the characters were still legible. One said, "Money and wealth are like dust and dung;" the other, "Benevolence and justice are worth a thousand gold pieces." Inside was a long counter and on the board partition behind it were several wooden shelves crowded with large and small tins, packets wrapped in paper, balls of twine and cotton yarn, and jars of peanuts, watermelon seeds, puffed-rice candy, tobacco and many other items. There were three square tables and ten or more long benches in the center of the room and a big clay stove near the rear wall. The inn not only offered a place where travellers could lay their pallets on the ground and sleep, but also sold noodles, rice and many other daily necessities. No one was at the counter. A woman was sitting by the stove feeding the fire. She was about forty and appeared to be the innkeeper's wife. Great-aunt led me in and sat down at the table furthest from the door. She set her bundle on the bench beside her. The innkeeper's wife came over immediately, smiled at us, and asked us what we wanted to eat.

"Please bring us two cups of tea." Great-aunt took out her handkerchief and wiped the sweat from her forehead and face. She asked, "Do you have any food prepared? We got up early this morning and haven't eaten for many hours."

"We have plain rice and rice fried with eggs. We have noodles cooked with salted vegetables and shredded pork, or with minced scallions."

Great-aunt ordered two bowls of noodles with scallions.

The innkeeper's wife was about to turn away when Great-aunt stood up and whispered something to her. The woman nodded and beckoned us into a dark room, partitioned off from the main room by thin boards, which contained a big wooden bed. We put down our bundles and she immediately brought us a small wooden basin of warm water and half a soapberry pod. First Great-aunt and then I washed our faces and hands. Then we took out our unlined clothes and changed. We immediately felt more comfortable. When we came back out into the big room, two steaming cups of tea were waiting for us, and by the time we had drunk half of it, the innkeeper's wife had brought us our noodles. She looked us over and asked the natural question, "Where are you going?"

"I'm taking my granddaughter to visit relatives," my great-aunt answered curtly. She did not look up but gulped down the noodles, took out the handkerchief in which she kept her change, and asked the innkeeper's wife for the bill. As soon as she had paid and we had finished our tea, my great-aunt hurried us away without saying another word.

She had spoken to only one other person that morning. We had been winding along so many little roads that she had lost her sense of direction and had asked a man we met coming towards us how we could get to the highway.

"Get to the highway? Where are you going?" asked the man who was carrying jars of rice wine on the ends of his pole. It was a friendly, routine question.

"Where are we going?" Great-aunt had repeated, keeping her face wooden. "To the highway." She was determined not to let him know we were going to Lugang. I thought to myself that she was being very cautious and that her son had been more anxious than necessary in warning her the night before.

The rest, food and change of clothes gave us renewed strength. The paths we were following were almost deserted, and most of the people we met looked like country villagers. Sometimes we met bamboo sedan chairs and wheelbarrows, or businessmen on horses or mules, and sometimes we met little bands of soldiers in their grey uniforms. But they all seemed to hurry by and no one paid any attention to us.

After about an hour, we reached a little market town where the main street was lined with low brick houses. Great-aunt said this was where her in-laws lived, and that since we were there she wanted to take the opportunity to see them. She led me to a house where an old woman, about sixty or seventy, was sitting on the threshold drying bamboo shoots and soybeans. When she saw us, she set down her big, round basket and greeted us with smiles. She ushered us into the house and said it was a pity that her daughter-in-law had taken the children visiting and would not be back until evening. She insisted that we drink some tea before continuing our journey.

Although Great-aunt had been careful not to talk with strangers, now that she was with a relative, she relaxed and became trustful. When the old woman said it had been six months since they had seen each other and asked who I was and where we were going, I was surprised that Great-aunt spilled out the whole story. In an indignant voice, she recounted all that had happened to me and how the Shaos had people watching everywhere so that we had to take a circuitous route, and how we were going to get tickets and go by boat—I kept wanting to stop her, but did not feel I could. But when I realized she was going to describe all the details of our route, I went over to her and pulled on the corner of her coat. She turned and told me, "It's all right. She's a relative. I know what I'm doing."

After the old woman heard the whole story, she came over to me and took both my hands in her own and, shaking her head, sighed and said she felt sorry for me. She then started towards the kitchen to make us some food, but my Great-aunt stood up and said it was late and that we had to go on. She gave the old woman a message to her in-laws. "Tell her not to worry, that everyone in the family, old and young, is well and happy. Come to see us when you are not busy." Still chatting, we finally left the house, but I kept worrying until the town was behind us and we were back on the highway. It was fortunate that Great-aunt had no other relatives on the last part of the overland journey and met no one she knew, because she did not know this area as well and we had to keep to the main roads. She became very cautious again, and stopped speaking except to ask me anxiously from time to time if I was too tired to go on. I hated having only feet, and not wings. I could not let myself be weary. I could only keep my eyes on the ground, muster all my energy, and keep on going.

The highway went up hills and down and seemed endless. The trees that lined the road and the fields were soft green and golden-yellow, and some were as red as fire. In the clear light of early autumn, the clouds and mountain colors were reflected in the gently-rippling streams and ponds dotted with wild ducks. Heaven and earth were in complete harmony. It was as beautiful as a picture—but my great-aunt and I had no time or serenity to enjoy the scenery.

We walked and walked, but still the road stretched before us. The deep-red sun sank gradually behind the distant mountains. There were fewer and fewer people on the road and as darkness fell the countryside grew even quieter. Great-aunt took my hand and murmured reassuringly, "Child, don't worry. It's not far now. We'll soon be there." Without realizing it, we both clutched our bundles more tightly and began walking in the center of the highway. We wanted to walk faster, but our feet and legs were too tired, aching and weak. We continued walking until it was quite dark. We were both growing more and more anxious. Suddenly we saw a patch of light in the distance. Great-aunt sighed with relief and said, "It's all right now, child. We've reached Lugang."

"We've reached Lugang! Now I'm finally out of reach of the Shaos!" My heart was pounding with joy, but I dared not say anything, because when hope first appears we tend to fear it will disappear, and I was afraid if I said anything disaster would overtake us and my fortune be turned into misfortune. But when I finally looked at Great-aunt in the pale cool light of the newly-risen moon that hung in the tree branches, I saw that her lips, which she had kept compressed the whole way, were now relaxed and slightly parted.

Lugang, a little county town, was much smaller than Wuhu. It had only two main streets, which were brightly-lit and busy. My great-aunt avoided the main streets and threaded us through the smaller streets, as Laoda had directed, to a small inn across the road from the river. There she asked for the least expensive room. The attendant, with a tiny glass lamp in one hand and a big teapot with a broken spout in the other, led us to a tiny, windowless back room that smelled of mold and rot. It contained a little wooden bed covered with a straw mat and surrounded by grimy, yellowed curtains. There was also a small square table and two broken wooden chairs. A rusty metal washstand stood behind the door. The interior three walls were thin board partitions covered with impromptu poems and folk sayings. The slanting, crooked lines of the characters told of the sadness and depression of the guests who had been stranded there.

Great-aunt told the waiter to bring us some prepared food and to buy us a piece of bean curd cured in soy sauce. After she washed her face and drank a few mouthfuls of tea, she went to the office to inquire about boats. Luck was with us, because she returned with a smile on her face and told me a steamboat would be leaving for Datong at daybreak. We hurried through dinner and went to bed right afterwards. My great-aunt pulled the chairs and the washstand over against the door to make us feel safer.

As the night deepened, the inn grew quiet, but the same could not be said of our bed! Just as we were on the verge of falling asleep, we were attacked by legions of bedbugs and fleas. Because I had walked all day and had not gotten much sleep the night before, I fell asleep as soon as my head touched the pillow, but not my poor great-aunt. She tossed and turned but could not close her eyes. From time to time she would sit up with the oil lamp in one hand and catch the bugs and fleas. She started at her end of the bed and then she hunted for them under me, waking me up. By two o'clock, there was a little mountain of dead insects piled up inside the chimney of the oil lamp. Then, just as she was about to lie down to sleep, a light suddenly shone through the cracks in the partition from the front room and we heard men talking and laughing. Then we heard tables and benches being pushed around, followed by the clack of mahjongg tiles and coughing and spitting. Then the smell of cigarettes drifted into the room. As if there was not enough confusion, a while later we heard someone playing the *erhu* and a woman began to sing. Her voice was soft and low, and she sang a ballad about love and longing. At first she sang loudly enough that we could make out all the words:

"When first we met—hardhearted man
We knew we'd loved in lives before.
I loved you for your bright eyes
By which my passions you did rouse.

"How could I know how bold you are and daring?
You burst at midnight into my chamber
Oh, at midnight you burst into my chamber!

"And kneeling down you begged me
Little me, my heart said yes
But the words would not come out of my mouth.

"Yet how you used
Words of beauty and guile
Until you had me coaxed into your arms!"

As she went on, her voice grew softer, as if she were weeping quietly, and I could no longer make out the words. But then, as she reached the last lines of the song, I could hear her sing:

"Oh, my beloved, my hardhearted man,
What have I done to displease you?"

And the man's rough voice would answer, "Oh, my little sister, my little heart and soul, your singing has made your lover ache!" And then the others would all shout with laughter.

It sounded as if they were minor military officers who had taken a room for the night to play mahjongg and be entertained by sing-song girls.

The bedbugs and fleas had not bothered me much, but the noise made it impossible to sleep. Great-aunt kept sighing and complaining in a whisper, "Soldiers! They're all scum! Beasts!"

But it seemed that because they were officers, neither the inkeeper nor any of the other guests dared complain. The commotion continued until almost dawn, when I saw the light beginning to come through the skylight and realized the sounds of voices and mahjongg tiles had stopped. Our lamps had long since burned out. Great-aunt and I did not dare sleep. Before long, the attendant tapped on our door and said that if we wanted to catch the steamboat we should get up. We rose immediately, washed hastily, combed our hair, and, without even taking time to drink any tea, took our bundles, and left the inn.

A grey-white morning mist lay over the Yangtze River. The air was humid and heavy. We could see several little boats anchored near the river bank, but we could not even make out the shape of the steamer. The bank was dotted with small stands that sold breakfast foods, and men and women passengers, with bundles on their shoulders and children in their arms, crowded around. We knew it was too early to board the steamer and we wanted to avoid the crowd. We sat down on a pile of lumber some distance away. Before long, a little boy carrying a basket came over shouting, "Hot sesame cakes, hot doughnuts! Just off the stove!" Great-aunt took out some money and bought four sesame cakes and two long fried doughnuts, all still warm. Then she went to a nearby stand and bought two big bowls of the steaming, fragrant, soybean milk. We sat on the lumber and ate our breakfast.

Soon we heard the sound of the whistle. It was the first call for the passengers. By now the mist had started to burn off and we could glimpse a big smokestack, half red and half black and belching black smoke, in the middle of the river. The passengers immediately rushed forward and crowded into the little boats near the bank. Great-aunt and I were among them. The boatman waited until every inch of space was filled and then shoved off. The little boats sculled forward, rocking and bouncing on the water. Just as we reached the steamer, all the passengers stood up. The little boat almost tipped over and water began coming in. It looked as if we were going to sink, and again there was great confusion. But with great difficulty, Great-aunt and I scrambled out of the boat and squeezed into the crowd on the steamer. We seized an empty spot just inside the entrance to the third-class cabin, put down our bundles and sat on the floor.

We stayed there until late that night when the steamer reached Datong.

Chapter 37

IN Datong our luck was not as good as it had been in Lugang. We spent four days and four nights in a small inn there before a steamer left for Hankou.

I will never forget that time in the inn. Although Datong was larger and more prosperous than Lugang, the inn was not that different. We spent our days and nights surrounded by the same kind of flimsy wood partitions, spotted and dirty, and when I woke at night it was in the light of the same kind of sputtering oil lamp. During the day I could read the same kinds of verses and popular sayings that had been written, who knew how long ago, in everyday language and often incorrectly, by the nameless people who had been marooned there. Those words, which told of their aching hearts and disappointments, made me feel that every place on earth was full of people who had suffered bitterness and oppression.

Great-aunt and I did not dare step outside the door. We crouched in our dirty, dark little room as if we were in a prison cell. The depression we felt was suffocating and almost indescribable.

Two weeks had already gone by since I had escaped from the Shaos. By now they would have received Father's reply and would know that I had not gone to Shanghai. They might guess that I would be trying to get to my aunt's, and they might also guess my route. If they moved fast, they could overtake me. I was already far from home—if they should find us here, among strangers and in a strange city, we would not have anyone to turn to for help or anywhere to hide. Great-aunt said nothing, but I guessed from the tension in her face and the continued frown she wore that she too was worrying about these possibilities. Sometimes I wanted to talk with her about them, to ask her what we should do if the Shaos were to catch up with us and try to block us from boarding the steamer. But we both seemed to want to avoid even mentioning the name Shao. If I tried to say anything, Great-aunt would immediately interrupt, "Child, it can't happen. Heaven will protect us and let us get onto the steamer in peace, and once the boat is on its way we'll have passed another milestone and the worst of this difficult journey will be over." But she would sigh, and her frown would grow even deeper.

We finally left our prison-like room at the inn at dusk on the fourth day. We walked along the dark, wet street that ran alongside the river to the pier. We were both breathing fast with fear and dared not to lift our heads as we pushed through the crowds boarding the big steamer. We found the third-class cabin. Under the dim light cast by a few bulbs in the ceiling we saw a scene of great confusion. All the new passengers were busy seizing places for their bedrolls, while the passengers who were already on board were busy bargaining with the peddlers who had come to sell local products. Fortunately, we did not see a single familiar face, and no one took any special notice of us. Great-aunt and I found an upper and lower berth against the hull. We put down our bundles, sat quietly on the lower berth, and did not move. It was only after the whistle had blown, and the peddlers and well-wishers had all left the ship and the steward had looked at our tickets after we started moving that my great-aunt finally relaxed. She sighed in relief, stood up, and patted her clothes with both hands as if she could brush away all the worries and fears of the last few days. Then she went to the steward and rented two quilts. I helped her make up the berths. The quilts were small, dirty, and yellow. We folded the quilts in two so we could have half under us as a mattress and half above. We had no pillows, but Great-aunt divided her bundle of clothes into two parts as substitutes. I slipped off my cloth shoes and climbed into the upper berth. Great-aunt slept in the lower berth. The steady sound of the ship's engines and the lapping of the water against the hull gradually helped us to relax.

I was awakened at dawn by the coughing of the passenger in the berth across from me and by the sound of the steward as he brought washing water into the cabin. I sat up and looked out of the porthole above my berth. The river breeze was damp and salty. Tiny waves pushed against the ship and flew upward into countless clean white blossoms of foam. I was looking out onto the Yangtze. It was so wide I could not see the banks. I felt that Great-aunt had been right—the hardest part of our long journey was over. Now I really had escaped from the Shaos and left my home region and old way of life far behind. It was the first time in the two weeks since I had run away that I felt even a little security. I felt my lips curve in a small, involuntary smile of relief and happiness. It seemed that Great-aunt felt the same way, for when I crawled out of my bunk I saw that her frown had disappeared. But we dared not be careless. We huddled on Great-aunt's narrow bunk all day and did not move a step except to go and wash our hands.

The only other women passengers in the third-class cabin were an old woman and a young mother holding an infant three sections away. They looked as if they were all members of the same family. Like us, they moved around very little and spoke to no one. The rest of the passengers looked like small businessmen or peddlers. Most of them went out to the deck after breakfast to chat and to watch the scenery. It was said that the scenery along this stretch of the river was most exotic and beautiful. Some of the passengers passed the time by playing cards with the stewards. There was also one old man of fifty or so in the upper berth at the foot of mine who liked to drink wine. All day along he would sit alone with his legs hanging over the edge of the berth and a small rice bowl full of wine in his lap. He also had a packet of peanuts and another of cured bean curd that he would nibble on as he drank. After a few sips of wine he would get very talkative. Sometimes he would climb down from his berth and offer peanuts to the other passengers. Whenever my great-aunt saw him coming towards us, she would make her face expressionless and shake her head, refusing to say a word to him. After he had offered us peanuts several times, he stopped coming.

In the lower berth opposite us, there was a middle-aged man with a yellow face who lay sleeping all day. He paid no attention to anyone and no one paid any attention to him. In the evening, when everyone else was preparing for bed, he woke up, called the steward and whispered a few words into his ear. Soon the steward brought him an opium tray and lit the lamp for him. After a few puffs of opium and some tea, he became more wide-awake. Because his berth was less than two feet from ours, the smell of the opium floated over to us. Great-aunt and I did not dare complain; all we could do was to put our handkerchiefs to our noses. He did not seem to notice, but he did notice that we were women and kept eyeing us. Once I woke up in the middle of the night and saw that he was still lying beside the lamp and staring at it. When he saw me lift my head, he bared his yellow teeth and leered at me. I quickly turned over with my back towards him and pulled the quilt over my head. I no longer cared how sour and dirty it smelled. Fortunately, when we woke the next morning he was gone. He had probably left the ship at Jiujiang. Two teenaged boys who looked as if they were on their way to school were sharing his berth.

I had been the only young person in the third-class cabin. All the other passengers were middle-aged or older. The two young men, with their constant talk and laughter and whistling of popular tunes and running around inside and outside the cabin, enlivened the scene. They seemed to be interested in me because I was a student too, and kept smiling in our direction. I did not mind but my great-aunt became very uneasy when she realized that they were paying attention to us. Her expression became even more forbidding than when she had rebuffed the old man who drank, but this did not seem to worry them. At lunch time they looked over at us and talked between themselves for a while. Then one of them came over with a pottery jar in both hands and invited us to share the food they had brought with them from home. Great-aunt shook her head and snapped "Thank you, but we have our own." He then offered the food to me. I shook my head, too, but I could not stop myself from smiling an apology. I knew it would not be proper for me to say anything. I also knew that Great-aunt was treating him coldly not only because she wanted nothing to do with strangers, but even more because young men and women must be kept apart. If the two students came over and started talking with me, everyone in the cabin would have noticed and it would have caused gossip. I wished that Great-aunt had treated him a bit more gently, but he did not seem to mind. He went back to his schoolmate, shook his head, smiled, and said something amusing in English. When Great-aunt heard him speak in a foreign language, she looked even more displeased. The two did not dare come over to speak with us again.

The steamer was to have reached Hankou about nine or ten o'clock in the evening, but it did not arrive until after two in the morning. None of the passengers had slept and we all had long since gotten our baggage ready and were sitting and waiting. Great-aunt and I had changed our clothes, shoes, and socks, and were sitting on her berth. As the steamer entered the slip at the customs house pier we saw many men swarming onto the ship from little wooden boats that crowded around like bees. Each man was holding up a sign with the name of the inn he represented and they all ran around shouting and seizing the passengers' baggage. It was a scene of chaos, and the intonations of the people's speech were different from what I was used to. Great-aunt and I felt nervous and bewildered and did not know what to do. Fortunately the other student came over and asked us if we were planning to stay at an inn. Great-aunt shook her head. He told us that there was always much confusion when the ship docked and that once it tied up there would be an even bigger crowd. He said it would be best for us to follow them when we left the boat. They would watch out for us. This time my great-aunt accepted his kindness, nodded, and said, "Thank you very much."

When the steamer docked, one of them led and the other followed, with us in between. We slowly pushed through the crowd and onto land. The students wanted to hire a horse carriage for us but Great-aunt did not want them to learn where we were going. She said hastily, "It's not necessary. We can do that for ourselves." She grabbed my hand and pulled me across the street. A horse carriage was coming towards us. We waved at the driver and before the carriage had even stopped completely we climbed inside. We heard the two students, who were still standing on the other side of the street, call to us, "See you again!" I looked out and waved to them. The driver asked us where we wanted to go. I could not remember my aunt's address, but I told him to take us to Xiude Girls' School, on Sanming Lane in the French concession. The driver asked no more questions but just raised his whip and his horses' hooves began clop-clopping slowly along the wide cement-paved streets.

Things and places seen in childhood can look very different to grown-up eyes. I remembered my aunt's school as a large, three-story, foreign-style building of red brick, with a wide archway that led into the lane. When the carriage stopped beside a low, narrow gateway and a faded red-brick house I thought the driver had made a mistake, but the signboard carved with green-painted characters was clearly visible in the weak light of the street lamp. I jumped out of the carriage and ran to the gate—I had seen through its two black-lacquered leaves more times than I could count when I was young. At first I dared not pound on the gate, but merely tapped the iron ring against it a couple of times. The house was dark and no one answered. I knocked several more times, but there was still no sound from inside. I had no choice but to pound on the gate with my fists. Great-aunt paid the driver and then came over and helped me pound. A head appeared at one of the third-floor windows. "Who is it? Who's pounding on the gate in the middle of the night?"

"It's Baogu!" I could not see the face, but I could not mistake that voice, with its Hubei accent. It was my aunt, whom I had not seen for seven or eight years. "Please! Come down quickly and open the gate!"

"Baogu! Is it really you? Have you really come? Mrs. Liu! Hurry and get up! Go and open the gate! We have guests! My child, how did you get here? Are you alone? Did someone bring you? Just yesterday, I got a letter from your father!"

Before I could answer, a light shone between the leaves of the gate and the doors grated open. A yawning maidservant of about forty ushered us in and led us up the narrow stairs to the third floor. My aunt was standing at the top of the stairs. She was dressed as usual in a grey gown but had not had time to fasten all the buttons. She did not seem much changed, but was somewhat plumper and had some grey hair at her temples.

"Oh! It's Aunt! I would never have imagined that you would have come here. I was very surprised by Baogu's father's letter. I never expected her to come here to me."

My great-aunt sighed. She and my aunt had not seen each other for almost twenty years, and now the unexpected meeting had moved them so much that they could not speak. Aunt led us to her room. Soon Mrs. Liu came in with hot towels and tea for us. My aunt and great-aunt talked a little about the difficulties of the journey and of what had happened during the years they had been apart. I then heard the sound of slippers, and a beautiful, graceful young woman came into the room followed by a tall thin man of about thirty. As soon as I saw her, I recognized my cousin Biying, and knew that the man had to be her husband. My aunt introduced us. My great-aunt went to Biying and took her hands. She looked at her searchingly and smiled, but had to take out her handkerchief to wipe away her tears. We all sat down, and my aunt asked us why we had come so unexpectedly.

My great-aunt sighed deeply and turned to look at me. She had to hold back her tears as she recounted everything that had happened to me. Her emotions came through in her voice, which was soft and mournful in the silence of the dead of night. We all felt her sadness—even I could not have told it so movingly. My aunt, Biying, and her husband listened intently, and when she had finished, they all sat in silence for a while. Great-aunt gestured at me and told my aunt earnestly, "Now I'm placing her in your hands. You must not let your duty to others interfere and you must not heed anyone else. You must carry out your duty to your dead husband and to her dead mother—help her and take her in! She has nowhere else to go, no other relative. If you turn her away, if you send her back, she will kill herself."

My aunt remained silent. She looked at me and then at her own daughter. After a long time she too sighed deeply and said, "I never imagined that this child would be so unfortunate ... losing her mother when she was so small. For all these years, I've heard nothing. Now, suddenly, I got a letter from her father saying that she had disappeared. I was surprised. Why should a fifteen-year-old girl disappear for no reason? I knew there had to be a reason, but I never thought it would be that! Imagine —sending her to another family's home as a child bride!"

There was another silence. From the street came the sounds of horses' hooves, the wheels of heavy carts, wooden tubs bumping against each other and water being poured. The city was waking up. The street cleaners and workers who took away the garbage and night soil had come.

My aunt stood up and said, "Aunt, it will soon be dawn. You must be weary from your long journey. Go and sleep, and I will talk with my daughter and son-in-law. We'll think of a way to help this little girl. Don't worry—we won't add to her sufferings. It has been almost twenty years since we last met and I would like you to stay here with us for a while. You can meet your great-grandson. He'll cheer you up—he's only three, and very lovable. You'll see him later in the day." As she was talking, Biying and Mrs. Liu set up two cots for us in the back room.

Both my aunt and Biying went downstairs to teach early the next day. They were too busy to talk with us, and we were worried about what my aunt would decide. Sometimes we stood at the window on the third floor and watched the gay, busy scenes on the street below, and sometimes we played with Biying's little son. Although I did not know what my aunt and the others would decide, I thought from what she had said that she probably would not send me away.

In the late afternoon, after school was out and all the students had gone, and after dinner, when the day's activities were winding down, my aunt told Mrs. Liu to brew a pot of tea. She had all of us sit down at the table in the living room. Then she pulled down the electric light overhead, put on a pair of silver-rimmed glasses, and picked up two sheets of thin red-lined writing paper. It was the letter she had written to my father.

Chapter 38

Although my aunt had always had a reputation for complete honesty, she had broken the habits of a lifetime and lied in her letter to my father. After first showing concern and surprise that I was lost, she had then asked questions. She had written, "In my humble opinion it is almost unimaginable that my deceased sister-in-law's only daughter should have had to face so much misfortune. If she comes here to me, I will of course keep her safely and look after her, and write to you immediately to inform you. If she does not come and meets with misfortune, it would shame the family. Not only that, but how would we ever pacify my deceased sister's spirit?"

After reading the letter, my aunt explained it to my great-aunt, who had not quite understood the formal style my aunt had used. Then she said, "If it were not that the Shaos have the law on their side and that we would not be able to protect Baogu if the story gets out, I would prefer to stand up and speak out on her behalf and make the Shaos face what they have done. I'd like for them to learn that the Lu family is not to be trifled with. Aunt, what do you think of the letter? Is there anything you'd like me to add?"

"No, nothing. What you wrote is well thought-out. We couldn't have put it into words so fully or so well. So how could I have anything to add?" She turned to me and sighed, "My poor child, you've been very unlucky, but your good fortune in having such a talented and kind aunt must be the result of your having led a virtuous life in a previous incarnation. Now that you're here, you don't need to worry any longer and your grandmother and I will feel reassured about you."

"But as my son-in-law says, she can't stay here too long." My aunt looked over at him. He said nothing and kept his face expressionless. "He's right—if the two families still fail to locate her, her father and grandfather will probably come here to look for her. So I can't guarantee that she'll be safe here in my home. But we can work out a permanent plan in a few days. For now, she can stay here." As she spoke, she sealed the letter. Then she called Mrs. Liu and told her to go to the post office the next morning and to send the letter by registered mail.

My great-aunt felt very reassured when she saw that my aunt was taking over. But after three or four days, she began to worry about how things were at home. She decided to return to Wuhu before a final decision had been reached about where I was to go. During her stay, however, she and my aunt would sit in my aunt's room and drink tea and chat about their relatives and friends and times gone by. But they never mentioned my mother's mother because my aunt had already told my great-aunt, "I'm very happy that you've come here, but I implore you never to mention Biying's grandmother." On the day she was leaving, however, my great-aunt could no longer hold in her feelings. After several false starts, she managed to tell my aunt a little about Grandmother's loneliness and isolation, and about her longing to see Biying.

My aunt listened silently but made no reply, nor did she reveal what she might have been feeling. But that afternoon, after she returned from buying my great-aunt's steamship ticket and some food for the trip, I saw her go into Biying's room. She slipped some bills into Biying's hand and told her, "Child, wait a while until I'm not around and then give this twenty dollars to your great-aunt and tell her that you're sending it to your grandmother, behind my back, to use as she likes."

The same evening, before my great-aunt left, I gave her my rings and asked her to take them back to my grandmother. My great-aunt promised my aunt that once she returned home, her son Laoda would write to us immediately if they learned of any movements on the part of the Shaos or my grandfather. In return, my aunt promised to write as soon as my affairs were settled. Then she and Biying went with my great-aunt to see her off at the ship. I could not go. I could only stand at the third-floor window and watch until their carriage disappeared among the throngs of passersby.

Less than a week later my aunt received two special-delivery letters from my grandfather. They resembled my father's letter but included the story of my engagement and my move to the Shaos' household. He begged my aunt to take me in and care for me if I came to her and to write immediately so that the Shaos could immediately send someone to get me. My aunt answered him the way she had answered my father and denied that I was there. Her tone in this letter was even more emphatic than in the one to Father: "I think that any fair-minded person would have to conclude that Baogu was driven away by her persecution by the Shao family. And if she comes to any harm I will stand on my legal rights and demand justice from the Shaos." In the meantime, she kept looking for another place for me because she felt it would be too dangerous for me to stay there.

One Saturday morning, when there were no classes, she took me into the little back storeroom after breakfast. She closed the door and we sat down side by side on an old carved red lacquered chest. She told me earnestly that she wanted me to feel safe and that she would treat me as she treated Biying. The only thing lacking, she said, was "the ten months I carried you in my body." She also said she would do her very best to make arrangements for me because it was the only way she would be able to face her late husband and my mother. Then she said that before she could decide what to do, she had to ask me some questions. I was to answer truthfully and not hide anything.

Although she and Biying had treated me with nothing but sympathy and kindness, Biying's husband had seemed cool towards me. I sensed that he did not approve of my aunt keeping me. Once while we were talking he came right out and said that the Shaos' treatment of me could not have been as bad as my great-aunt described it. There seemed to be areas in which my aunt and her son-in-law were not in agreement. I had been feeling uneasy about this all during my stay, and I had become even more uncomfortable when my aunt told me she needed to have a serious talk with me. For all I knew, she might have changed her mind about keeping me. So I said nothing, but listened quietly to her questions.

"Child," she said, patting me on the shoulder, "I must ask you if you have any plan for your future. What about Zhongyao —what about the two of you? Is there any affection between you? Biying and I asked your great-aunt but she did not know. All she could tell us was that your grandfather had said that, after you left, Zhongyao shut himself in his room and wept. I must ask you whether you still hope to marry him. I must know these things if I am to make plans for you."

Ever since I had run away from the Shaos, I had had neither the time nor the energy to make any plans for my future. My only idea was to escape. But when my aunt asked me whether I still wanted to marry Zhongyao, I realized I had long since made up my mind. I had made my decision the moment I had determined to run away. So I turned and looked at her pale, kind, and gentle face, and stated, "No matter what happens, I will never willingly enter the Shaos' house again. Not only do I not want to marry Zhongyao—I don't want to marry *anyone*. I want to remain single. I'll never marry anyone."

My aunt frowned slightly and shook her head.

"Aunt, I'm telling you how I really feel. Every single word is true." She kept on shaking her head, and that made me even more anxious. "Aunt, if you don't believe me, send me to a Christian convent or a Buddhist nunnery. I'd willingly enter a convent or a nunnery, but I will not go back to his home and marry him."

She sighed and said, "There, there, don't worry. I believe you. You're still too young to understand. And no matter what happens, I'm not going to send you to a convent or a nunnery or anywhere else. You're talking this way because you've been hurt. It will pass. If I took you seriously and sent you off to a cloister now, you'd always regret it, and you'd blame me, too."

"Regret it? Blame her?" I thought. "Perhaps I am young, but I've already suffered so much on account of marriage that I'm clear in my own mind. Look at Biying—so intelligent, so beautiful, with such a good, wise mother to love her. Her marriage should be full of happiness and contentment, but I've seen her husband get angry at her and I've seen her, sitting in her room silently wiping away tears while her little son hid his face in her lap and cried. I've seen that in a society that favors men and treats women lightly and gives parents complete control over arranging marriages it is difficult for marriages to be satisfactory."

"Child, do you understand that I'm right?" My aunt interrupted my train of thought.

I shook my head but did not answer. She sighed again.

"Oh, child, life isn't that simple. It's not that easy. Some day you'll understand what I'm saying. There's no need to decide anything now about your getting married. We can wait a few years to talk about it—it won't be too late. I asked about the Shao boy because I need to know if you care for each other and what you want to do. It isn't that I must make decisions and act right now. It's that in order to plan I must first understand."

She thought for a while and then sighed again, this time as if from the depths of her heart. "I've already made one big mistake that I'll never be able to undo. I've made lifelong trouble for Biying because I did not send her to college to learn a profession.

I was wrong—I thought that all I needed to do was choose a good husband for her, a man of ability who'd be willing to come here so she would not have to be a daughter-in-law in another home. I thought that that way our family name would survive, that even if the man were poor or older, it would not matter. I never considered Biying's wishes. Poor girl! She was such a dutiful daughter! When she came back from the meeting arranged by the matchmaker she said, 'Mother, did you see how cruel he looked? He frightened me!' I thought she said it because she was young and bashful, and I ignored her.... Oh, my poor child! Now, the rest of her life ..."

She fell silent and tried to calm herself. "Their first year of marriage, there was no trouble between them. But then he began staying out all night gambling, and we have not had a peaceful day since. Our home is not a home and our school is no longer a school. After the years of trials and tribulations I had endured since I was left a widow, now almost all my savings, the little I had managed to scrape together, has gone to pay his gambling debts. I don't know how much longer we can maintain our home and keep the school open, no matter how hard we try. If it were not for my little grandson it would be much easier."

"I'm going to tell you this so you can understand why I feel so strongly about this and why I must be so very, very careful. Biying and I have talked things over many times these past few days. If you don't want to marry the Shao boy, it will be best for us to house you somewhere safe and quiet for two or three years. That way, any changes in our lives here would not affect you. Also, if we can keep you out of the way for a year or two, the Shaos will find another wife for Zhongyao and the matter will be settled. They won't wait forever. It looks to me as if the Shaos are trying to keep up appearances and hush things up. Otherwise, wouldn't they have long since advertised for you in the papers?

"But I'm having trouble deciding where to send you. If my life were still the same as before, it would be easy to send you to a good private girls' school in another province for a couple of years. Now I can no longer talk that way ... But I've had a stroke of good luck—your aunt from the Gu side of the family has been a friend of mine for more than ten years. She is a person who believes in fighting every kind of injustice. Last night I went specially to talk over your situation with her. She immediately offered to help and said that very fortunately her son-in-law had just been appointed to a position in Changsha. I've heard that there are several public normal schools there that don't cost much, and also a school that teaches girls to spin. There's also a big hospital, run by Chinese and Americans both, with a medical school and a school for training nurses. Aunt Gu said we could send you there to learn to be a nurse. All you'd need is a little financial backing and some spending money. I think nursing would be a good specialty for you—it's a profession that can always be relied on. But I'm afraid you're still too young. Usually they only take students who are at least eighteen. Also, the work might be too hard for you, you're so thin. Maybe it'd be better for you to attend normal school for a year or two. Then, if you still wanted to study nursing, it wouldn't be too late. Aunt Gu also said that her son-in-law has just found a house in Changsha and that she was sending a servant to take her daughter's furniture and possessions to her. If we decide you should go to Changsha, you could go with that person. Aunt Gu would tell her daughter to look after you and that would ease my mind. What do you think? Take some time to think it over, and give me an answer."

What my aunt had just told me was better than I had ever expected, first, because I had never even dreamed I would have the opportunity to go to school again, and second, because my aunt was trying so hard to take care of me despite her own difficult circumstances. I felt very grateful, but also troubled. For a while I could say nothing because I was so busy thinking about how to keep my expenses down so I would not be too much a burden to her. I thought that learning nursing was a good plan. It would not cost too much and I would learn a special profession. I did not need any more time to think about it. I exclaimed, "Aunt, I do want to study nursing. I'm thin only because I didn't have any care when I was recovering from my illness. Once I settle down safely somewhere, I'll gain back the weight I lost. I can work hard and I like to work hard. I'm not old enough, but I'm tall—I can always add a few years to my age. Aunt, I've always wanted to learn a profession and to be like you, to live alone and not have to depend on anyone else. This is the very best opportunity I could have. Don't worry, dear Aunt, send me there to study, and when I get there, I'll devote all my strength to learning so I can become a useful adult."

My aunt did not wait until I had finished before standing up and opening the door. "Biying! Biying!" she called. "Come here! Come and listen to what your younger sister is saying."

My aunt's face looked happy and less tense, and that gave me even more courage. When Biying came in, I repeated what I had just said, but even more firmly. This was the first time in my two weeks at my aunt's that I was able to speak my mind without fear.

Biying was standing near the door with one hand on the brass doorknob and fiddling with the off-white braided silk shoulder button of her blue silk gown. Her soft black hair hung down loose and shining behind her high curved collar and her green jade earrings. Her eyebrows were delicate. She looked just as I remembered, but now that she was married and a mother, she seemed more mature, gentler, and calmer. When she had heard me out, she tilted her head and smiled at my aunt. "Mother, I told you that Baogu does not lack ambition. This is the best decision we could make. Take advantage of the weekend, go back to Aunt Gu and talk it over again. Find out what we should do, and when the maid is leaving. Aunt Gu's daughter has not been married long, so we should not cause her too much trouble."

My aunt too was smiling. "Of course. I'll go this afternoon and take Baogu with me to meet her. Biying, come and help me look through the clothes boxes. Your poor little sister has no clothes at all, and it will soon start turning colder. I think that some of your old clothes are too small for you. We should be able to find some lined and padded, and even some lighter things, for her to wear. She carried a chair over to the upper cupboards and was standing on it to open them when she thought of something else. "One more thing ... We must give Baogu another name for this journey. It would be best if we even changed her surname. Biying, think quickly, think of a suitable name."

This did not take much time. They talked it over and soon decided that I should use their surname Lu and in my given name I should, according to custom, take part of my cousin's name, and be called Biling (Azure Bell). From that moment on my aunt said, I was to be called Lu Biling and should count myself as having been adopted by her.

My aunt's adopted daughter! Another thing I had never even dreamed of! "Lu Biling, Lu Biling." I kept repeating it to myself and thought it indeed sounded as melodious as a bell. I could not help laughing out loud in delight.

My aunt also laughed. "Second child," she said, "your smile is like your mother's. I see her in you. It's a good smile and should be smiled often. You're at the age when young people should laugh and be happy."

Biying joined in our laughter and cautioned me playfully, "Younger sister, from now on you must remember not to call her Aunt any more. You must call her Mother, as I do."

Mother! The word rang out in my heart, but I was too bashful to say it. I looked at the pleased and loving smiles on their faces and I wanted to run over, hold out both arms, and hug them tightly. But when I stood up, I saw that my aunt was taking two suits of clothes out of a box. So I put out my hands and she gave me a coat-and-trousers suit of leek-green brocaded silk lined with flannel and a coat-and-skirt suit of fine, light-blue linen.

I felt as if the clouds that had been hanging over my life had been blown away by the wind. I felt Zhou Baogu and her whole unhappy, sorrowful life had ended.

Now I was Lu Biling and a new way of life was opening before me.

Chapter 39

WHEN I left my aunt's home a few days later, I looked like a different person from the girl who, a month earlier, had stolen away like an escaping criminal. I was no longer helpless and frightened. I was like any other student on my way to school. My adopted mother and sister, as well as kind, warmhearted Aunt Gu, all went with me on the ferry across the Yangtze to the railroad station in Wuchang. I was neatly dressed and looked my best in a light lined coat of pale blue cotton printed with tiny white chrysanthemums and a finely pleated skirt of sky-blue cotton twill. Both were almost new. I was also wearing low-heeled leather shoes that Biying had taken me to buy the day before. I had two pieces of baggage, a yellow leather suitcase and a rattan basket. Although my baggage could not have been called elegant —both pieces were well-worn—I had everything I needed. My cross-stitched purse held my train ticket and enough money from my aunt for food and tea on the train and for rickshaw fares and tips when I reached my destination. That morning, Biying had sewn four ten-dollar bills and two five-dollar bills into my inside pocket. I was to entrust them to Miss Gu when I arrived; they were my entrance fee to the school. My aunt said that if the fifty dollars were not enough, I should ask Miss Gu to lend me what I needed and she would repay her.

Before the train left, my aunt and Biying squeezed into the compartment and reiterated all their advice to me. Aunt Gu was too fat to squeeze onto the train, so she stood outside on the platform gesturing and giving last-minute instructions to Mrs. Lin, the serving woman who was taking the furniture and who would watch over me on the journey. Aunt Gu told me affectionately, "Niece, I hope this journey is just as you wish it and that you have nothing but good luck in the future. When you arrive, my daughter will look after you. She has a kind heart, but I feel sorry for her because she's so far from home and has no relatives there. You'll be company for her. Tell her that I said that the first thing she must do is be careful of her health, and that when she is not busy she should write to me."

I nodded at everything she said. A column of thick black smoke rose from the train engine and blocked our vision. The whistle shrilled a series of long and short blasts. The train began to move. Biying and my aunt, squeezed in among the noisy crowd, followed the train for a few steps and waved to me. My aunt's lips were moving, as if she was trying to tell me something, but I could not hear. I waved to them and nodded reassuringly, trying to let them know that I would remember their advice and my promises to them to work hard and discipline myself so I would become a responsible, useful adult who would never disappoint them.

The train snaked along the shiny, grey-black iron rails. My thoughts were as busy as the engines. My first thought was that I was headed in a new direction and had to forget my old way of life entirely. "The past died yesterday," I told myself. "Now everything is as if born anew. I must go forward and live the right way and feel free to lift up my head again."

In fact, I had no wish to look back; I was already full of visions of the future. I felt as if I had already seen Changsha, which was a big provincial capital. I remembered from my primary school geography classes that Hunan Province was rich and prosperous, that it had mountains and lakes, and that its people were brave and simple. I saw myself as taking a warm, friendly heart into this new world, and saw its people treating me with corresponding warmth and friendship. I could see myself walking into a big, spacious hospital where white-garbed doctors and nurses were busy tending the sick. I saw myself, also wearing a white uniform and a cap, walking with them to care for the sick. "You must be patient and careful. You must not complain even if the work is hard," I instructed myself. "Yes—patience, hard work, and humility must be my goals as I work to grow up and mature."

My reflections continued as I watched the scenery outside the train. It was early autumn and the land was spread with alternating strips of green and yellow. A few small clouds floated in the far distant sky. Sometimes they drifted along comfortably and sometimes they stopped. The golden sun made the air soft and agreeable. The countryside was peaceful and alive and seemed to be smiling at the haste of the speeding train and its imperious steam whistle. As the sun began to set behind the hills, the red and green trees on the slopes reflected its rays and seemed to be covered with a transparent red and gold gauze that made the leaves even redder, as if they wanted to compete with the radiance of the sunset. The flocks of birds hurrying home to their nests were like black threads in the sky, sometimes forming a giant "v" and sometimes flying in a straight line. The evening colors faded gradually. The woods, the hills, and the water all seemed to be deep in thought, and the whole earth seemed peaceful, majestic, and eternal.

Mrs. Lin had never been on a train before and was sick the whole way. She slept most of the time and talked with me very little. This suited me because I could think my own thoughts without being interrupted and also enjoy the autumn scenery outside the window.

The arrangements in the third-class compartments were simple and poor. The passengers were crowded together on four rows of hard wooden benches that faced each other across two aisles down the length of the car. Dust and coal-smoke covered everything and all we could smell was smoke and the sour odor of body sweat. We ached all over from sitting. Each time we dozed off, we would awaken to find a neighbor's head lolling against our shoulders. I did not mind any of this, because I had only one thought—that the train was bringing me and my destination closer together each second and each minute.

The afternoon of the second day I was aroused from my thoughts by noise and confusion. The wheels and engines had stopped. I saw all the passengers pushing to get out of the train and realized we had reached Changsha. I hastily gathered myself together. Mrs. Lin asked me to stay on the train and watch our luggage while she went to call a couple of porters to carry it for us. I asked people about the address Aunt Gu had given me and learned that her daughter lived near the railroad station. Our two days and nights of sitting on hard benches had left our feet and legs stiff and numb, so Mrs. Lin and I decided to get some exercise by walking behind the porters.

We were on a long, wide, dirt highway surrounded by empty fields. I could see green fields and scattered thatched houses far down the railroad track, but not a trace of anything resembling a city. The distances seemed greater than I had imagined. We followed the porters a few hundred yards and around two corners and came to white-walled houses with black-tiled roofs. The porters stopped in front of a big black-lacquered gate. They put down their bamboo carrying poles, and knocked the iron ring against the gate several times. Before long, the gate groaned and opened and a smiling maidservant of about forty, wearing jacket and trousers of black homespun, came out. She asked us where we had come from and when we said "Hankou," she nodded and immediately beckoned us to come in.

Inside the gate was a large earthen courtyard with a small bamboo pavilion in its center. We walked along a narrow dirt path lined with masses of chrysanthemums of all colors in full bloom. When we reached the house at the rear of the courtyard, a young woman wearing a white silk suit printed in lavender with a pattern of old copper coins came down from the veranda to greet us. I knew she was Aunt Gu's daughter because her round face looked very much like her mother's, but she was delicate and lovely and had a charming smile. She greeted Mrs. Lin first, with a smile and a few words. Then, still smiling, she came to me as if my sudden appearance was no surprise at all. "You're here, good," she said, taking my hand. "A couple of days ago I received a letter from Mother and also one from Biying, so I knew you'd be coming. Come in and sit down." As she spoke she led us into the living room.

The living room was almost bare. The house was spacious but did not have many rooms and it appeared that there was another family living in a partitioned-off apartment to the left. The oblong living room also served as a dining room. On the right was a large bedroom and behind it was a little storeroom where the maidservant also slept. After we had washed and drunk some tea, Miss Gu led us to the storeroom and told us that it would be crowded but we could sleep on board beds there for a few nights. She then asked me to treat her house as my own and not to act like a guest, because she and Biying had been schoolmates and good friends for many years. About my wish to enter nursing school, she said she thought it was already too late in the fall. But she added that I was not to worry, and we would talk over how to proceed that evening when her husband came home. Miss Gu was like her mother, sincere and simple and sympathetic. And because she did not overwhelm me with sympathy, I felt at home immediately. After my first two days there, I consented to her request that I stop calling her Miss Gu and began calling her Big Sister Gu.

Her husband, Mr. Cui, had returned from studying abroad not long before. He too was sincere and simple, with none of the pomposity of the returned student nor any of the snobbery of the West. He was now working for the railway as a consulting engineer. The Cuis' life was simple and harmonious. They got up early and went to bed early, and their relationship was full of love and mutual understanding. On evenings when they did not go out they would play table tennis in the living room or tend the garden. Every evening when Mr. Cui came back from work, he would give a soft whistle as he entered the courtyard. His wife, who would already have been waiting for him on the veranda for some time, would run to meet him and say lovingly, "You're back!" Then the two of them, laughing and talking and holding hands like children, would walk back through the chrysanthemums to the house. They seemed to be an ideal, loving couple. Perhaps because I had become so used to harsh voices and angry faces, I felt that such a pleasant, gracious household was more than I could expect. I felt grateful for their warmth and sincerity, but I also felt that it would be inconvenient for me to stay with them long, so I hoped I would soon be able to enter school.

Mrs. Lin stayed a week, until all the boxes and furniture had been brought from the station and she and Miss Gu had arranged them all in just the right places. Then she returned to Hankou. I gave her a short letter for my aunt. I told her that everything was fine but that I had reached Changsha too late to start school. I said that that was the only difficulty, and that the Cuis were trying to help me. I added that I would write to her as soon as a decision had been made and that she and Biying should not worry. I wrote a similar letter to Aunt Gu in which I thanked her again for all her concern about me and all the trouble she had gone to on my account.

I had been at the Cuis' for more than two weeks before we decided what to do about my schooling. The schools had all started and the time for taking entrance examinations had long since passed. Miss Gu and her husband thought that since I wanted to be a nurse, it would be good for me to use this time to learn some English, so that when I took the examinations I would have a little more background. They asked a friend to help get me into a nearby mission school, a middle school for girls. It was agreed that I could go there on a trial basis for a few months. Then if I finished lower middle school with good marks, I could transfer to nursing school.

I wanted to enter nursing school right away because I had made up my mind not to be a burden to my aunt and wanted to earn my own living, but I could not object to the Cuis' arrangements for me because they had gone to so much trouble. I also realized how fortunate I was to be going to a school where I could get a general education. Once the decision had been made, Miss Gu and I both wrote to my aunt.

We received a special-delivery letter from her the day before I went off to school. She had written it after receiving the letter I had given Mrs. Lin. She wrote that she and Biying were very relieved to know that I was settled in the Cuis' home. She also said that since they were so far from me, I should consult Miss Gu about everything and that if I followed her advice and that of her husband, I would make no false moves. She told me that once I was in school I should settle down, study hard, and not to worry about anything. And she also told me that my great-aunt had written to her to say that the Shaos had had the wet nurse let out of prison because she had never confessed anything. That was certainly happy and comforting news! My aunt added that Mrs. Shao's mother had died the previous week and that the family was busy with funeral arrangements, and that for the time being they would probably not have time for other matters.... I felt more reassured than ever.

The next day Miss Gu went with me to the school, a twenty-minute walk from her home. We hired a porter to carry my luggage. The school was in the country, outside the city, and near the railroad station. The buildings were wide and long, with white walls and black-tiled roofs, in a mixture of Chinese and Western styles. It was surrounded by whitewashed brick walls topped with shards of broken glass that reflected the autumn sunshine in bright, sparkling flashes. We went in through the heavy iron gate and showed our entrance permit to the gatekeeper. After putting my things in the gatehouse, an old manservant led us along a path paved neatly with pebbles and bordered with trees all cut to the same height. We went into a two-story building and were led in to meet the foreign headmistress, Miss Smith. Miss Smith looked about fifty and was very thin and tall. She was wearing a Western-style dress of blue silk with a white collar and cuffs. She sat writing at her clean, shiny desk and her expression and manner were very serious. We stood in front of the desk and waited silently for quite a while before she lifted her head and greeted us with a slight smile and a nod. The servant handed her my entrance permit. She picked up a letter and a calling card from the desk and compared them with the entrance permit. Then, in halting Chinese, she asked a few questions about the relationship between Miss Gu and me. Miss Gu answered, "We are relatives." Miss Smith then asked me my age and how many years of schooling I had had. I answered everything truthfully. She then asked me why I was so thin and whether I had some illness. Miss Gu hastily answered for me, saying, "She has just recovered from a long illness, but she's now completely well and there's nothing wrong with her." Miss Smith scrutinized me again and finally wrote a few words on the calling card. She then told the manservant to take us to see the Chinese dean and matron, Mrs. Yuan.

Mrs. Yuan was the exact physical opposite of Miss Smith —short, fat, and loquacious. She looked about forty and was wearing a blue cotton jacket and a skirt of black twilled cotton. She looked at me up and down and then asked me my age and what schools I had attended. I answered all her questions. She measured me again with her eyes and finally told me about all the major and minor school rules. She talked about the classrooms, dining hall, and exercise field, and the bathrooms and bedrooms. She told me about when the lights were to be turned on and off and when we were to get up and go to bed. She also told me about health and personal hygiene, how many times a week we were to bathe and change our uniforms, and so forth. She told me all this in a very business-like way and then asked me, "Have you understood everything I've said? Do you have any questions? If you do, ask now."

She spoke very quickly, especially when she outlined the rules. She spoke as if by rote and recited them in one breath. I was not yet used to the Hunan accent and understood only that some things were against the rules and that other things were permitted on holidays and weekends but not on ordinary days. She looked so serious and forbidding that I could not tell her I had not understood her or ask her any questions. When I said nothing, a little smile appeared on her face. She stood up, clapped her hands, and said, "Good, you've been told everything and understand it. You must abide by all the rules. Because you're new, you should follow the example of the older students, those who know how to behave. Don't learn any bad habits. Now, come with me and I'll take you to the dormitory."

The dormitory was a clean, neat, spacious three-story building. My room was on the third floor. It was long and quite large, with twelve little single iron beds that faced one another in two rows. The white bedspreads were all alike. The glass windows on the east and west walls were open. The east windows looked out over the distant rolling hills, covered with trees whose green leaves were turning yellow. The west windows looked out over the railroad track, green fields, and scattered thatch-roofed houses. The scenery was very beautiful.

Miss Gu helped me make my bed and arrange my things. Then, when two students about my age and wearing blue cotton jackets and skirts came in, smiling, to lead me to the classroom, she left.

Chapter 40

FROM that day on, my month of wondering ended. I now had a secure place to live, at least temporarily. I had a home. What made me happiest of all was that in addition to my other classes I was allowed to enroll in a pharmacy course as preparation for nursing school.

It took me about a month to get used to living with a crowd of lively young girls my own age. When I heard them laughing and singing and calling my name, "Lu Biling, Lu Biling" in their Hunan accent, the spirit of youth and gaiety that had been suppressed in me so long rose up spontaneously. But I could not feel completely at ease because I was always afraid that my teachers and new schoolmates would find out about my background. And I was still afraid that one day the Shaos would suddenly catch up with me. When I was with my schoolmates, I would often look at their strong bodies, at the red blood flowing under their fair skins, and at their thick, glossy black hair. Compared with them, I was thin and weak. My face was still pale and my hair thin because I had lost so much after my illness. My manner was even more different—they moved and spoke briskly and freely, but though I wanted to be friendly and to melt into my new surroundings I always felt constrained, wooden and stupid, and unable to be free and natural.

As for my studies, because they had been so neglected over the previous year all the knowledge I had gained seemed to have evaporated. And because I was still very anxious, doubtful, and worried, it was not easy for me to concentrate during classes, to listen to the teachers, or to prepare my lessons. I found English and mathematics especially difficult.

However, I knew how precious an opportunity I had been given. I knew that my being able to go to school again was a matter of great good fortune and that I could not afford to be easy on myself. My circumstances would not allow me to stay in one class too long. I had entered the second year of lower middle school. I had to work my hardest during the coming few months.

So whenever I had trouble concentrating and my thoughts flew to other places, I would bite my lower lip with my teeth or slap my forehead and tell myself, "You must pay attention! Concentrate!" After lunch, when all my roommates would nap, I would use the same methods to drive away my midday sleepiness so I could study.

Fortunately my new schoolmates were kind to me and did not mind my sluggishness and lack of sociability. They knew I came from another province and was far from my own home and that I had just recovered from a severe illness and could not help being subdued. They were all sympathetic towards me and my eleven roommates were especially warm. Because we all lived together, we all looked after each other. When they saw that I was having trouble keeping up with my classes, they took turns helping me. Sometimes, when they saw me sitting in a corner with a book in my hands and a frown on my face during recreation periods, they would come over and tell me, half-comfortingly and half-teasingly, "Lu Biling, put down your book and come for a walk with us. Don't worry! Since you want so much to stay in our class we won't let you down! We'll help you with whatever work you can't finish!"

In this way, minute by minute, hour by hour, and day by day, I slowly began to overcome my difficulties. After a month my class work began to show improvement, my spirits suddenly rose, and my appetite improved. School food was much the same everywhere; it was seldom very nourishing and did not have enough oil, but there was always enough rice at every meal. In Hunan, hot red peppers were served at each meal. At first, I was not used to them, but then I learned that they could stimulate the appetite. A plate of fresh red peppers sautéed with preserved black soybeans could make me eat two or three bowls of rice. Sometimes I could have eaten more, but I was afraid that the others at the table would laugh at me. In a month I gained four or five pounds. My face began filling out again and the color started returning to my cheeks. And though I did not realize it, laughter began again to bubble up in me.

My schoolmates and teachers all noticed the change in me and were happy to see me getting stronger. Once, a delegation of students from the upper classes went to Miss Smith to complain on behalf of all the students that the food was not good enough. But Miss Smith countered, in her broken Chinese, "You say the food not good. You look, Lu Biling, she comes our school, a month and a little. She fat has grown. What she eats, is it not, same you all eat? She eats school food. You look Lu Biling."

The students were disappointed that their negotiations had failed, but they used Miss Smith's words to tease me.

"Hey, Lu Biling," they would say, laughing. "You'd better hurry up and get thin again, for us. Then we'll see what Miss Smith's excuse is for not giving us better food."

And I would laugh with them.

Outwardly I was now like all the others. Most of my nervousness had disappeared and there were few barriers between us. But on Sundays and holidays, after morning services were over and the students who lived in or near the city would invite those of us who came from other provinces to dinner in their homes, or to go shopping, or boating or sightseeing, the other students would agree with delight. Only I, it seemed, did not appreciate my schoolmates' generosity and always poured cold water on their invitations by saying, "Thank you, but I'd rather not go out." I could not of course tell them the real reason. I could only keep my face expressionless and let them think me odd. When I went to Miss Gu's home, even though she lived in a quiet section outside the city, I would always watch carefully. I knew I could not risk going about as I pleased. The black shadow of the Shaos could appear suddenly at any time, anywhere, and take me back.

And indeed I soon received a letter from my aunt warning me to be careful. I received it from Miss Gu because the school censored all our letters, both incoming and outgoing. So my aunt sent any letter dealing with the Shaos to her. The letter said, "Child, you must remain alert and watchful. Do not leave the school grounds unless you must. If anyone except Miss Gu and her husband comes asking for you, you must not see them! This is most important!" She had drawn many little circles by the phrases, "Do not leave the school" and "you must not see them!" to emphasize their importance.

The letter made me anxious for several days. I knew that my aunt must have had some special reason for sending me such a warning. Two weeks later, a second letter from her showed me I had not been mistaken. My aunt wrote, "... Now that the episode is over I can write to let you know that you need no longer be anxious. Two weeks ago, a man from the Shao family came here. As soon as I saw him I knew who he was, even before he said, 'I've come to find my daughter-in-law.' I replied that it had been many years since I had seen you and that you had not been here.

I said I was worried about you and had been planning to contact the Shaos to find out where you were. He could make no reply. He stayed for a while and then left, but kept coming back every day and asking questions. He was a great nuisance to Biying and me. Last Saturday he came again. Fortunately Biying's husband was at home. He went out to see him, had words with him, and made him leave. After that, Mr. Shao did not come onto the school grounds again, but he would walk up and down in front of the gate all day every day, watching us. However, I have not seen any trace of him for the past three or four days, so perhaps he has returned home ..." At the end of the letter she added, "In short, child, for the time being you must be as alert and watchful as possible."

For a long time after this, her letters contained no more news about the Shaos, and I gradually stopped worrying about them. Time seemed to fly, and before I realized it, it was winter again. One afternoon, Miss Gu, wearing a dark-grey padded silk gown and wrapped in a dark-red wool scarf, braved the wind and came to see me. She stayed in my room for a long time, until all my roommates had left. Then she took out a letter and gave it to me. When I opened it, I was surprised to see that although the address on the envelope was my aunt's handwriting, the letter itself was not from her. The handwriting was uneducated and it was addressed to her. My aunt had written two lines of small characters at the top, "I hope, child, that you will read this letter carefully and thoughtfully. I will wait for your decision before I make mine and will then write an answer." I read through the letter quickly and saw from the signature that it had been written by my great-aunt's son, Laoda. He had written as my grandmother and great-aunt had told him to. After a few words of courteous greetings, the letter said, "During the past few months, the Shaos' eldest son Shao Zhongyao has been coming every Sunday to see my mother's eldest sister, Baogu's grandmother. When he comes, he always brings cakes, candy, or tea, or other gifts. My mother and her elder sister have studied him carefully during his visits, and they believe he is young and handsome, and of good character. His behavior is good, and he is also respectful to the older generation. It is rare to find a young man with so many good qualities, and they now feel he would be a suitable husband for Baogu and that they are meant for each other. This is why they have asked me to write this letter. We earnestly hope, sister-in-law, that you will consider these circumstances carefully and that you will not keep this couple apart. Please tell us what you plan to do. Your younger brother, Laoda."

I reread the letter more slowly. It made me very uneasy. I thought that since the Shaos had spent so much time and energy trying to find me, they were now trying a softer approach and had sent Zhongyao to charm my grandmother and find out where I had gone. It was clear that the family still suspected that my grandmother had had something to do with my escape. They knew that she was very old and had spent most of her life in the countryside, so that she was not very sophisticated. They also knew that she had no sons and daughters of her own left alive and that she was lonely, so they had sent Zhongyao to beguile her and win her over in order to get information out of her. What a crafty plan!

Miss Gu, who had been sitting beside me, saw that the letter had made me very thoughtful and asked gently, "Is it more bad news?"

I had never hid any of my aunt's letters from her, so I handed it to her and told her about Laoda. She read the letter and said nothing for several minutes but looked at me as if trying to guess my thoughts.

"I must write to my aunt immediately and tell her that I have no need to think it over. No matter what happens, I will not go back."

"Good! That's right. Of course you must not go back." Miss Gu looked relieved. "If you're going to write, you had better do so right away. I'll leave now, but I'll send Mrs. Liu over in a little while to get the letter and mail it from outside the school."

After I had accompanied Miss Gu to the gate, I went back to my room to write the letter. But I could not stop worrying about how much danger I was still facing. Fortunately, my aunt showed foresight in everything she did. She had written to my great-aunt after I had left Hankou and told her that I had been sent to another place to go to school, but she had not told her where it was. If she had, Zhongyao might have already found out and the Shaos have located me. I knew I had to show great firmness in the letter and say that my will was as immovable as a mountain and that I would never change my mind. I begged my aunt to write and tell Laoda how I felt. I begged her not to mince words and to make it clear to my grandmother and great-aunt that it was out of the question that I would ever return to the Shaos. It was a hasty, excited letter. I could not worry about careful composition and I repeated myself many times, but my only concern was to get my ideas down so they would be understood.

Winter examinations began a short time later. They lasted for five days. Then winter vacation began. The schoolmates who lived nearby packed their things and went home to spend New Year's with their families. Only about four or five of us were left at the school. Ordinarily, we were not aware of how big the school was, but now it seemed huge and empty and quiet. It was the very coldest time of the year, when the north wind blew, strong and cold, and there was no heat in the dormitories. The views from my windows were very different from when I had arrived. All the hills and fields seemed to be covered by a thick, grey woolen blanket. When the north wind blew and the rain or hail fell too hard for us to go outside into the garden to walk, I could not help feeling depressed. And it seemed that the newly-healed wounds in my heart were opening up again. Besides, Laoda's letter had reawakened my memories of the events I had begun to forget. Several times, I was awakened in the middle of the night by my roommates, who shook me and said, "Lu Biling, Lu Biling, wake up! Are you homesick again and having a nightmare?"

When I wakened my face would be wet with hot tears and questions would be racing through my mind. "Has anyone ever treated you well? Wanted you? Your father? Your stepmother? Mrs. Shao?" Their faces would swim before my eyes in the dark night, but wherever I looked I could see no smiles. The Shao woman glared at me. My stepmother gazed at me impassively but she was watching coldly to catch my mistakes. Father's face was wooden, as if he were angry.... I would turn over and rub my left chest because deep inside there was a little place that ached as if it had been bruised with a hammer.

Fortunately, Miss Gu came five days before New Year's to take me to their home for a holiday visit. The snow had been falling, thick and heavy, all morning, and by afternoon it was several inches deep on the ground and on the rooftops. Miss Gu, with her red scarf around her shoulders, had braved the snow and walked over. She laughed as we held the yellow oilcloth umbrella over us. As we walked back across the white, glistening fields, she told me, in a clear, sweet voice full of excitement and anticipation, about the preparations for the New Year celebrations: how many catties the red candles weighed, how many delicious New Year's dishes and sweetmeats were being prepared, how many kinds of flowers she had bought, how many catties of the best charcoal, how many strings of firecrackers and how many gifts she had bought, how she had decorated the living room, the bamboo pavilion and the courtyard, how we would all sit around the charcoal brazier on the night of the thirtieth and see the old year out ... Her talk made me feel very warm and comfortable.

Her happy little household was full of the New Year's spirit. From morning to night Miss Gu ran back and forth from the living room to the kitchen. And while I helped her, we would both listen to her husband play his Western violin. Without my realizing it, the activity and excitement made my dark, bitter mood crumble and melt away.

Two days before New Year's, I received a special-delivery letter and a parcel from my aunt. She had sent me a new long-sleeved padded gown of red raw silk, trimmed with rolled black-satin piping. In her letter, she said she had had it made especially for me to wear at New Year's. It was more than I had ever expected, but the new gown was secondary to my happiness. What made me feel so warm and comfortable was that my aunt had thought of me. In her letter she also said she was happy to see how determined I was and had written to Laoda in very strong terms. She quoted, "Even if the Shaos find out everything, even if they take it to court, and even if you should all confess, I will never confess." And she told me not to worry any more. Her letter only increased my admiration for her way of doing things, for her sense of responsibility and her courage. Only someone with strong character could have led the life she had. So I also felt that, although she believed she had ruined Biying's whole life and put both of them in danger of losing both their home and the school, I knew she would find a solution. I was sure that she and my poor cousin would grapple with their many difficulties, find a new road, and create a new life for themselves.

On the last day of the year, the sound of firecrackers, gongs, and drums began at daybreak and continued without let up all day. When dusk came and the lamps and candles were lit, the noise and gaiety increased. Miss Gu and I put on our new clothes before the New Year's dinner. She wore a brocade satin jacket lined with white lambskin and black satin trousers with embroidered cuffs. She put a cross of two small white narcissus blossoms in her loose, hanging knot of glossy black hair. I wore my new red gown. Miss Gu took two tiny sprays of yellow winter-plum blossoms and put them in my hair behind my ears. Then she and

I went out to the courtyard and stood watching hand-in-hand as her husband set off a long string of firecrackers that hung from the bamboo pole he was holding. The sparks flew in the cold, dark air and exploded in all directions. The noise was deafening. Miss Gu covered her ears with her hands and doubled over with laughter.

The big table was completely covered with plates and bowls full of food of every kind, color, fragrance, and flavor. The two tall red holiday candles burned with sweet-scented light on the long wall table. A tall copper charcoal brazier stood in the middle of the living room. Its coals gleamed a brilliant red and sent flames bursting upwards. The house was full of peace and happiness, warmth and harmony, and surrounded by noise and gaiety. Every family in every home was busy seeing the old year out, and new hope was born in the hearts of everyone, men and women, old and young, as they met to celebrate the new spring that would soon come.

At midnight, the noise became even more deafening. Suddenly we heard two tremendous explosions that seemed to rend the heavens—someone had set off some huge fireworks that drowned out all the other noise. Both heaven and earth seemed to be shaken, as if presaging some great event that would take place in the coming year.

BOOK IV

Chapter 41

The rushing river roars and fills
With wave-dashed reed catkins.
A single lantern, a thousand eyes,
A bunch of wick grass, ten thousand hearts.
The future is like fire, promising and bright.

SOON after New Year's, school reopened and I went back.

The bright pendulum of the clock in my dormitory room made me think about how time passed. The pendulum swung one way and my wounds had reopened; it swung the other and they healed again. My aunt sent me no further news about the Shaos. I felt as if everything that had happened and all the people in that family, how they spoke and how they looked, were being drowned out by the tick-tock of the pendulum. The longer it ticked the further away they went, and the further away they went the less distinct they became to me.

The story of my little, unimportant life could end now—if the times into which I had been born had been peaceful. If the China of my birth had been independent and self-governing, instead of subject to the foreign powers that treated it like a possession, my life would perhaps have not been shaken by any more upheavals. Perhaps I would have been able to do as we had planned—studied until the following summer and then taken the examinations for nursing school, spent three years of training and become a professional nurse, worked hard in that little hospital, served my society, and lived in peace and security. But people's destinies cannot be separated from the times in which they live. The times are like the ocean and the destiny of a person is like a grain of sand—in periods of great confusion, when the winds blow and the waves beat, the grains of sand are scattered in all directions. I and everyone else of my generation were all blown about by the story of the revolution that was breaking.

The tide of the Chinese people's resistance to the aggression and control of foreign powers, the warlords, and the feudalistic system had been rising, and as though those in front might be suppressed, those who came behind kept advancing until the waves reached their peak. In the south, the National Revolutionary Army had risen and raised the banner of the Northern Expedition,* and the people too had risen in response to the banners that floated in the wind and to the urgent calls of the bugles and drums. The army swept north as if to push over the mountains and attack the oceans. The whole earth seemed caught up in this great tidal wave of revolution. Even we, as segregated from the outside world as we were in our peaceful little school, were touched by this wave.

At first we knew very little about the great changes that were coming. Like other mission schools, ours made us concentrate on lessons and religious activities and did not allow us to have much to do with outside events. We had very little opportunity to hear about the current situation and political trends—ordinarily, the daily paper was not even to be found in the reading room. Because of this, we were indifferent towards outside events. Nor were current problems ever discussed between the teachers and the students.

But now it was different. The forces of the Northern Expedition were about to reach Changsha. We had all heard the rumors and were all curious. We knew that this army was not like the old warlord armies. We had a vague idea that its coming had something to do with improving the lot of all the people of China. At first, the only news that reached us came indirectly, a little here and a little there, from schoolmates who lived in or near the city, but later new rumors spread almost daily. In the summer of 1927, the situation grew serious. The provincial authorities put the city under martial law and every day at dusk armed military police would patrol the city and the suburbs and no one could cross the major intersections. Policemen were stationed every few steps on the big business streets and there were sentries on all the small residential streets. The whole region was full of soldiers. We kept hearing about arrests and shootings of revolutionaries. Young people dared not walk about on the streets, and went out only when absolutely necessary. Even in our peaceful suburb, we could see bands of soldiers, with their guns and equipment, starting for the front.

---

*The military movement to smash the warlords and unify China that began in July 1926.

Among the precautions our school took was doing away with the regular half-day holiday on Sundays. Only students with homes in the immediate area could go home, and then only if their parents or another family member came in person to get them.

One morning, just after our first class had ended, Mrs. Yuan came running towards us clapping her hands and saying, "Be quiet, all of you! Be quiet and listen! Miss Smith is waiting for you in the auditorium. She wants to talk to all of us. There will be no more classes this morning. Hurry up!"

We thought that some important person from the church had come and that we were to go and listen to him preach, or that since the situation was serious Miss Smith had called a special prayer meeting, but when we got to the auditorium we saw her standing alone at the long table on the speaker's platform. Her manner was as calm and dignified as always, but her habitual slight smile was missing from her face. When we had all settled down, she began speaking to us very slowly in her broken Chinese. "I think, you all, all have heard. Many, many days, events outside, all not good, all not peaceful. Your Chinese soldiers, they again fighting! Our school, these times, you must be careful. All must not to front gate, to back gate, go and come. Already Mr. Cao told, front gate, back gate, early close, not let outside idle persons into school come.

"The rooms, you sleep night, early put out lights. In night, big guns, cannon hear, not frightened be, not make noise. Wait Mrs. Yuan, lead you downstairs, little reception room.

"All you, must not, please, discuss matter. Most important, your hearts, at peace. No fear. Pray constantly, heavenly father protect us, in peace, give wisdom. Now I ask Mrs. Yuan, come platform, say few words, to you." Miss Smith took two steps forward on the platform and nodded to Mrs. Yuan, who was sitting on the front bench.

Mrs. Yuan stood up immediately and went to the platform. She stood at the center of the long table. Her round face was flushed and we could see tiny beads of sweat on her forehead and the tip of her nose. It was now midsummer and the weather was hot. Because Mrs. Yuan was short and fat, she did not tolerate the heat well. She took out a white handkerchief, wiped her face, cleared her throat, and raised her right arm as if to tell us to pay attention.

"No doubt you have all understood Miss Smith, so there is no need for me to say much. In short, the situation is getting worse each day. Rumors keep spreading. We do not know whether there will be a revolution." Mrs. Yuan always spoke fast and her voice was high. She was so excited that she spoke even more quickly and shrilly than usual. She was the exact opposite of Miss Smith. "Fortunately, we here need not be afraid. We are a church school and come under the protection of the foreign church. The soldiers will never dare come here or create an incident because it would have international repercussions. So, no matter what rumors you hear, you must not get upset or panicky." She paused and looked around the auditorium. When she saw that we were all quiet and that none of us seemed agitated, she lowered her voice and spoke a bit more slowly. "Although I do not think the soldiers are a danger to us, we are still a girls' school and we must prepare for whatever might happen. We must be careful and alert. Every evening, the electric lights in the teachers' and students' bedrooms will be on for half an hour. You can wash, prepare your beds, and tidy up then. The lights will then be put out.

"If you hear guns or artillery in the night, you must not panic or run around in confusion. Put on your clothes, keep together and be quiet. Wait until I come. I'll take you downstairs to the small reception room, where you will be safer than you would be upstairs.

"Also, remember not to gossip about this. This is not a joke to be laughed over and talked about as you please. In short, there's no need to worry. We will go on as usual...." Then she added contemptuously, "Northern Expedition or Southern Expedition, we have nothing to be afraid of."

After she finished speaking, she went over to Miss Smith. They whispered to each other and then Miss Smith dismissed us, but asked the teachers to stay and go on with the discussion.

We students were not disturbed or frightened, as Miss Smith and Mrs. Yuan thought we would be, by the changes that were coming. We all surmised that the school had heard that the provincial army had been defeated by the forces of the Northern Expedition and was in retreat. That afternoon when Mr. Lin, the youngest of the men teachers, finished his lecture on the Chinese language, picked up his books, and was about to leave, he stopped still and looked around at us. Then he said in a very serious voice, "Fellow students, there will soon be a great change in the situation in China. We, you and I, are all Chinese, and since we are all part of China's younger generation we should pay even more attention to these new developments." Although he did not explain what the new state of affairs might be, it was clear from his expression and voice that he had spoken out of great hope and faith.

In times of crisis, the more one attempts to suppress discussion, the more curious people become and the more rumors grow. None of us could get to sleep after the lights went out in our dormitory rooms. We would huddle together on our beds in little groups and whisper about what we knew. The students who lived nearby repeated all the rumors and vivid stories they had heard about the progress of the Northern Expedition and about revolutionaries. The people were all on the side of the forces of the Northern Expedition and all the stories had been passed on by word of mouth so many times that they had become exaggerated and had taken on the flavor of legends. This gratified our adolescent craving for excitement. Often we got so caught up in these stories as we listened that the slightest noise outside in the quiet of the night would startle us. We were sure it was not an ordinary noise, and would wish, half-fearfully and half-excitedly, that we could go outside the school walls and see what it was. Perhaps the noise was coming from the soldiers and horses of the Northern Expedition.

The general impression we got from all the rumors was that the soldiers of the Northern Expedition were on the side of the people—that they were coming to release Chinese people from want and oppression, especially the workers and the peasants, whose lives were hardest. They had both a plan for saving the country and a way to carry out that plan: regarding the outside world, China should throw off control by foreign powers and become an independent, self-governing, strong nation; internally, she should do away with the warlords and old feudal influences and release the women from centuries of oppression....

This was a strange, new language. We had never heard words like these in our classrooms. But they seemed to hold special meanings for us. When we heard these words, we felt moved, as if they were raising new hopes that we could see fulfilled. We could no longer pay attention to our classroom lessons or to the sermons in the church.

Things stayed this way until late summer, when school let out for the summer vacation. One day after summer school had started, we suddenly heard that the forces of the Northern

Expedition had reached Changsha. The school's front and back gates were still bolted shut and we could not hear any guns or artillery. We did not know what to believe, but early the next morning, as we were eating breakfast in the dining room, Mr. Cao came running through the grounds from the gatehouse to the school garden. He was panting and dripping with sweat, and kept pointing towards the city as he shouted, "They've really come, they're really here! The forces of the Northern Expedition! The Revolutionary Army!"

We all dropped our bowls and chopsticks and ran to the dormitory, to the big window over the stairway to the third floor, where we could see over the school wall to the long dirt highway that led from the city to the countryside. Oh! A sea of people! What colors! What excitement! What tumult! The people were like an endless, many-colored dragon rolling along a mighty river. The singing, the shouting of slogans, the shriek of whistles roared like thunder to the heavens. The dragon had almost reached the school before we were able to see that it included soldiers, students, workers from labor unions, peasants associations and every kind of people's organization, men and women, old and young. They were hand in hand, shoulder to shoulder, walking and running and pressing forward, probably on their way to a big meeting. The soldiers wore neat grass-green cotton uniforms and carried guns on their shoulders. Some wore leather leggings. Some wore glasses. They all looked very young and strong and full of spirit, not thin, hungry and ragged like the soldiers we usually saw. From their gun barrels hung colorful little paper banners with slogans written in ink, but we could not see them clearly. At the head of each group of students and of the different organizations, marchers held high a long cloth banner with the group's name on it and everyone marching behind was waving banners with slogans. The banners fluttered past us like gay, brightly colored butterflies under the clear bright sky and between the green summer trees.

It seemed as if the hordes of people would never finish passing. We crowded in the window and hung over the sill as if we could never see enough. The bell for going to class sounded before all the groups had passed, and we still did not want to leave the window.

Every day after that new throngs of soldiers and people marched past. The sounds of slogans and new songs invaded our classrooms and echoed throughout the peaceful, quiet countryside:

> Workers, peasants, merchants, students
> Workers, peasants, merchants, students
> All unite
> All unite
> Down with foreign powers
> Down with foreign powers
> Get rid of the warlords
> Get rid of the warlords

Before one group had finished singing, another would drown out the first:

> Great compassion, great sympathy
> Save the people, save the world
> Soldiers of the revolution show the way!
> ......
> How brave and strong the sons and brothers of Sanxiang,
> Unite, down with the warlords and foreign powers!

Sometimes, as we crowded around the window, we would listen and watch until we had forgotten ourselves. We would not hear Miss Smith's footsteps as she came up behind us and would not know she was there until she tapped us lightly on the back. She would order us gently, "All of you, hurry back to your dormitories. Do not look, do not look. They soldiers, soldiers dangerous."

Although Miss Smith's voice was always soft—she never raised it, even when she scolded us—we were all a little afraid of her. So, though we did not want to go back to our rooms, we had no choice.

But as soon as she went away we would all creep back to the window.

Chapter 42

THE ferment outside the school walls seemed unending and our calm days inside those walls seemed to have disappeared.

When the schools in the area reopened for the autumn term, all of them except the mission schools added lecture courses on current events. The students in those schools had joined the central students' association of the province and were called upon to join in patriotic activities.

The gates of our school remained tightly closed. Strips of paper with slogans written on them began to be pasted on the outside walls. The school workers washed them off, but they would reappear the next day. Amateurishly-printed pamphlets that urged us to wake up, join the students' association, and devote ourselves to patriotic activities, were tossed over the walls. When the bands of men and women students saw us, behind the wall that separated us from them, they would shout slogans at us.

"Fellow students of the mission schools, stop reading dead books! Arise and save yourselves!"

"You too are Chinese! Stand up with us! Join the revolution!"

"Stop depending on foreign powers! It's shameful to depend on foreign powers!"

"Root out foreign influences!"

"Down with foreign slavery!"

"Times have changed! Stop being contented foreign slaves!"

"We welcome you! Come out and join our ranks!"

Inside the school walls we would stand silently at the upstairs window and look out unhappily at the smiling, excited young people who looked up at us with their arms held high and waved their paper banners to show how much they welcomed us.

Although we did not like them calling us foreign slaves, the words did lead us to think about many questions we had never considered before, questions about the country, about the school, and about ourselves.... We were full of doubts. As Mr. Lin had told us, we were China's younger generation. We were concerned about our country. We wanted to know more about conditions outside and also about what was happening, but the school still refused to give us any opportunity to meet with outsiders and also tried to forbid us to discuss the situation. This, we felt, was not right.

Our lives now seemed empty and colorless. The teachers seemed to feel as we did—when they lectured, it was not with their old enthusiasm and interest. The dormitories and the school garden, which used to be full of lively, laughing chatter, were now oppressive and dull. Even the sound of the church bell seemed muffled. These were like the clouds and the oppressive atmosphere that came before a storm.

The school authorities also felt the tension and uneasiness. Miss Smith and Mrs. Yuan began coming around very often to inspect our sleeping quarters and reading rooms. Mrs. Yuan kept warning us every time she spoke that the school would never allow us to join the students' association. She told us we should have more self-respect than to spend so much time looking out the third-floor window, and said that we should pay no attention to the young men and women who shouted like devils outside the school gates. "I really do not understand," said Mrs. Yuan earnestly, clasping her hands together, "how you can listen to them call you names. What pleasure can you get from hearing them? From now on, just let them go by and pay no attention to their screaming. Let them make themselves hoarse shouting, pay no attention. Once they see that, I guarantee that they'll lose interest in us."

But no matter what Mrs. Yuan said, we did not stop wanting to learn more about the changes that were taking place outside the school walls, or about the new ideas that were in the air. On the contrary, her words only increased our discontent and strengthened our determination and desire to join the students' association. This lasted for almost a month. And then, one clear, cold, autumn evening, the gate that opened onto the vegetable garden, which had been closed so long, was very quietly opened. And it was in this way that the tide of change finally reached our school.

Earlier that day, at lunch, when Mrs. Yuan was not present, Yang Jingru, an upper middle school student, suddenly stood up just as we were about to begin eating. She tapped on her bowl with her chopsticks and announced, "Fellow students, I want to announce a joyous event, one we have all been hoping for a long time. We have invited someone from outside who is familiar with the present situation to speak to all of us at seven-thirty about the recent events in our country."

The buzz of voices arose immediately.

Yang Jingru tapped on her bowl again. "Please be quiet! Please be quiet. When the time comes, please leave your dormitories and go down to the small reception room. For reasons I'm sure you're aware of, we will not ring the assembly bell. Please be sure to attend, but please do not talk about this."

By seven o'clock, after dinner, we were already all gathered in the reception room. The curtains on the windows on three walls had been drawn tightly, the long table moved to one side, and about ten long benches from the dining hall were lined up in rows across the room. Two of the women teachers and four or five of the upper middle school students were conferring in whispers near the wall. The students, whether sitting or standing, looked excited and tense and murmured questions among themselves. We were all wondering who had been invited to come this evening.

Seven o'clock struck. It was very hard to wait the last half-hour until seven-thirty. We all sat up straight and stopped talking. We waited a long time but nothing happened. The students began to be a little restless. No one spoke, but one could hear feet shuffling. Several of the upper class students went out and bustled back in, showing a certain amount of impatience. Suddenly we heard quick footsteps and Yang Jingru and one of her classmates ran in. Yang Jingru said breathlessly, "It's all right. It's all right. He's come! Please sit down, and sit up straight."

We heard the sound of leather shoes, and then Mr. Lin came in followed by a young officer of medium height wearing a light-brown military uniform and a soldier's cap, and with a leather belt crossing his chest from his shoulder to his waist. This was more than we had ever expected! We all sat up and stared at him stupidly. Yang Jingru held out her arms towards us and motioned to us several times before we finally woke up and jumped to our feet. The officer sat down facing us and we all sat down again.

We stared at him as he took off his cap and put it on his knee. Mr. Lin stood at the little table and made the introductory speech:

"Fellow students, we are much honored this evening to have with us Secretary Wei of the Fifteenth Division of the Army. He has squeezed out a little time from among his many duties to come to our school—"

"Secretary Wei?" I thought to myself. "Strange. Why is his face so familiar? It seems to me that I have seen him somewhere."

"—Secretary Wei is an experienced revolutionary soldier—"

"Be sensible," I told myself. "There are many people who look alike. He's been a soldier for a long time—where could I ever have met him?"

The students clapped and Secretary Wei, smiling slightly, stood up. He placed his cap on the table and, as if it was habit, brought his legs together and clicked the heels of his high leather boots.

"Fellow students, I feel honored to be here at your school to meet you. This school is a mission school, run by foreigners—"

"Oh!" The exclamation slipped out of my mouth before I could stop myself. Immediately, the students on either side of me nudged me hard to make me be quiet. I gulped and looked around, but fortunately everyone was absorbed in his speech and no one was paying any attention to me.

"—Now, I think I will tell you, my fellow students, about the history of China over the past hundred years, from the time of the Opium Wars, about the aggression of the other world powers and their oppression—"

"No, there can be no mistake. It is Mr. Wei! His voice still sounds the same as it did when he taught us at he Women's Normal School. It *is* Mr. Wei. No wonder I thought his face looked familiar. But now he is wearing plastic-rimmed glasses instead of gold, and his face is thinner and darker, and he has cropped hair like a soldier. He is now in the Northern Expedition—"

"—So I ask you all to open your eyes and look—look at the map of our country! Year by year it changes color. Year by year the land of our nation is being lost to outsiders! I beg you all, fellow students, to open your ears and listen! Listen to the cries of your people, who are in pain and trouble, trampled under the iron hooves of imperialism and warlordism. The common people of our nation are worse off than horses or cattle!" Secretary Wei's voice was filled with pain and he looked indignant. He looked more heroic in his uniform than he had in his long scholar's gown, and his soldier's life had made him lose his former leisurely manner. As he spoke, he gestured constantly and held out his hands to us in a way that was earnest and moving.

"—In Shanghai, in Hankou, in Guangzhou, in Hongkong,

blood has flowed time after time as foreign soldiers and police have shot Chinese people to death. In our own China, we Chinese people cannot walk, cannot talk, cannot act as we please. No matter where we are, we are in danger of being shot by foreign soldiers—"

Suddenly we heard someone knocking on the door of the reception room.

We all froze. Secretary Wei stopped speaking. Mr. Lin and Yang Jingru both got up at the same time, and Mr. Lin gestured for all of us to be quiet. Yang Jingru hurried to the door, hesitated, and then opened it a crack.

"Miss Yang, Miss Yang," we heard Mr. Cao say.

"Mr. Cao, why have you come here?"

"Miss Smith and Mrs. Yuan want to talk to the young ladies. They are now in the corridor and have told me to come and announce them."

"Oh, that cannot be. We're having a meeting." Many voices broke out.

"Mr. Cao, please go and tell Miss Smith and Mrs. Yuan that we are in the midst of a meeting and that it is not convenient for them to talk to us now."

Mr. Cao did not answer. Yang Jingru waited and then added "Mr. Cao, go and tell them. It is not your responsibility. What are you afraid of? Just go and tell them we say it's not convenient because we're in the midst of a meeting. Hurry and go tell them."

"All right ... I'll tell them." Mr. Cao's voice faded away with the sound of his footsteps.

Yang Jingru closed the door and sighed with relief. No one at the school had ever disobeyed a command of the head of the school before.

Secretary Wei went on with his lecture.

As he spoke he seemed to be the same as when he had lectured to us about history. His voice was still the same, as was his height. He was not yet thirty, and, though his face was thinner and darker because of the wind and the sun, he did not look older. He did, however, seem to have a new strength and depth that he had not had before. I did not know why, but as he stood there before us he seemed tall and heroic. His glasses could not hide the warmth and wisdom that flashed in his eyes. He used no abstract, foreign terms and no slogans. Even much less did we feel he was giving us instruction. He did not tell us, you must do it this way or you must do it that way. What he said was simple and easy to understand, and he gave facts and evidence. It was as if he were rolling out a picture scroll for us inch by inch and letting us see for ourselves, so we could think and understand.

It was deeply moving. He had strong feelings and the hearts of all of us who heard him ached and we all forgot ourselves. At the end when he said that one of the goals of the revolution was to root out feudalism and to liberate women, my heart ached even more. My forehead felt tight, as if something were pulling on the nerves between my eyebrows. There was a queer feeling in my nose, as if the air were stopped there and I could not breathe. "This won't do," I thought. "I can't burst into tears in front of all these people!" I wanted to force myself to smile, but the more I tried, the more my breath stopped. I knew that I was neither smiling nor weeping, but something in between, and it was more difficult to bear than weeping would have been.

I looked around me and saw that everyone else looked as if they felt as I did. I had thought I had been so easily moved by Mr. Wei because I had suffered and because he had been my teacher. I had not thought that my fellow students would be like me, and that they too would all look as if they wanted to smile but not smile and wanted to weep but not weep. When Mr. Wei finished speaking, the emotions we had all suppressed for almost two hours flooded out in enthusiastic applause. Now we could all really smile. Everyone gathered in a tight circle around Mr. Wei.

I stood at the edge of the circle, against the wall, and tried to decide what to do. "Should I squeeze in? Should I make myself known to him? Should I speak to him? But what would happen if he called me by my real name? ... But if I don't go up to him now, I will have lost this one chance in a thousand. In a little while he'll be gone and if I ever wanted to see him again it would be difficult to find him. He himself said, 'The present is not like the past.' Even if he does call me by my real name, what does it matter? But ... should I go or not?" Suddenly the circle opened and Mr. Wei walked out through the crowd, which stepped back to let him go. As if something had pushed me from behind I ran over before I could hesitate any longer and pushed my way past the students surrounding him. Though I was trying to control myself, I could not keep the excitement out of my voice as I said, "Mr. Wei! Mr. Wei!"

Looking surprised, he turned towards me.

"I ... I ..." I laughed in embarrassment. "Mr. Wei, do you remember me?"

He looked puzzled and then he suddenly seemed to realize who I was and a smile spread over his face. "You—you?" He pointed at me with his right hand and seemed to be trying to recall my name.

I said in a rush, "I am *now* called Lu Biling."

"Oh, oh, I remember, now. You are Zhou—"

Before he could say any more, I broke in, "I am called—*now* I'm called Lu Biling."

"That's right." He nodded his understanding. "How is it that you're here? How long have you been here? Good, good. You have not had an easy time of it." He seemed to look happy. He pulled out a little book from his pocket. "Please write your name for me. Who would ever have thought I'd see you here?"

"What is it? Have you two known each other before?" Mr. Lin, standing beside us, asked with a smile.

"Oh, she was one of my students. I taught her for half a year."

I wrote "Lu Biling" and, afraid that after a while he might forget, I wrote "Zhou Baowen" in characters as tiny as ants. He took the book, looked at what I had written, and put it back in his pocket. "I never would have expected to meet you here. When are you free? I'd like to talk with you. Oh, perhaps it isn't convenient for me to see you here." He turned to Mr. Lin, who shook his head. "Then this is what we should do." He took out a card. "When you have time and can get out, write a note to me and come to my place for a visit. I live not too far from here. For the next two weeks, I'm going to be very busy—I'm afraid I must go on a short trip—but I'll be back by the end of next month." As he spoke he put on his cap and nodded to us all. Then he and Mr. Lin walked out of the reception room.

We followed him out to the back gate and stood watching silently as they crossed the vegetable garden and headed down the long, narrow, dirt road under the chilly moonlight. When we could no longer see them we turned and came back inside. I was clutching his card tightly. All my schoolmates surrounded me. Their questions about him rained down on me like a summer shower. I gave brief answers to a few of them but then pushed my way through the crowd and ran back to my dormitory room. I was excited and could not tell whether it was joy or sorrow or some other emotion that moved my heart. Everything seemed to have happened too quickly and to have ended too quickly as well. I had to be alone for a while to think.

Chapter 43

WHAT we had feared the night before came to pass in the morning, when Miss Smith posted a notice on the big bulletin board outside the door of her office: "Students must not organize any meeting without first getting permission from the school authorities. Since last night's meeting was a first offense, the school will be lenient. Yang Jingru will receive one demerit. If there are any more unauthorized meetings there will be no leniency. The leaders will each be given three demerits and expelled." If Mr. Wei's speech the night before had been like setting a match to a brazier piled with charcoal, Miss Smith's notice was like pouring a can of kerosene over it—the flames rose high and red and could no longer be put out.

That very day, the students organized a students association. Yang Jingru was elected chairman. Mr. Lin and two other teachers were invited to be advisors. That same evening they took their demands to the school authorities. The only terms that related to the meeting were a request that students have the right to assemble and that Yang Jingru's punishment be rescinded. The other demands dealt with problems that had been rankling us all for many months. We asked for freedom of religious observance and that non-Christian students not be forced to study the Bible and go to church services. We requested that private letters should be sent and received without censorship. We asked also that Mrs. Yuan inspect the dormitories only at stated times in the mornings and evenings, and also that she be forbidden to search our books and belongings. We also made some suggestions for improving living conditions.

The school authorities ignored our demands. After this, events moved like fallen leaves driven by a strong wind, rolling forward and unable to stop. The students association posted a strike notice the next morning, telling the students not to go to classes, and appointed representatives to contact the central students association. The association's representatives arrived that same afternoon to offer us support and to bring us a formal letter inviting us to join the association. All day long, representatives from all the men's and women's schools in the region streamed through the reception room offering us their support. We were all very excited, because only three or four days earlier we had listened as they had shouted at us from outside our walls to stop being "foreign slaves." Now, after one short day and night, we had joined them and become one with them. The new songs that had been sung only outside our walls now welled up from time to time on the grounds. Several other mission schools in the area joined us in the strike when they heard the news. Each of the schools made demands similar to ours, which added to our courage.

The authorities of all the mission schools also banded together and took the same counter measures. They decided to close a month early for the winter vacation, and sent notices to all our homes. The notices also stated that no more food would be available at the schools a week later. The students all joined together and decided not to leave the schools until their demands were met. They also sent out notices asking other organizations for help. Both the school authorities and the students thus created a stalemate, a situation that could not last long. A week later, the authorities at all of these schools, and ten or fifteen other Westerners in the city, were ordered by their governments to board ships that would take them back to their own countries. After Miss Smith's departure, Mrs. Yuan also left. The staff and students then held a meeting at which we organized a temporary committee to take care of the school and carry on classes.

The student movement flowered in one short month. We could not have foreseen its rise. Although at first glance all these events seemed unexpected and inexplicable—and we were all too excited and busy to examine them closely—a closer look would have shown that they all followed one from the other, and had been inevitable. As the proverb says, "Water comes from springs and trees from roots"—everything has its causes. The student upheavals were not limited to a few mission schools with a fev foreign heads and a few hundred middle-school students. They were a tiny ripple in a great wave—the whole nation's opposition to dominance by foreign powers. As Mr. Wei had said in his lecture, "The fire of the anger of the common people in every part of the land against the aggression of foreign countries has been suppressed for almost a hundred years." Now that the forces of the Northern Expedition had come, it was as if the fuses had been lit. The explosions were happening everywhere and could not be stopped.

At this time the Northern Expedition had the unanimous support of people everywhere and we kept receiving word of one victory after another over the warlords. There was a celebration or parade almost every day. The day Miss Smith left, we were all out at a meeting to celebrate the Northern Expedition's victory in Wuhan. That night every social group in Changsha—students, artisans, and tradesmen—decided to hold a lantern parade. When darkness fell, the main streets and the residential lanes were dotted with red lights. Torches and silk and paper lanterns of every size and shape stretched for many *li* along the prosperous and lively main business streets of the city. As they flashed and flew and danced, from a distance they looked like a long, shining dragon of fire. The sound of firecrackers accompanied the singing and shouting of the groups as they marched along. No one could make out any of the words, but we all shouted and sang as loudly as we could. People crowded against people, lanterns followed lanterns, and torches followed torches. No one knew who was who, but we all felt that everyone else was our own brother and sister and that we were all going in the same direction. It was a rare scene of unrestrained enthusiasm and gaiety. The whole city of Changsha became a place of flashing red flames and sparkling white stars.

The next morning, we heard about Miss Smith's departure from Mr. Cao, who said he had carried her luggage and accompanied her to the rickshaw. He said she wept when she left because she did not know if she would ever return to China. When we heard this, we all fell silent. We had all been somewhat afraid of Miss Smith because she was so serious and rigid, but none of us had ever had any ill feeling towards her. She had always been conscientious about the school, concerned about the students, and diligent in her work. We all knew and appreciated her good qualities. If she had left in ordinary times, we each, in our own way, would have told her how we felt about her, but now we could not speak. No one showed elation, and no one showed sorrow. What was happening was not something between Miss Smith and us, but something bigger than all of us. We all seemed to be caught up in the great wave, which was turning as a water wheel turns, and in the turning of the wheel personal likings or hatred seemed to be but tiny pegs on one of the spokes, too small to be seen.

Classes were held very seldom during this period. There were meetings and parades every day, and if occasionally we went to class it was difficult to quiet our minds and listen to the lectures. The atmosphere outside the school seemed to be always dancing and moving and our nerves seemed to have been caught up by the beat and to be dancing in rhythm with it. This went on for several months before things began to return to normal.

A month after Mr. Wei had come to the school, I thought that perhaps he had returned to Changsha, so I wrote to him at the address he had given me and told him about the rise of the student movement and its course. I also wrote that it was now easier for us to receive visitors and that we had more freedom to come and go. I added that I hoped he would tell me a time when he could come to visit me at the school, if he was not too busy, or I could ask for leave and go to see him. But two or three weeks passed and I received no answer. At first I thought he had to be very busy with important matters, and perhaps did not have time to be concerned with something so trivial as answering my letter. Then I thought that he had never been a person who said things he did not mean, or who forgot what he had said, and that he had perhaps been detained by business and had not yet returned. I thought about writing again, but decided I should not write too often. Soon afterwards, winter vacation came. Because Miss Gu's husband was often away on inspection trips for the railroad, she had me come to spend the vacation with her and to keep her company. Gradually my feeling of expectancy faded.

One Saturday not long after the spring term had begun—the staff and student committee had kept classes going and our lives were continuing in the same busy way—Yang Jingru asked all of us to write slogans chosen by the women's association for the Women's Day celebrations. The twelve of us in my class were given a big roll of colored paper and we were gaily cutting the paper, preparing the writing brushes, grinding ink, and chatting as we wrote slogans in the sunny classroom. We had finished a few when suddenly a fellow student came running into the room, smiling and shouting, "Lu Biling, Lu Biling! Hurry! Your teacher, that Secretary Wei, has come. He's downstairs in the big reception room waiting for you. Hurry!" I dropped my pen and without even taking time to wash the ink stains from my hands, I ran down the two flights of stone steps and down the long corridor to the reception room door. Mr. Wei was standing near a chair with his back to the door, looking appreciatively at a long piece of Hunan embroidery that depicted the famous Yuelu Mountains.

He must have heard my swift footsteps, because he turned and smiled and said, "It's again been many months since we met. How are you?"

I nodded and smiled too. I was still a little out of breath. I walked hesitantly into the room and asked him to sit down.

"It was only yesterday morning that I got back from Xiangtan. I did not think when I left that I would be kept there so long." As he spoke he sat down. "I saw your letter as soon as I got back and wanted to come to see you yesterday, but could not get the time." He laughed. "Did you think I had forgotten to answer it?"

"How could I? Of course not. I thought that you must be busy or that perhaps you were still away."

"Oh, you must sit down, too." Mr. Wei, seeing that I was still standing near the table, stood up and gestured for me to sit.

I sat down across from him and noticed that he was not wearing his military uniform, but a dark-brown Chinese tunic suit of wool. Instead of his high leather boots, he was wearing black cloth shoes. But his face was still the same, tanned and roughened by the sun and wind. He was full of vitality and energy. I noticed that he seemed to be studying me as if he had noticed something different about me. His gaze travelled to my hair several times and stopped there. Embarrassed, I could not help reaching up and pushing the ends of it aside where it hung down to my shoulders.

"You still look the same as you did at the school. You haven't changed much," Mr. Wei said, and smiled.

I smiled, "We all cut our hair two months ago."

"Good." He seemed slightly at a loss. After a moment he said, "Very good!" Then he began asking me about the development of the student movement and the present situation. I told him what I could. There were many things I wanted to talk over with him. I wanted to ask him about what had happened in the two years since I had left the Women's Normal School. He too seemed to want to talk, but because of the long separation, because we had known each other only as teacher and student, and because we were in the big reception room, it was difficult for us to begin talking intimately about what had happened to us. We chatted about many things and then Mr. Wei picked up his dark-brown felt hat and, turning its edges in his hands like a wheel, hesitated and then asked, "Can you—do you have any classes this afternoon?"

"It's Saturday. We don't have classes in the afternoon."

"Oh, that's right ..." He looked at his wrist watch. "It's only a little after two. It's still early. How would you like to go into the city and look around? We can eat an early supper in one of the restaurants and talk some more. I'll bring you back. Can you?"

I nodded and asked him to wait a while. I left the reception room and flew to the student on duty to fill out the form asking for leave. Then I went to the classroom and told my classmates, and then to the dormitory, where I quickly washed my face and combed my hair. I picked out a bright-colored jacket-and-skirt suit and changed. Then ran back to the reception room. When I reached the end of the corridor I saw Mr. Wei, his hat already on his head, standing outside the door waiting for me.

We walked through the gate and out onto the road into the city. The cool breeze caressed our faces, but the sunlight was warm on our bodies. It was almost the end of March. Though the cold of winter had not entirely gone, it was much warmer than it had been a month earlier, when it was so cold it hurt to breathe. Hints of green and yellow could already be seen on the sides of the road. Tiny blades of grass that had hidden their faces in the ground as if afraid of the snow were now sticking out their heads, as if to test the strength of the wind. The branches of the big trees looked brownish-black in the distance, but when we got nearer we could see they were dotted with fresh yellow-green shoots. The willows were even more impatient. They had not waited for the warm, gentle spring winds but had already put forth long, slender, pale-gold yellow strands that looked like a yellow mist under the light blue sky and white clouds. Sometimes, as we passed the bamboo fences in front of homes, we could see scattered early-spring flowers swaying gently, their faces turned to the sun as if they were afraid or ashamed of having opened too early. From time to time, we caught a whiff of fresh earth.

I did not talk much as we walked along. Although Mr. Wei had been my teacher for one semester and I had always admired and respected him, this was the first time I had been out alone with him. I was excited and happy, but could not help feeling a little distant and constrained. And Mr. Wei, who had always been so articulate in the classroom or when lecturing before an audience, also seemed constrained and at a loss for words. But whenever I turned to speak to him, I could see that he looked pleasant and relaxed, with none of the tension or seriousness that he had when speaking in public. We chatted about our acquaintances at the Women's Normal School. He told me that two of the leaders of the students' association had been arrested and put in prison because of their patriotic activities. He also said that Miss Hai and Xiao Ming, the jeweler's daughter, had joined the Army of the Northern Expedition. He did not, however, ask me anything about my own experiences—about my illness, my leaving school, or my escape from the Shao family. It was as if he was reluctant to stir up unpleasant memories.

I had not met anyone from my home region in almost two years. Now, as I walked beside him, I not only did not fear hearing him talk of the past, but felt warm and comfortable. I felt like a wanderer who has suddenly met an old, old friend, and the meeting filled me with an indescribable sense of closeness and trust.

When we reached the end of the highway, we walked a little farther and entered the city. The busy, gay main business street was packed with men and women, old and young, coming and going. They all looked cheerful. The gay, multi-colored shop signs that lined the street seemed to be smiling and waving at all who passed. There seemed to be a holiday atmosphere in the air. Side by side, we slowly made our way through the crowds. As we chatted and watched the scenes on the street, the feeling of constraint that we had felt earlier seemed to vanish on the cool breeze without our realizing it.

Chapter 44

IT was still light outside when we came out of the little restaurant where they served Tianjin-style food. As we passed a big bookstore, Mr. Wei suggested that we go in and look around. The electric lights were shining brightly and the store was full of people, some in military uniforms, some in suits like Mr. Wei's, and some in ordinary clothes. But most, men and women alike, looked like students. Two of the men in uniform came over, smilingly doffed their caps, and saluted Mr. Wei. He and I looked at the books on the stands and as we were leaving, he bought several magazines on current events and literature and also three or four books of modern stories. He kept the magazines but asked the clerk to wrap the books, which he put under his arm.

By the time we came out of the bookstore the street lamps had been lit. Mr. Wei stopped and asked, "What do you think? Is it too late? Would you like to ride back in a rickshaw?"

"It's not too late. Now, we're not counted as tardy if we get back before eight."

Mr. Wei looked at his wrist watch. "Then it's still early, but it's a long way back to the school and you've already walked quite a bit today. Are you tired?"

"I feel like walking—even if it were farther, I'd still feel like walking." Then, as we were about to set off, I asked, "Mr. Wei, What about you? Can you walk so far?"

"Me?" He smiled. "I'm a soldier. If we could not walk, how could we march and fight?"

When he said soldier, I could not help looking at him. His life in the army and his suit made him look very heroic, but the time we had spent together laughing and talking about whatever came to mind had made me see that he was still the cultivated scholar he had been when I had met him two years earlier. All the way, as we walked slowly along the main street, people were making noisy, busy preparations for the evening trade. The itinerant peddlers were setting up their stands on both sides of the street. The theatres and the restaurants were all brightly lit. Appetizing smells came from the restaurants and from the cauldrons carried by men on the ends of poles and on the streets. The smells and the clanging of the iron ladles against the cooking pots whetted the appetites of the passersby. The crowds grew thicker. Some people idly watched the scenes on the street; others stopped to listen to the men and women students or soldiers from the political section of the army, who were holding up banners and making animated speeches about current affairs. As we reached the end of Main Street, we saw a crowd of laughing people. They were gathered around a little toy stand. The peddler, a man of about forty who was wearing a short blue coat of coarse cotton and long trousers, held up a fat little clay figure and shouted, "Look! Look! Greedy officials, grasping underlings, local rascals, oppressive gentry! Knock them down, knock them down! Cheap! Cheap!"

Mr. Wei went over and bought one of the clay busts and gave it to me. I took it and we examinined it closely. The features were well-modelled and though it was only clay, it was lively and well-executed. He was wearing a foreign tophat made of paper lettered with, "Local rascals, oppressive gentry." A white cord hung down behind the little figure. When I was not looking, Mr. Wei followed the peddler's example and suddenly pulled the cord gently. The clay figure made a crying sound, "Wa!" and stuck out a red tongue, half an inch long! It was so funny that I could not help doubling over with laughter. Mr. Wei too could not stop laughing. So we walked, laughing and talking, towards the countryside.

Outside the city, twilight had fallen. The wide fields were hushed and there were few people about. The air suddenly felt colder than it had in the city. The setting sun was just sinking behind the faraway hills. The banks of clouds in the east reflected the radiance and glowed a deep red through the black branches of the trees. But soon the colors faded and night fell. My short jacket of leek-green brocaded silk was lined with wool but though it had been just right in the afternoon it was no longer warm enough.

"I love this time, when the sun goes down behind the mountains, best of all. It's too bad that it's also the very shortest time of the whole day." Mr. Wei looked at the distant mountains, which were like a picture, and said reflectively. "When we marched with the army, we often saw the sun rise in the distance across the wide, borderless plains. The sun would come up like a red ball from the horizon. It was so exotic and beautiful. But daybreak is never as beautiful as twilight. Twilight is so full of peace. It calls for reverence."

I listened but said nothing. The scene was so peaceful and tranquil and Mr. Wei's words so full of poetry that I felt that even the slightest cough would have destroyed the mood.

Mr. Wei said nothing more.

The cool wind blew the ends of my hair against his shoulder from time to time. The hem of my loose, wide skirt occasionally brushed against his knees. We walked forward silently in our cloth shoes, and the scenery around us changed as the night deepened.

When we neared the school wall, Mr. Wei suddenly seemed to come back to himself and exclaimed, "Oh! We're here already! So soon?" We arrived at the gate. Its leaves had been drawn together but not closed. A dim light shone through the crack, and I knew that Mr. Cao was waiting in the little wooden gatehouse for the late-returning students.

We stopped at the gate. Mr. Wei held out the bundle of story books and I took it with both hands. The words, "Thank you very much," crept to the edge of my lips, but I could not speak. I looked at the black night around us and could not help saying anxiously, "It's completely dark. You won't be able to see anything when you go back."

"It doesn't matter. I'm used to walking on dark roads. And besides, one person walking alone goes much faster. I'll be back in the city in no time."

We stood there silently for a while.

"I want you to know," Mr. Wei said, "that today has been a rare one in my busy life—it has been a day of pleasure and happiness."

"It has also been an unusually happy day for me."

"If I had not met you again so unexpectedly, I would not have had a day like this."

I looked up and saw him gazing down at me. I could not help blushing. It was as if suddenly I realized that this man standing before me was not only my former teacher but also a man not much older than I. It was also the first time that I had ever gone out alone with a young man. Alone and close together in the night, we stood face to face. My heart began to pound, and for a while I could not answer. Fortunately the night was dark, and I was standing with my back to the light, so he could not see my face.

"I ... nor did I ever imagine that we ... that I might meet you here." I finally got out the words.

Mr. Wei did not answer. I knew he was still looking at me but I did not have the courage to lift my eyes again.

"You'd better go in. I'm going now," he said at last.

"I want to watch you leave before I go in."

"Take good care of yourself. When I have time next week I'll come to see you again."

He turned and walked down the dark road.

I stood by the gate and watched him leave and my heart was filled with loss. I waited until the sound of his footsteps had faded in the distance before I turned and ran through the gate.

For the next few days I felt expectant, as if something were about to happen. I could not calm myself, and could not decide why I was feeling this way.

It was difficult for me to analyse my feelings. I was clearly aware of some of them, but others were indistinct. My emotions seemed like the bits of colored glass in the kaleidoscope I had played with when I was small. Sometimes I felt happy, sometimes I felt sad. Sometimes I wanted to cry and sometimes I wanted to laugh. Why? I was not sure.

But whether I was happy or sad, Mr. Wei's voice was always in my ears and his face was in my mind and nothing that had happened that afternoon ever left me. I kept remembering him sitting across from me in the restaurant at that table loaded with dumplings, *jiaozi*, noodles and other dishes, and how he had asked so sympathetically and indirectly about my situation, about who had helped me enter the school and whether I had any relatives and friends here. I remembered how he had said several times that he and many others at the Women's Normal School had not thought it possible that I would have the courage to defy such an old social pattern and two such traditional families all by myself. I remembered him telling me that I was intelligent and courageous and that it certainly had not been easy.

When he had referred to what I had been through over the past three years, I had not been able to keep from feeling sad and lonely, even though it had been hard for me to answer his questions, and once or twice my throat had choked with tears and my voice had trembled a little. Several times I had to stop before I could force myself to go on. He had pretended not to notice, but had gaily poured me a cup of hot tea and changed the subject.

He had told me about his experiences travelling with the army and how he and the soldiers had been welcomed everywhere by the common people, who had helped them win the war. Once, in a rural area, he and two comrades had been overtaken by a heavy rainstorm. Because it was late in the day and they could not reach the main army, they had sought shelter in the home of a poor peasant and his wife. The old couple were at first reluctant to let them in but when they learned that they were soldiers from the south, they had been very hospitable. They not only gave the three soldiers all the rice they had; they boiled their only old hen for dinner and lit a fire to dry their uniforms and army blankets. At bedtime, the old couple took down the leaves of their door and made a makeshift bed for their guests to sleep on. The three had planned to make pallets on the ground but could not refuse the kindness of the old couple and had to get on the big bed. But just as they were falling asleep, they were attacked by so many bedbugs that they could not endure it. But they did not want to awaken their hosts, who were on the other side of the partition, so all the three comrades could do was creep off the bed and sit up all night on the long benches against the wall. Mr. Wei laughed as he talked and kept picking out the best bits of food for me and asking me if I liked northern-style cooking and whether I preferred noodles to rice, and whether I wanted to try any other dishes. He was like a patient, sympathetic older brother who was comforting a wronged younger sister. I felt extremely grateful to him for his kindness and felt it would be ungrateful of me not to show my appreciation by laughing with him even when what he said was not especially amusing.

After we had eaten and the waiter had cleared the table and brought us a pot of tea and a plate of watermelon seeds, I asked him if he was working too hard and whether he would have to follow the army north. He said that he had now returned to teaching and had been appointed to the provincial education department, and that he would not be leaving again for a long time. This made me feel happy. He had then asked me what books I was reading and whether or not I liked literature. He asked with a smile if I remembered taking the entrance examinations for the Women's Normal School, and that he had praised my essay as the best in the class. I remembered that he had been the teacher who gave out the essay topics and had monitored that part of the examination, walking up and down the aisles to look over our work. I also remembered that he had stood over me for a while and had seen a wrong character on my paper that he had corrected for me. And I could not help remembering that later time, when I was in his class but the Shao woman was forcing me to knit gloves even during classes. I remembered my humiliation the time my composition had been too short and he had commented that a student who could write so well should write more. At that time, he had just graduated from Beijing University. He was the youngest and handsomest of the men teachers. His vigor and new ideas had attracted the attention and admiration of all of us.

I had put aside all these memories, but now, instead of being like scattered beads from a broken string, it was as if a threaded needle were stringing them together again. Sometimes I wanted to cut that thread and stop thinking, but the thread kept getting stronger and tighter. It was as strong as steel wire, and I could not cut it apart.

"He is your teacher," I told myself over and over. "He has treated you with concern, sympathy, and kindness. But it's because of our relationship as student and teacher. He said so himself many times that day. As we were walking into the restaurant, he said, 'You're my old student. Who would ever have expected that I'd run into you thousand *li* from home.' Clearly, he looks at you as a former student. If he were to meet another former student of his he'd no doubt treat her the same way.

"But he was so understanding and so warm! And he was so spontaneous when he bought me that clay figure.... And when we were walking along side by side in the tranquil twilight it seemed to me that I could hear the tips of my hair blowing against his shoulder and each breath we took and each heartbeat ... What was he thinking then?"

The more I thought, the less I felt I understood him.

"And then, when we reached the school, why did he say, 'Oh! We're here already? So soon?' And then it seemed as if he wanted to say something else, but he did not speak—as if he wanted to go but he did not move. He stood there silently. And then, when he finally turned to leave, his voice was so full of emotion when he said, 'I'm going now. Take good care of yourself ...' Is it perhaps because you've suffered so much coldness from others, and because you feel so solitary, that a little kindness and sympathy from someone can move you and make you feel so intensely?"

Emotion and reason—reason and emotion! It was as if I were

tightening or loosening the two strings on an *erhu*, plucking them and trying to tune them into balance. But it was also as if I were only beginning to learn the instrument and was not sure how tight or how loose the strings should be, or how high or low the pitch. I could not create a balance or a tune that pleased me.

I told myself, "What's more, Mr. Wei is a man of learning and a scholar. He is sophisticated and experienced in the ways of the world. Who knows what he has gone through in his two years in the army as he has travelled through the wind and frost, rain and dew? How could he possibly be interested in or care about a naive little middle-school student like me?" As I thought about him in this way, I grew calmer and I began to feel I should be ashamed of myself for thinking about him in that other way, ashamed of being unable to forget him and of longing for him.

But then I rebuked myself: "He may be a scholar and a man of learning, but you must not belittle yourself! You too have struggled with life, and you've won. The world is different now. There are many important new events and problems facing you. You must think about them. You must learn and do. Your admiration for him should make you even more diligent and eager to learn from him. You must fill yourself with knowledge so you can join him in the revolution and work for our country and our people. That is the right thing to do. How can you continue to let your thoughts spin around in such a disorganized way?"

I knew this was the right way to think. But why, why could I not calm my emotions? Why could I not be at peace?

Chapter 45

LIFE is like the Yangtze River. Before one wave dies away, another arises in its place, and there never seems to be a time when all is quiet and at peace.

During the more than six months since the forces of the Northern Expedition had come, equal rights had been established for men and women, as had freedom of marriage. So my hidden bondage to the Shaos and my parents' control over my life were no more. I no longer had to fear that the Shaos might find me. I was free. Now I could hold my head high and walk with dignity and confidence, just like other people. But although this old problem no longer weighed on me, others came to take its place. In the beginning, especially during the first months after the arrival of the Northern Expedition, we scarcely noticed these problems because we were swept along on the tide of enthusiasm. No one had time to study or analyze, but after six months, when the tension had lessened and our heads had cooled, we could no longer evade dealing with the problems we faced.

The school had become more careless about classroom work each day, and there were fewer classes because both the teachers and students did not consider studies important. Our attention was on national affairs, on the Northern Expedition, and on the activities outside the school; none of us could concentrate on our studies. Mr. Lin and two other teachers had long since left to go north with the army. We students began to agree that it was not much use to stay at the school, but we would only find the same conditions if we went somewhere else. We all wanted to join the army or find work in a government agency. Yang Jingru, along with almost a third of her class, had joined the army a month before and gone to Hankou. The rest of her classmates were waiting to join the army until after they got their middle school diplomas. The spring passed very quickly. I too was thinking about where I should go once summer came and I had my lower middle school diploma.

There had also been great changes in my aunt's family during that six months. I learned about them after the fact, though I had known from one of Biying's letters, that her relationship with her husband was growing worse each day. He was interested only in carousing and took no responsibility for his family. He would often fail to come home at all for two weeks at a time. Biying was very depressed. Her letters hinted that she hoped to find a way to solve the problem. After that letter, I almost stopped hearing from her, and my aunt wrote much less often as well. One day I saw a notice in the Hankou newspaper that Miss Lu Biying was getting a divorce. I turned to the page and read, "My husband and I were mismatched in temperament and had very different interests in life. For ten years we shared a life and a bed, but our dreams were as incompatible as fire and ice. Now that freedom in marriage is the law for both men and women, I have been given a judgment from the court and am now released entirely from all marriage bonds with the person named. From this day on both of us may remarry with no interference from the other." I realized that because of the social changes and new laws in China, Biying had at last found a solution to her problem, an old, old family problem that could never have been solved in the past. I felt glad that she had at last freed herself from a marriage in which there was no warmth and no love. I wrote immediately to comfort her and to ask about her son and my aunt's school.

Two weeks later, the letter came back stamped "undeliverable." I did not know what to do, so I took the letter to Miss Gu, who said she would send it to her mother and ask her to make inquiries. It was another two weeks before we received an answer from Aunt Gu. It also contained a letter from Biying that put my worries to rest. Biying wrote that she and her mother both felt they had just awakened from a ten-year-long nightmare. But though they had now been released from the dark prison that their home had become, Biying's former husband was unwilling to let go entirely and kept threatening to snatch away the little boy. Biying and my aunt had been forced to act to protect him. My aunt had closed the school and was now living in hiding with her little grandson and Biying was staying with relatives until her plans became clearer. She said she had not been able to write sooner to reassure me because her life had been in such a tangle. At the end of the letter she added that she did not know when she would be able to live with her mother and son again. The letter breathed sadness and loneliness. I realized that although Biying's unhappy marriage had been dissolved, her problems were by no means over. Laws could be changed overnight, but old social patterns and the ways people looked at things were very strong and harder to change. I felt that however unfortunate the situation was for my aunts and Biying, it was even worse for the little boy, who was not responsible for the marriage or the divorce but had now, through no fault of his own, become a pawn in the struggle between his parents.

Because of these changes in my aunt's situation and because I knew they were having trouble taking care of themselves I could not bring myself to add to their problems. I decided that my original plan to enter nursing school would take too much time and money. Besides, I had also learned that the directors of the school had all returned to their home towns and that the school was not accepting any new students. I realized I would have to find work in the summer to support myself. This practical necessity meant I had to put aside all the impractical, romantic ideas I had had of doing something big for my country and its people. Instead, I had to answer a few simple but crucial questions I had never given much thought to: what skills did I have and what could I do? And what job opportunities were there and where should I look for them?

I thought that with my amount of training I could take the examinations for becoming a clerk in a government office or perhaps those for entering training in a propaganda group. But getting into either of these would not be easy. Whenever these examinations were given, many, many people responded, but few were selected. If neither of these opportunities worked out, perhaps I could find a job teaching in a small country school. Women now had many more opportunities to work than they had in the past. It was still more than three months before summer vacation; I knew I could have to look seriously for work as well as practice my writing. I also wanted to read some of the many new books that were being published.

Like my classmates, I was afraid of being left behind. I wanted to go forward. Knowledge, scholarship, and advances in thinking are like mountain peaks that pierce the clouds—easy to drop onto from above, but difficult to reach when climbing step by step from the level ground below. The problem of earning my own livelihood had made me more practical. I began to realize that learning and progress lay not in the ability to mouth the latest progressive maxims, or to shout slogans at meetings and in parades, or to skim a few progressive books. That kind of progress was like trying to jump up a whole flight of stairs at once—it would be impossible to reach the upper story. I thought and felt more deeply about these things as Mr. Wei and I saw more of each other and grew closer. During the months I had been seeing him and writing to him, I had often mentioned my problems and asked his advice about my studies and about looking for work. He did not think I should be too impatient to find work for the summer. He urged me not to worry and told me to study hard so I would be able to understand the new ideas of the era of change we were experiencing and have a solid educational foundation so I could always find work in the future. The more I learned now, the greater my contribution would be in years to come. Whenever he came to see me, he always brought me books, books of recent literature and new ideas. He told me to read them carefully and to ask him questions about anything I did not understand. I was grateful to him and understood what he was telling me, but I also understood my own circumstances and the uncertainties I was facing. I could not tell him much about my financial situation or that my source of funds would soon be cut off, because I knew that if I did he would want to help me. And that kind of help I did not want to take from him. My feelings for him made me unwilling accept his generosity, and all my upbringing, from childhood on, as well as the values I had learned in school, had made me reluctant to be careless about money.

In the month after the evening we parted outside the school gate, we never spoke openly or wrote about our feelings. But it did not matter—our mutual concern was obvious. We could not hide the happiness we felt when we met or how hard it was to part, because we were so drawn to each other. It seemed as if there was something very special and affectionate behind every word we said and everything we did. I now began to feel that he felt more for me than a teacher would ordinarily feel for a student. Because of this, I wanted his understanding and respect even more and did not want to put out my hand and accept his generosity or pity. How deeply aware I was of the difference between my emotions for him and those I had had for Zhongyao. With Zhongyao I had been walking the ancient road followed by my grandmother; I had felt that since my fate had already been decided when my parents betrothed me to him, I belonged to him and should love him. In that relationship we had not sought mutual understanding or respect; they had not seemed necessary. Even less had I experienced the sweet excitement of exploring the depths of our emotions.

Now, however—how much more I loved life! How much I wanted to march forward into the future! No matter how many stones lay in my path, no matter how many thorns lined it, no matter how many times I stumbled or how often those thorns pierced me and made me bleed, I knew I had to get up and struggle on. I had no fear of what lay ahead, and no desire to retreat. If anyone had reminded me, "You once thought about killing yourself, about giving up and dying," I would have reacted with astonishment. That had been another person; I was no longer that person. My changed outlook on life and my positive attitude towards the world came partly from the new social currents washing over me, partly because Mr. Wei's positive, optimistic attitude was contagious, and partly from my new emotions.

Although I did not speak about the pressing financial needs I was facing, Mr. Wei seemed to have guessed. In one of his letters, he approached the matter indirectly:

"Baowen,
From the very beginning I have had every confidence in you. Your past struggles and unbending spirit keep impressing and touching me. There is no limit to what you can accomplish in the future if you only persist and work diligently.

Baowen, please do not keep your problems or difficulties to yourself. Tell me about them. I am slow and not as wise as I would like, and have few practical ideas to offer you, but you know I will always stand beside you and help you. Wouldn't your load be easier and lighter to carry if there were another shoulder next to you, helping you? Why, oh why won't you let me help you?

I've noticed that you haven't been happy recently, so I can't be happy either. I think about you constantly and wish I knew how to solve your problems. We can discuss the problem of your finding work; it will be soon enough to make a decision once summer vacation starts. Please set your mind at ease. You have enough to deal with already. Please tell me if you have any difficulties. Although my income is small, I'm wealthy compared to you! (I am smiling as I write this!) We could share it and use it together."

These simple, sincere words moved me greatly. Even now, in the long years of bitter struggle and uncertainty that have followed, I still feel a boundless gratitude towards him whenever I think of them. If I had not been feeling all those emotions and had not always been made to feel insecure and dependent on others, I might have done as Biying had suggested and gone to live with her in Hankou for the summer or waited, as Mr. Wei suggested, until summer to look for work. But my past and present insecurity made me long for independence and to stand on my own feet.

I was so wrapped up in my own thoughts that I did not stop to think that there might be an important reason why Mr. Wei wanted me to wait until summer to look for work. Like countless other young people, I was full of faith in the changes going on in China and unconcerned about other developments, even when Mr. Wei and I went into the city and chatted with his fellow workers, who sometimes said strange things were happening in the government and in the party of Kuomintang (KMT). Many KMT members had become arrogant in the wake of victory. Their lives had become comfortable and easy. Though they always mouthed the words, "the people," their lives were diverging more and more from those of the people. Some of them were prejudiced and dogmatic and did favors for one another. There were also many opportunists and reactionaries who had infiltrated the side of the revolution and set themselves in high places. Then they became officials, they began acting as masters rather than servants of the people and administered the laws arbitrarily as if they were the lawmakers, though their salaries came from the people. Although I was disillusioned by this, life in school was too limited for us to experience the kind of oppression and pain common people had suffered.

We understood the political situation even less. I thought these disorders were temporary consequences of the upheaval and would soon be corrected. I did not realize that the situation had already become very serious and that before summer came the revolution would be betrayed and threatened.

Mr. Wei had had experience in many political struggles and, like an old sailor who knows the ocean, could make forecasts based on changes in the wind and the clouds. I heard him say more than once, "A military victory alone cannot fulfill the promises given the people or ensure the attainment of a democratic policy. This kind of victory is short-lived. It may be a victory for the warlords and for ambitious politicians, but it is not one for the Chinese people." One afternoon as he and I were

walking back to my school and he was speaking that way, I could not help feeling that the future looked very uncertain. I asked, "If the victory cannot last long and the current situation is as bad as you and your fellow workers fear, perhaps there will be a change. What do you foresee for China? What do you think we should do?"

He did not answer immediately. We walked along silently for quite some time before he marshalled his thoughts and replied, "China will continue to be unsettled and in disarray. The struggle for independence and freedom will be even more bitter and more protracted and our responsibility, yours and mine, will be even greater."

"Our responsibility, yours and mine, will be even greater," I repeated to myself. He had said "our," including me with him and his fellow workers. The young men and women who worked with him had never excluded me from their discussions or treated me like an outsider. They were all young, enthusiastic and pleasant, with none of the formality or superficiality of the old society. They always called me "Comrade Lu." "Comrade Lu"! How sincere and lovely a name! "It's too bad that I'm still not able to make a contribution to my country and society," I thought, feeling very humble.

"Don't lose heart," Mr. Wei added in a somewhat lighter tone of voice when he saw how silent I had become. "We believe that the situation will not reach a crisis soon, but the indications are not good. We must all be alert, so that if disaster strikes we will be ready."

Chapter 46

THE spring and early summer of 1927 were filled with unrest and disorder. The situation changed constantly and rumors multiplied. Everyone had heard stories but no two were alike. It was as if we were enveloped in a thick layer of clouds. We all understood that a fearful storm was about to break.

During this period Mr. Wei and I saw very little of each other. He was busier than usual and my fellow students and I were often called upon by the students' association and other groups to join in meetings and parades outside the school. Though we were all uneasy, we carried on with our usual activities. We went on this way until suddenly the black cloud that hung over us burst and the crisis erupted.

One morning we heard that the local militarists, under control of the landlords had risen the night before and taken over all the government offices and the headquarters of all organizations. They had arrested and killed many people. Communications between the city and the outlying districts had been broken off and there was great confusion. But, just as when the Northern Expedition had first arrived, we had heard no gunfire or artillery. We did not know what to believe. My first thought was to go down to the office and telephone Wei to ask him for news. I was running towards the door of the office when a fellow student came running out and almost knocked me down. She was shouting, "It's true! The telephone's been cut!" I ran back to the dormitory with her. Fear and indecision filled my heart, because we had no way of learning what the situation was in the city.

Both school gates were closed and bolted. None of us dared leave the school because there had been a rumor going around that if the militarists took over, any girl student who had cut her hair would be treated as a revolutionary. We did not know if this was true, but since we had all cut our hair, we dared not risk going outside to find out. The countryside around the school was very quiet all day and evening and we saw very few people. There was none of the usual laughter and singing inside the school and we barely spoke above whispers. We all believed that the situation was very serious and that disaster could strike at any moment, but we could not predict when or from what direction.

Soon after we put out the lights and went to bed that night we heard the dogs suddenly begin to bark. Although it was summer and the nights were hot, their barking that night made me shiver because it sounded different—they were howling in long-drawn-out wails. We realized that something sinister was happening in the black night. How many unfortunate people were being arrested and taken away? I lay in bed tossing and turning and unable to sleep because I was so afraid for Wei's safety.

The sun rose high in the sky and shone warmly on the earth and on the greenish-grey hills to the east of the school. The countryside around us seemed quieter than usual. One noon, about two weeks later, we saw two bands of people approaching each other, one from the south and the other from the north, in the distance near the hills. When my roommates and I leaned out the dormitory window, we could see that some of the people in the band from the south were wearing blue coats and trousers like farmers. A few others were dressed in the grey uniforms of the forces of the Northern Expedition. They were carrying what looked like either rifles or hoes. The people coming from the north were all wearing grey military uniforms and armed with rifles. Suddenly we heard gunfire—it sounded like a long string of firecrackers going off. We saw many of the men at the front of the company from the south fall. Those behind them continued to press forward, but soon even more fell. The southern company seemed unable to stand its ground and turned back, but the northern company pursued them. In a few minutes silence returned and the two groups disappeared. The only ones left were those who had fallen at the foot of the hills—and they would never rise again.

The indifferent summer sun shone on the fallen men. Who were they? Did they have fathers and mothers, wives, sons and daughters? Who were their brothers and sisters, relatives and friends? No one knew and none of us dared ask. Their bodies lay quietly at the foot of the hills. But after a day or two they were gone.

Some people said the soldiers had buried them; others said their bodies had been devoured by hawks and wild dogs. Some said the soldiers' fellow workers and relatives had retrieved the bodies late at night, when the soldiers on watch were drinking and seeking pleasure, and buried them. Only the hills knew the truth, but they could not speak—and even if they could, perhaps they too would not have dared.

The sun was as hot as fire. It beat down on the earth and its light and heat made the clean fragrance of the earth and leaves rise in waves. The summer mountains and rivers were as green and lovely as jade. All of nature—the flowers and plants, the trees and animals—flourished in the sunshine. But among us human beings, there was sadness and cold because fear had sapped our ability to enjoy the beauties the world offers us.

In times of social chaos, today's friends may be tomorrow's enemies. Many people lost their lives at this time because of their beliefs and ideals. Many others, countless others, died needlessly. Many young students—men and women, boys and girls—were pulled out of their classrooms and off their athletic fields. All this news came to us on the hot summer winds.

Human life became as weak and unimportant as the weeds of the fields in the face of a ruthless wind. There was no one to pity or protect us. A single word, a single modern book—especially if its cover was red—could cost us our lives. Then we heard a rumor that the rickshaw pullers, like the peasants at the foot of the hills that day, were planning to revolt. The rickshaws disappeared from the streets and the rickshaw pullers hid in their thatched houses and dared not show their faces on the streets.

Rumors and fear penetrated everywhere like the summer heat.

But as yet the police had not come to the school; perhaps our reputation gave us some protection. The students who had been active in the central students' association had stolen away a few days after the mutiny. Summer vacation was approaching and we were all preparing to leave. I was not worried about where to go; if it came to it, I could go to Hankou, to Biying. My great worry was Wei. It had been more than two weeks since the mutiny but he had disappeared as completely as a needle dropped in the ocean. I wanted more than anything to stay at the school until I heard from him. I would not leave until the last moment.

Every morning when the postman brought the mail, I would run to the gatehouse to make inquiries. Every day I would stand at the dormitory window, waiting and watching, from sunup until long after the sun had set behind the hills before I could bear to go to bed. My heart was filled with an anxiety that grew every day, but I did not give up hope. I was convinced that he was still alive. "No matter how fine the net, it can never catch all the fish in the sea," I told myself. Moreover, he had been involved in all the patriotic movements since his student days; he had been in danger before and was experienced and alert. I believed that he and I were still breathing the same damp, oppressive summer air of this earth.

As I stood at the window looking down the long road from the city to the country, always hoping he would suddenly appear, my feelings were mixed and contradictory. What an unimaginable joy it would be to see him—but how afraid I was that he would be in danger. My anxiety was bound up with hope and my hope was bound up with anxiety. Like a silkworm spinning its cocoon, loop by loop and layer by layer, I could not sort out my emotions. I did not know what I should hope for or what would be safe.

Each day that passed brought summer vacation closer, but I still had no news of Wei. One afternoon when I was feeling depressed and sad, I went to my room and began writing to Biying to tell her that once school closed I would probably return to Hankou and stay with her for a short time while I looked for work. I was in the middle of the letter when one of my schoolmates came running in and told me that the gatekeeper had come over to say that a man named Zhang was asking to see me. My heart jumped. I knew no one named Zhang, but thought that he might be a friend of Wei's, and that perhaps he had brought me a letter from him. I flew downstairs but there was no one in the reception room. I ran out of the dormitory building and saw a man wearing a long blue gown and a wide-brimmed felt hat. He hurried across the lawn to meet me as soon as he saw me. Oh, heaven—it was Wei! My heart was in my throat. I do not know how we managed to reach each other, we were so agitated. He made for the back garden and I followed right behind him. He had changed. He was thinner and his eyes were bloodshot, as if he had not slept for many nights.

"How did you get here?" I murmured once we reached the bamboo fence in the garden and I had looked all around to be sure no one else was there. "I've been so worried! Are you well? Why are you so thin?" Suddenly tears were running down my cheeks and I could say no more.

"Don't worry, don't worry. I'm fine," he answered. A tiny smile appeared on his dark, haggard face as he looked at me. It was the only thing about him that had not changed. "How are you, Baowen? Look! You're much thinner, too!"

383

I shook my head and tried to smile but my tears continued to flow and I still could not speak.

He took my hand and we began walking alongside the bamboo fence that bordered the garden. His fingers were cold and his palm was wet with sweat. I had been upset and unhappy, but now I had the greatest consolation—he was safe, he was here walking beside me again! "Is this real or is it a dream?" I asked myself over and over. And over and over I looked at him. "It is he! It really is!" The man I loved so dearly was alive and walking beside me! I wanted to walk with him like that to the ends of the earth. I did not care how hard the winds blew or how high and dangerous the waves were. No matter how bitter life might be, I wanted to share it with him and never be parted from him again.

It was a midsummer afternoon. The wind was blowing gently. Row upon row of big, shiny green cabbages and red pepper plants festooned with peppers grew in the crumbly black earth. The sun hung like a big red lantern over the peaks of the hills and glowed through the clouds that half-covered the sky. How quiet and beautiful this summer twilight was! As Wei had once said, the loveliest time of day was sunset. But that night, the beautiful evening sun and twilight seemed only to heighten the sadness of our situation.

When we had walked halfway around the garden he began talking about what we should do. Though time was short, he spoke slowly and calmly. He first told me that I should leave Changsha as soon as possible and go to my relatives in Hankou, where it was safer. He said he would follow later and that we could discuss work and other plans there. He also said that the militarist uprising had happened too quickly, that the whereabouts of many of his friends were unknown, that all lines of communication had been broken, and that some of his friends who wanted to get away could not. He wanted to wait until things were clearer before he left. He told me to be careful when I travelled and encouraged me not to be afraid if I met trouble.

As he talked he kept clearing his throat and I saw that there were beads of sweat on his forehead and nose. I wondered if he had gotten chilled and caught a cold, or if he was perspiring because of the tension and anxiety he was feeling and because he was wearing too many clothes. I listened to every word he said. Sometimes I wanted to say to him, "No, I want to stay here until you go and go with you." I also wanted to say, "If it's too dangerous here for me, it must also be too dangerous for you!

Why not come with me now?" And I also wanted to tell him, "Wei, Wei, I love you! I swear before heaven and earth that I will stay with you until the sea become a desert and the stones melt into water. I will never leave you!" I wanted to say many, many things to him—things I had wanted to say many times, but now in this time of crisis, we seemed to understand each other without words. I knew that the times were not ordinary and that we could not act according to our own desires. Our decisions were controlled by the situation facing us. He could not go with me, either because he had to avoid the secret police or out of loyalty to his responsibilities and to his friends. He had to wait until he had first made arrangements for his friends to escape. Only then would he go. I felt that the best way to comfort him and keep him from worrying was not to ask too many questions, but to show that I understood him and would do what he told me to do.

"Here is the railroad fare to Wuchang and some more money for incidental expenses." He pulled out a little envelope and placed it in my hands. "I cannot buy the ticket for you but fortunately the railroad station is nearby. You'll probably need someone to help you carry your things when you go. Can you leave tomorrow or the day after?"

"Yes."

"Good. Now give me the address of your cousin in Hankou."

"Do you have a pen and paper?"

He felt around in his breast pocket and brought out a short pencil but could not find any paper. He thought for a moment and then took off his grey hat. I was surprised to see that underneath he was wearing a small black satin cap with a red button. He smiled and tucked the cap inside the big hat. I understood at once that in an emergency he would put it on and pretend to be a small merchant. He pulled out the paper lining from the yellow leather sweatband of the hat and I wrote Biying's address for him. He wrote the address of a friend of his in Hankou on the envelope of money and told me to go to see him if I had any problems.

We stood facing each other near the bamboo fence. We looked into each other's eyes, wanting to reassure one another but unable to speak. We smiled. He took out a handkerchief that had once been white but was now so grey with grime that he put it away again and wiped the sweat from my forehead with his coat sleeve. I wiped his forehead and nose with my little handkerchief. He put on his hat. Involuntarily, we both turned to look at the path that led out of the garden. I took a step forward and clutched at his sleeve. "You—please be careful—"

"I understand. Don't worry. Take good care of yourself on the trip to Hankou. Baowen, you—you must not be unhappy. We'll meet soon in Hankou. And then how happy we'll be!" The smile spread over his face again, but this time I could not smile back. He turned and began walking away. "I'm going." It took him only two or three steps to reach the gate.

I held on to the bamboo gate and watched his figure, in his long blue cotton gown, grow smaller and smaller in the twilight. When he was about to turn the corner, he looked back and waved. Then he disappeared. How much I wanted to run after him, but my feet could not move. I looked at that dark, deserted road and the words of a song I had often heard and sung came back to me. It was the song of farewell to heroes as they went away to do their duty:

> We hope your bright red blood
> If shed, will flowers of freedom be
> Blooming o'er all the land.

But our parting might be for life, and I could not sing a word. My heart sent up a silent prayer. "May he travel in peace and safety. May he come back to me alive and well."

Chapter 47

TWO days later, I rose early, packed the worn yellow leather suitcase and rattan basket my aunt had given me two years earlier, bought a third-class ticket on the morning train, and started for Wuchang and Hankou.

During my two days on the train, my heart was full of dreams for the future. Whenever the train stopped at one of the stations I could not help putting my head out of the window to look at the passengers who were waiting to board. I hoped that perhaps Wei would be among them. Perhaps, that evening after he had left me he had managed to finish what he had to do, and perhaps, since it would not be safe for him to try to leave from Changsha, he had taken a roundabout route and would catch the same train I was taking. In my heart, I knew this was only a fantasy, but I continued to dream.

Most of the time I kept my eyes closed while the train was moving. I heard his voice in the sound of its wheels and his face floated, sometimes indistinctly and sometimes clearly, before my eyes. I saw him not as he had been in the past, but as he had looked when we had last parted, in his ill-fitting blue gown, with his bloodshot eyes and hacking cough and the tiny beads of sweat on his face. At other times I seemed to see him wearing that little black satin cap—but also a short jacket and long trousers and looking like a peddler. He would be walking along the main street, but his hands were tied behind him and soldiers were guarding him ... His face had its usual slight smile, but it only made me feel even sadder and more depressed, and I did not know why.

The crying of the children and the comforting and scolding of their mothers all around me never stopped, and would pull me out of my dreams and into the present. Sometimes I wanted nothing more than to push away my frightening thoughts. I would tell myself that if he had been able to survive the militarist backlash without coming to harm, he would certainly survive the present crisis. These thoughts eased my mind and I would think about the happy future that lay ahead of me in Hankou: that he would soon follow me there and that he would be himself again, full of energy and vitality. As soon as he arrived he would come to look for me at Biying's home, and when she met him, how surprised and happy she would be. And after he left she would certainly say to me, "Younger sister, I think Mr. Wei is a good person." She would ask me how I had met him and I could then go back to the very beginning and tell her everything.... If only I could be with him, I would fear nothing. I would become even more diligent and would learn to work. Had he not said in his letter that a load is lighter if carried by two people instead of one?

The nearer I got to Hankou, the stronger these thoughts became. I was impatient to see Biying and to reach her home so I could begin waiting for him.

The train arrived in Wuchang at noon on the third day. I took a rickshaw to the river bank and boarded the ferry to Hankou. The streets in Wuchang were as narrow and crowded as before. People bustled around in the hot sunshine. They all seemed busy and sunk in their own thoughts. No one seemed to have time to notice anyone else. Certainly there was no one to notice one young woman who had just arrived from another province, or to wonder what changes and anxieties she had experienced during the previous two weeks. The ferry was so crowded that I had to stand up in the bow. Soon it began moving. A hot wind blew across the deck. The white waves churned up by the prow of the boat rolled past my feet and subsided in the muddy, yellow water of the Yangtze. I could see green hills in the distance. They reminded me of the sad ten-scene ballad that I had often heard Biying sing when we were children:

In the third scene is the high Tortoise Hill
The Serpent Mountain with its broken back
And the Hanyang River rolling.

Almost ten years had rolled by, like the water of the river. The Biying of that time had been an innocent young girl. I had never known what kinds of sweet, beautiful dreams she had had at that time. Since then, she had experienced more than a few misfortunes and heartaches in the adult world. As for myself, I had been only a "little bean" of seven or eight and had not yet learned anything about sadness or sorrows. Since then, I too had endured many hardships. I did not know what Biying's life was like now. In her last two letters, she had hinted that she and the younger brother of one of my aunt's students were thinking about getting married. They had been friends since childhood. I hoped that my arrival would not inconvenience her and that I would not be a burden.

When the ferry reached the customs house jetty, the clock on the tower was indicating twelve-thirty. Biying's new address was still in what had been the French concession, near the river. The rickshaw sped me to a whitewashed brick wall surrounding a long two-story building with white walls and black roof tiles. The house Biying had rented was the last one in the row. As I got out of the rickshaw, she ran out to meet me. She had seen me arrive and had hurried downstairs. We went up to her apartment, two big rooms with a spacious living room between them. My suitcase and rattan basket were once again in the presence of their old owner. Biying quickly brought me water so I could wash my face and told her woman servant to brew some tea and serve lunch. We then sat down facing each other across the square table and began a leisurely meal. We both felt happy, but also a little sad. Biying scrutinized me for some time and then smiled and said, "Little sister, you've turned into an adult in the two years since we last saw each other. You've lost all your childishness. You look much stronger, and your haircut is very becoming. You look beautiful. If my mother were here and could see you, I can't tell you how happy she'd be." She sighed.

As I studied Biying, I felt she looked much the same as she had two years ago. Her hair was still long and she still wore it in a long horizontal coil that hung low on her pale pink collar and braided black buttons. Her leaf-shaped gold earrings swayed gently against her delicate, pensive face. I asked her about my aunt and her little son. She sighed again and said that they were both safe. They had first gone to Shanghai, but had moved to Jiujiang the previous month. They were staying with an old schoolmate of my aunt's who had several vacant rooms in her house. She had asked my aunt many times to visit her. The cost of living was lower in Jiujiang and they had more room. My aunt was just beginning to teach her little grandson to read. All was well except that the three generations could not live together, so their happiness could not be complete. Biying told me that her former husband had recently married one of her old schoolmates. She thought it was a good thing because perhaps his desire for revenge on my aunt, Biying, and her son would gradually fade away and that they would soon be able to stop worrying and return to Hankou to live with Biying.

I asked her about her plans to remarry. She laughed bashfully and said that she would wait until autumn to decide. Her friend was away clearing up some business and would not be back until then. Also, she wanted to wait and not act hastily. As she went on speaking about him, she became more and more animated. She told me that he was a childhood friend and that he valued their relationship, could care for her family, and was a diligent worker. They had not seen each other for many years, but when he had heard about her divorce he had hurried back from another city to see her and had done everything he could to help her. That my aunt and Biying's son had been able to find a safe place to live was due in no small part to his help. Biying said he treated her the same way as when they were children and had not changed. Such a friend is rare.

Both her words and her manner revealed clearly that she and her future husband felt a deep affection and tenderness for each other.

After lunch Biying asked me what I planned to do. I told her I wanted to stay in Hankou and look for work as a primary-school teacher. Then I added that I wanted to stay and wait for my good friend before deciding on anything definite. Biying asked no more questions, but said only, "Don't worry. You've arrived at just the right time. You can keep me company. I'm bored with being alone." And she prepared the room across from hers for me.

The next day, after breakfast, I went to the middle school whose address Wei had given me to look for his friend. I wanted to ask him about the situation in Hankou and also about opportunities to teach. The address was in the city, some distance away, so I hired a rickshaw. When I got to the school and told the gatekeeper why I had come, he shook his head and said, "You've come too late. Mr. Tan went to the country two weeks ago and I'm afraid he won't be back until school opens in the fall." I was disappointed, but could only turn and go back home. I had not realized that because it was summer vacation, teaching positions would not be available. I would have to bide my time and make inquiries. As soon as I got back to Biying's home, I got out my pen and ink-grinding slab. I decided that I would practice writing characters every morning after breakfast and that I would also search the newspapers for advertisements for positions. In the afternoons, when I was free, I would help Biying with the housework and sewing as she prepared her new home.

But I could not stop worrying. Each day, I hoped Wei would come. I worried even more because the local situation was disintegrating each day. Rumors kept sweeping the city. The meetings and parades continued and I began to feel as I had in Changsha the previous month, that we were enveloped in a dense, threatening fog. And so it was. The backlash came to Hankou in midsummer. There was chaos and misery, and the warm winds carried the stench of blood.... It became even more difficult to predict when Wei might be able to come.

Biying was aware of my distress and urged me not to worry. What did it matter if I did not find work right away when there was so much upheaval? Besides, she worried that it might be dangerous for me, a young woman who had cut her hair, to be seen in the streets. She said that even if she had had less money, she would still not begrudge me the small amount of food I ate. Whenever she saw me run to the window because there had been a knock at the gate, she would ask, "Little sister, when is that good friend of yours going to come? And even if he can't come, why doesn't he write to you?"

But she did not know the full story and I did not feel I could tell her. She had been through so much, and it was only recently that she had been able to breathe freely and begin leading the life she wished to lead. I did not want to add to her worries. She had many lovable qualities, she was gentle and patient, could put herself in the place of others, and could endure hardships. But we were also very different. I might have said to her, "Big sister, my friend has devoted most of his life to patriotic activities and has served in the forces of the Northern Expedition. Now, with the political situation in so much chaos, I don't know whether he's alive or dead, or when he may be able to come." Or I might have said, "Big sister, I no longer look at life the way I did two years ago. Now I feel that we must live not only to gain security and independence for ourselves but that we must also work hard for our brethren, our fellow countrymen—for everyone whose lives lack security and independence. I now feel that life is not just a matter of food and clothes, but that we must also work for an ideal greater than ourselves."

Perhaps if I had told her these things, she would not have been opposed to my ideas. But I thought that if she learned what my friend believed in she would have been startled, and not necessarily because she disapproved of people who did patriotic work. She had already told me that if it had not been for the coming of the Northern Expedition, she would probably not have been able to escape from her marriage. If it were a year earlier when times were favorable to us, she would have understood and would not have thought it too strange—but now that the situation had turned against us and many people had lost their lives, she would not have understood why Wei and I still wanted to talk about freedom and revolution. .

Without being aware of it, Biying and I had been walking along gradually diverging paths in the two years since we had seen each other. We could not change this, but our relationship was close and we could sympathize with one another about the things that happened to us. However, the direction one's life takes depends not only on the period in which one lives but also on the environment. Although she and I were both living at the same period, our environments had been different. To be sure, Biying had lost her father when still very young, but her mother had always treated her like a living treasure and sheltered her from life's storms. Then, when she grew up, she had made an unfortunate marriage, but that too had passed, and now a bright new future lay before her. She had someone to support her, and had no need to go out and earn a living. So she had few points of contact and small concern with the outside world.

Whereas I had had to live as if both life and death were beyond my control. And though my family had helped me so much, I would still have been living under a cloud had it not been for the Northern Expedition. The prejudices of the old society would never have let me be free. People would have always looked at me with the same scorn and pointed the same accusing fingers they had pointed at my two grandmothers.

When the forces of the Northern Expedition had come a year earlier, I, like thousands of other young people, had held out my arms and rushed to meet it, as if rushing to meet a wave crashing upon the shore. I rushed to meet it because of what it represented, I had felt deeply that I and countless others had all been sinking into a bottomless slough that overwhelmed us and smothered us under the refuse and mud heaped on us by foreign powers and by our own feudal society. If it had not been for this great wind and tidal wave, which had washed away the slough and swept everything clean, how could we, the countless ordinary people, ever have risen to the surface?

Like my countrymen, I loved the land where I had been born and grown up. We hoped that China, with its beautiful mountains and rivers, would remain one nation and would not be occupied and carved into pieces by outside powers. We hoped even more that the people would become the masters and that they would have an honest, incorruptible government to serve them, that our five-thousand-year-old heritage would survive and flourish in independence and freedom, and that we would throw aside the oppression of the past hundred years and stride towards the future vigorously and in peace. These were the thoughts and beliefs of the ordinary people; they were also mine. They were thoughts and beliefs I had come to understand more clearly after I had begun to see so much of Wei, and I would never abandon them, even under the threat of death.

I held all my beliefs inside me and did not discuss them with Biying. I spent my days in uncertainty waiting, and hoping. The weather gradually became cooler. The nuts that hung from the branches of the tall parasol tree in the courtyard grew round and fat. From the upstairs window, I could see flocks of geese flying south, in pairs and companies, to their old, warm nests. Soon the autumn wind blew the fallen leaves back and forth against the courtyard wall, and a thin lined coat was no longer enough to keep off the cold.

One afternoon I was in Biying's room helping her unpack autumn and winter clothes. Suddenly we heard a loud knock at the front gate. Then a man's voice asked, "Is there a Miss Lu living here?"

The voice was not familiar. I dropped the clothes I was holding and ran to look out the window. A man in a long blue cotton gown was at the front gate talking with the maidservant.

"Yes! I'm Miss Lu!" I called.

He looked up and smiled and waved at me. Biying came over to me and whispered, "Little sister, is it your friend?"

"No. It's someone else," I whispered back. Then I called to the visitor, "Please, won't you come upstairs and stay for a while?"

"No, no need to put you out. Why not come down here for a few moments?" he replied.

"All right." I turned and hurried downstairs. When I reached the gate the man held out his hand, grasped mine tightly, and murmured, "Miss Lu, do you remember me? I'm An Tong. We met about six months ago."

An Tong? Of course I remembered him—he was one of Wei's colleagues. I had met him two or three times in Wei's office; he had been working in the education department as a secretary.

"When did you get here?" I asked and smiled at him.

"Yesterday afternoon."

"Secretary An, have you heard anything about Wei Hong? I mean, have you seen him? How is he ... I ... it's been a long time ..."

An shook his head and his voice dropped even more. "Miss Lu," he said earnestly, "I have come here on purpose to talk things over with you." He looked all around us. "But I don't think this a suitable place ... Are you free now?"

I nodded.

"Good. Let's go somewhere else and talk."

Chapter 48.

AN put on his grey felt hat and headed down the street. I followed behind him.

It was only the second time I had gone out that month. The first time was when Biying and I had taken a horse-drawn carriage to see Aunt Gu. On the return trip we had made a detour to the school where Wei's friend taught, but before we reached the building we saw that another signboard was hanging beside the one for the school. It was a police signboard. We had turned around and left immediately. Now as I walked behind An, I did not know whether it was because I was perturbed or whether other people had changed, but it seemed as if everyone was in a hurry and was watching everyone else from the corners of their eyes.

Neither An nor I spoke to each other.

Just as we turned outside the French concession, we saw people running in every direction. Some of them seemed to be looking for places to hide, while others were standing around watching the excitement. An was very alert. He grabbed my arm and drew me into the crowd in front of a grocery. The buzz of people's voices surrounded us.

"When will it end? They've caught some more bandits!"

"I hear they've caught a woman!"

"Look, look! They're coming!"

They all pushed forward in a wave and then back again. Suddenly all the voices were hushed, and we heard only the sound of horses' hooves clip-clopping down the street. Two big brown horses appeared carrying two fat officers. They had shiny faces and sat very erect. Their eyes were fixed in front of them and they looked fierce. They were each holding a huge sword. A blood-red cloth band with tassels hung from the handle of each sword. Behind them came two rows of grey-uniformed soldiers, each bearing a long rifle on his shoulder. The rifles' bayonets gleamed balefully. The soldiers also wore revolvers on the ammunition belts around their waists. Their expressions were as icy and unfeeling as their bayonets. The two rows of soldiers were guarding three rickshaws that were carrying the three criminals to the execution ground. Behind each criminal was mounted a three-foot-high wooden signboard with a poster listing his name, age, and crime.

"Look! The front one is a highwayman!" a voice near me murmured.

A man of about forty was half-sitting and half-lying against the back of the first rickshaw. His face was swollen and covered with dirt. His hair was loose and hung down over his eyes like scorched straw. His trousers were rolled up above his knees and pus was oozing from his swollen legs and from under the black medicinal plasters stuck all over them.

"Look! The one in the middle is a girl!"

Galvanized, the crowd pushed forward again.

"It must be a woman revolutionary again."

"Tsk-tsk! How beautiful she is! She's even more beautiful than the last one!"

"She's so young! What a pity! What a waste!"

A young woman of about seventeen was in the second rickshaw. Her hair was short—she looked like a student—and she was wearing a black coat and skirt. Tears were streaming silently down her round face. Behind her came the third rickshaw, carrying a young man in a short blue cotton coat and long trousers who looked like a working man. Both he and the young woman were as pale as ghosts. The posters behind them said they had both committed the same crime, "Communist agitation to mislead the people."

After the soldiers and the rickshaws had passed, the people began to disperse. An tugged at my sleeve and I jumped, as if I had been awakened from a nightmare. I shook myself and we started out again. We turned left and then right, and went down four or five streets before turning into a narrow lane. We stopped outside the back gate of a house. An knocked twice. A woman in her fifties poked her head out. When she saw him she immediately opened the gate wider and let us in.

An led me to a little room on the stair landing. A young woman wearing a red sweater and a black skirt was sitting by the window with a book in her hands. She rose when she saw us. He went over and whispered a few words to her. She nodded and smiled at me and then went out.

An indicated the round stool on which she had been sitting

buried my face in my hands, trying to calm myself and to conceal my feelings.

I heard footsteps coming up the stairs. An went to the door and peered out to see who was there. Then he came back over to me and said, "Comrade Lu, why don't you lie down on the cot. and rest for a while? A friend of mine has come and I must go and talk with him. I'll be back soon. I hope you'll have come to a decision by then."

I nodded. He helped me over to the cot and settled a pillow behind me, and then left, closing the door quietly.

I buried my face in the pillow. I felt as if I were in a void and the only thing that existed was my body lying sobbing on the cot.

"Dear heaven, how can the world be so cruel? Why must life be so sad and full of pain? Why can't I just run to the train station, get on a train, and go to him? Why must I go even farther from him? Oh, Wei! Wei, I can't bear it!

"I must stop crying—tears are a sign of weakness. I could weep a river of tears but they would not bring me any closer to him ... I have only two choices—shall I go with An to Shanghai tonight, or stay here unprotected and run the risk of being arrested and beheaded, like that young woman? Shall I listen to Wei and his sister and go to Shanghai to wait for him and then join him in the bitter struggle to do away with oppression and injustice, or shall I cower back and live in comfort, not daring to hold up my head? Two choices—go or stay ..."

"Comrade Lu ..."

I rolled over. An was bending over me. His face was full of sympathy and friendship, but there was a question in his eyes. I sat up. My head was still heavy and my throat was so tight that I could not speak for a few moments. He went and poured me another cup of tea. As he handed it to me he asked, "Have you decided?"

I nodded.

"And?"

"I think I will go with you tonight."

"Good. My friend is waiting in the front room. I will ask him to buy two steamer tickets." He looked at his wrist watch. "It is now only a quarter past five. We need not go aboard until about nine. Do you want to go back and get your things?"

I shook my head.

"You don't want to go back to your relative's house to get your clothes? You have plenty of time."

"No. I don't want to go out. My eyes are so red. If I go out looking like this people will notice me. And my cousin might try to persuade me not to leave. Secretary An, can you loan me a piece of paper and a pen? I would like to write my cousin a note."

"Paper and pen I have." He took out his fountain pen and got several sheets of white paper from a small rattan bookshelf on the wall. "It's almost dark and there's not much light in here. I'll go and bring you a lamp."

"No need to go to so much trouble. I'll sit by the window and write by the light there ... What ship will we take tonight?"

"The *Tianjiang*. It's a big steamer."

"There's something else I must ask you. After I write the letter, can you find someone to deliver it for me?"

"Of course. I'll send Aizhen's younger brother over in a rickshaw to take it for you. Is there anything else you need?"

"No. Thank you."

"Good. Then I'll leave you alone for a while."

He left and I sat down by the window with the pen and paper.

At dinner, in the front room, all eight seats around the square table were filled. Besides the people I had already met—the old woman who had opened the gate, the young woman in the red sweater, and the teenaged boy who had delivered the letter for me—there were three men who had attended military academy with An and had served in the same regiment with him. Two were Koreans. They all seemed older than An. The Korean who had been an officer, Lieutenant Colonel Li, had some grey in his hair. The house was his elder sister's home. She was the only one of the group who did not speak Chinese well. This room, like the other one, was almost bare and contained only the table, a tall clothespress, some chairs, and a big board bed. The reddish-brown walls reflected the light from the oil lamp, and our shadows played over them.

During the meal, An and his friends discussed their work. His Korean friends sometimes talked in their own language. Their speech sounded rapid and level and lacked rhythm and cadence. The old woman seemed to know something about me and kept picking out good bits of food for me and urging me to eat more. Her daughter acted as interpreter as she questioned me about how old I was, whether I had parents, and where I came from. After the meal she gave me two little apples and a pear and told her daughter to tell me that many pears were grown in the part of Korea she came from. She said that every autumn the trees hung heavy with pears and that although baskets and baskets were filled, the ground was still covered with them. Korean pears were sweeter, fresher, and juicier than Chinese ones but the local people seldom had a chance to eat them because the Japanese took most of them away by cart and boat. She sighed and shook her head. Then she went to the clothespress and rummaged in it for a long time before bringing out a faded four-inch-square photograph of a strongly-built middle-aged man with a drooping mustache. She indicated her daughter and pointed to her own hips, and then pointed to the boy and to her belly, speaking to me the whole time in her own language, which I did not understand. Her daughter waited until her mother had finished and then told me that the photograph was of her father, who had been devoted to the Korean independence movement. When she was tall enough to reach her mother's hips and her mother was still carrying her brother, her father had been seized by the Japanese secret police one day in Shanghai as he was passing through one of the foreign concessions. He had been in prison on a small Japanese island ever since.

"My mother says, 'Those who have suffered the loss of their country feel an inexpressible bitterness that those who have not suffered can never fully understand.' She says she hopes that your China will rise and be independent, because only then will Korea be able to hope for independence as well. The Japanese are strong and well-armed. Not only could we not protect our Korea, but even the safety of China, big as it is, cannot be completely guaranteed. The time will come when no one on earth can live in peace. My mother says that in Korea, the Japanese made nine families share one chopping knife, and would not let us shut our gates at night for fear of secret meetings...."

As the daughter spoke, the mother kept nodding. Her eyes were red, as if she were about to weep, and she took out her handkerchief and wiped her nose from time to time. The daughter's voice became more and more emotional as she went on speaking, and added to my distress.

A little later, An interrupted us by coming over and telling me it was eight o'clock. He said it was getting late and that he wanted to talk with me.

His three friends were talking together in the small room. When I came in, they offered me the stool near the window. An's leather suitcase and roll of bedding lay, packed and ready, on the floor. Everyone continued to discuss where he should go and what he should do once we left. They then asked whether we had a place to live and money for our immediate expenses once we arrived in Shanghai. An said he would ask his friends and relatives for help and that for a week or two there would be no problem. He added that I would certainly find work before long. Colonel Li took two envelopes from the wallet on his belt. One was a letter that he asked An to take to a friend in Shanghai. The other, he said, was a little gift from the three of them to An and me, so we could buy whatever small things we might need. Then, just as we were about to start for the pier, they discussed the precautions we should take. If anyone should ask how he and I, a young man and a young woman, were related to each other, what would we answer?

Colonel Li looked at both of us, smiled, and said, "You could say you are sweethearts, that you're betrothed, but not yet married."

An gave an embarrassed smile and said, "We can say we are brother and sister."

Chapter 49

WE boarded the *Tianjiang* about nine o'clock. In order to avoid attracting attention, only Colonel Li came along to help with the baggage.

We had third-class tickets and were fortunate enough to find an upper and lower berth together on the outer side of the cabin. An put our baggage away and we were just about to settle ourselves when a woman in a long blue wool dress came pushing through the crowd in the cabin. She had a leather suitcase in one hand and a cloth bundle in the other and was looking around in all directions. It was Biying. When she saw me she ran over, dropped the suitcase and bundle, and grasped my hands. "Little sister, you've frightened me to death!" she whispered, out of breath.

I had never expected Biying to come to the boat, and it made me both happy and unhappy to see her. Colonel Li and An jumped to their feet and I quickly introduced them to her. I could tell by her expression that she did not know what to think about them. I took her aside, out of earshot. She kept eyeing them, and finally asked in a whisper, "Little sister, tell me the truth. What is this all about? Who are those two men? You were living so quietly at home—what has happened to make you act so suddenly?"

"Big sister, I must apologize for having caused you so much anxiety. I've been wanting to tell you, but I was afraid it would make you worry too much."

"What is it? Are you in trouble? Tell me. Have you joined the revolution?"

I shook my head emphatically.

"Then I don't understand. Who are those men?"

"Don't worry, they are to be trusted. I'm leaving for a good reason. There's nothing sinister about it. Here, when you read this you'll understand." I took out the letter from Wei's sister and gave it to her to read. Then, as we sat together I recounted all that had happened since An had found me. I asked her not to worry and said that if I stayed in Hankou there might be trouble for me that could also involve her.

Biying listened to all of this and sighed deeply. "There is so much chaos that no one knows what to do. But going to Shanghai —suppose you can't find teaching position? You have no relatives there. What will you do?"

"Don't worry. I have friends there, and besides, it'll only be for six months. If I can't find a teaching job, there are many factories where I can find work and earn my living. In six months the situation will be completely different. Then there will be time enough to decide the best thing to do."

Biying sighed again and looked searchingly at me. She turned her gaze on An and Colonel Li and said hesitantly, "Biling, you're a very young woman. To be travelling alone with two men ..."

"No, only the young one, An, is going."

"Travelling alone with a young man! Little sister, how can you tell me not to worry?"

"Please—because you don't need to! Our relationship is not what you seem to fear. He's a good friend of Wei's, and of mine as well. He's not like feudal men, with old ideas."

"No, relationships between men and women never seem to change. You're too inexperienced. I'm older than you. I've been married and have a child—I understand. You must be very careful!"

"Biying, please believe me. Our relationship is different. I know I'm right. I know I can trust him!"

Biying still looked anxious. She put her hand on my shoulder and looked at me anxiously. I was worried because I thought it was insulting to talk about An that way. Although I knew much less than Biying about relationships between men and women, that day I had been exposed to human relationship that differed greatly from the secret emotions between men and women. These relationships contained no vestige of sexual attraction, only deep sympathy and trust. It was as if we were on a boat in a storm and all had to help each other. I was deeply grateful to An for helping me solve my problems and for exposing himself to danger by taking me with him. His three friends had also treated me warmly. Without ever even meeting me, they had opened their slender purses to give us travelling money. And that old woman's family had also treated me like one of them. These things made me unforgettably thankful. However rough and full of difficulties and dangers the road of life may be, fresh, beautiful flowers sometimes blossom by its side, and those flowers can make us forget our weariness and imbue us with new hope and new courage.

"Big sister, I beg you not to worry," I tried to comfort her. "When we reach Shanghai, An and I will each go our own way and will look for ways to support ourselves. I'm now a grownup and I know how to take care of myself."

"I know you can. You're intelligent. I also realize that An and his friend seem to be honorable men. It's just that I can't help worrying. These are dangerous times. But I can't do anything to keep you here." Biying seemed to be trying to make me feel better and also to be resigning herself to my decision. She sighed again. "If you can't find a suitable place to stay when you get to Shanghai, I think you should go to where Mother and my little boy lived. The people are relatives of my friend. They know Mother and will certainly be willing to look out for you. I'll give you their address and a letter asking them to help you." She took out a notebook and a pencil from the bundle of clothes she had brought and wrote the family's name and address. Then she pointed to the clothes and suitcase and said, "The bundle contains your spring and autumn clothes and your underwear, socks, pens and ink and writing materials. I put your long padded gown and interlined gown and two lined sleeveless jackets with seven dollar bills sewn into the linings in the suitcase. I couldn't fit anything else in, but will send you the rest of your things when you get there."

She sighed again. "Little sister, it's hard being a grownup. I have so many regrets. I've always felt that if it weren't for my mother and my son, whom I'm responsible for, I too would have liked to see the world. Take good care of yourself. Write to me when you arrive. Here is fifteen dollars—it's all I could get on such short notice. You should be able to live on it for a month. Oh, I hope peace comes soon! And that your friend is released soon. I also hope both of you will accomplish much that's worthwhile, for others and for yourselves."

I clasped Biying's hands tightly. I felt as if this was the first time she and I had ever truly understood each other. My heart was aching and I could not speak. Suddenly the gong clanged and the ship's whistle blared, signaling those who had accompanied their friends to leave the ship. An and Li came over to Biying and me. We jumped up. Biying stepped forward and told An earnestly, "Sir, take good care of her. I am placing my little sister in your hands."

"Please don't worry," he replied warmly. "We're in the same boat; we're both trying to escape from possible disaster. I'll use all my skill and strength to take care of her."

Colonel Li came over and shook hands with me. "May the winds favor you the whole way. I hope that the whole world will be bright and peaceful by the time we meet again. We will not let the fire die in our hearts, or lose hope for the future of mankind. Am I right?" A small smile crept across his wind-chapped, wrinkled face, but the smile was tinged with sadness.

All around us, people were hurrying to leave the ship. An and I joined the noise and confusion and made our way out of the dimly-lit cabin with Colonel Li and Biying. We watched them disappear into the crowd on the pier.

Soon after the ship weighed anchor, the passengers in our third-class cabin made up their beds and settled down. Some sat on the edges of their berths smoking cigarettes and talking idly. Others draped their bedding over their shoulders and drank tea. Opium lamps had been lit in the lower berths in the middle section and in the one diagonally across from us. An went to the steward and rented a quilt so I could have his clean one. As he opened his bedding roll he asked me whether I preferred the upper or lower berth.

I suddenly felt very shy, and hesitated. He then said, "I think you should take the lower berth. Then you won't need to do any climbing. Shall I spread my bedding down here for you?"

I hesitated again. "I think it would be better for me to sleep in the upper berth," I stammered.

My thought was that although the upper berth was also open and the people around me would be able to see me, it was a little better than the lower one because An would be able to see how I looked when I was asleep if he were above. That would be too embarrassing.

An said nothing, but climbed up and spread his bedding on the upper berth for me. I helped him spread his rented bedding in the lower one. Then I stood on the chair and began to climb up, but when I was halfway up I suddenly heard several voices saying, "Look at that girl with her hair cut!" I turned and saw four or five men in the berths around me staring at me open mouthed. One older man came over to An and said, as if both advising and criticizing him, "What kind of man are you, to let a woman sleep above you?"

"You may not be afraid of bad luck, but we are!" came several other voices.

An and I said nothing. Hastily, I climbed off the chair.

"Never mind. But we must not violate their social customs, feudal though they are," murmured An. "Never mind."

I crawled into his soiled rented bedding with all my clothes on. An took a new towel out of his suitcase and covered both sides of the end of the quilt with it. He also gave me his pillow. "Sleep well. See you tomorrow," he said.

"See you tomorrow." I turned my face towards the wall and closed my eyes. Then I felt a hand lightly caress the top of my head and heard An climb into the upper berth. I grabbed the towel and covered my face.

The autumn night wind blew more coldly on the river than on land. The Yangtze murmured in the darkness and the ship rolled from side to side. Soon the cabin was filled with the rise and fall of deep snores as the passengers gradually drifted into dreams.

I shut my eyes and tried to sleep, but could not. My weary brain was filled with the murmur of the Yangtze and images of the many events and people of my young life. It had been more than two years since I had been on that steamer with my great-aunt. At that time I had been running away from the Shao family. Suppose they had overtaken me. I would never have been able to stand up and be a free person.

My thoughts went back over the sixteen years that had been so full of wintry cold and so empty of spring warmth. My only regrets were for the days of childhood, which would never return. But I now felt no anger towards anyone, not even towards the Shao woman. Instead, it seemed to me that all the difficulties I had endured had given me a deeper understanding of the world. It was the social system that had let my family and society step on me, had let the strong oppress the weak. I had no desire for revenge, but I had grown to hate that unjust system.

My thoughts went to Wei, far away in prison, and I could not stop worrying. How difficult it was to achieve happiness! Six months earlier, he had told me that he had been concerned about national affairs ever since lower primary school and that from then on he had been so busy fighting to change society that he had neglected the most precious relationship of life—love. Now that he had found love, he said, not only did it not hinder his work, it heightened his commitment to his cause. It had been the first time he had ever really said what was in his heart, and I had considered myself fortunate that I had finally found safety and someone I could trust. But now the winds of change had blown us apart. How could we plan our lives, in such tragic and disordered times, and how many other young men and women were sharing the same fate? Fortunately, his family had some power, and we could hope he would be free by spring. Whatever the difficulties, I would wait for him calmly and steadfastly in Shanghai.

It took about four days to reach the huge, prosperous, bustling city of Shanghai. Foreign concessions were everywhere. Shanghai was a paradise for adventurers of all nations, including our own. The lust for gain, exploitation, and the struggle for survival were all more intense there than anywhere else. I realized that the road ahead of me was even more dangerous and difficult than the one I had taken to escape from the Shaos, but I was not as fearful as I had been in the past. I knew that the world had changed. It was bigger, wider and freer than it had been, and I was no longer walking alone, but with countless others of my fellow countrymen.

As soon as the steamer entered the Whangpoo River, we all went out onto the deck. The muddy yellow Yangtze was filled with gunboats from many nations. Imposing and awe-inspiring, their great grey guns were trained arrogantly on the many hundreds of thousands of people who lived in the city. The guns made my heart freeze. I stood with An in the bow of the ship, and the cold wind off the river tore at my hair and at the edges of my coat. In the city's business district, the tall buildings reached towards the clouds. The city seemed asleep. As the steamer neared the wharf, we could see throngs of ragged coolies, their backs bent under heavy cargoes. An slung his bedroll over his left shoulder and took his leather suitcase in his right hand. I followed behind him. We squeezed through the crowd to the landing. The rickshaw pullers crowded around, stretching their dirty hands out to us. An and I had already decided to go first to the home of his aunt for a few days because it would be a convenient place for me to stay while I looked for a teaching job. He hired two rickshaws and we went to the French concession.

An had to knock on the gate of the two-story Chinese style house in an inner lane for a long time before his aunt opened it. She was in her thirties and seemed well-educated. She was also very happy to see him and invited us in with a smile. Before An sat down in her living room, he took her aside and explained who I was. She nodded and glanced at me and said several times, "No trouble at all, no trouble at all." Then she showed us where to wash and offered us tea. When her woman servant came back from the market, she asked her to prepare breakfast immediately. She showed me to a little room upstairs, apologized for how small it was, and said she hoped I would be able to put up with the inconvenience for a while.

After breakfast, I was so impatient that I wanted to go across the river to the small school in Pudong immediately to make inquiries about work. An, who was unfamiliar with Shanghai, took out the address and asked his aunt for directions, but Pudong was a large area with many market towns, and she did not know it well. She asked her servant, who came from Pudong, and she told us that the town we wanted was far away. We would first have to hire a small boat to take us to the middle of the river, where we could board a small steamboat that made only one trip each way a day. If we started out in the afternoon, we would not be able to get back the same day. All we could do was write to the headmaster and introduce ourselves, so An wrote a two-page letter in which he introduced both of us and also recounted Wei's story. He also said that Wei's sister had expressed the wish that the headmaster would help us as much as he could. I wrote my letter carefully, in small, formal characters. I gave my age, my educational background, and the subjects I felt qualified to teach: lower-primary arithmetic, Chinese, singing, handicrafts, and recreation. I also said that if needed I could stretch a point and teach history. Regarding terms, I merely wrote, "I have just arrived in Shanghai and do not know the area or the people. If your school will add me to its staff and give me food and lodging, my needs will be met and whether I have a salary or not makes no difference."

Headmaster Sun's reply arrived three days later, on a Saturday morning. It was brief and said only that he had business in Shanghai that afternoon and hoped we could meet with him at about one o'clock at An's aunt's house. An, who was staying at a friend's home came over during the morning and was very happy to see the letter. He stayed for lunch. I was very nervous. I did not know what the headmaster would be like or if there was any hope of work at the school. His note gave me no indication. Fortunately, Headmaster Sun arrived soon after lunch. I was surprised to see that he was very young, only twenty-two or so.

He was also modest, pleasant, and sincere. Our meeting was informal. He and An discussed Wei's situation and the conditions in the provinces of Hubei and Hunan for a while. He spoke then with me about his school, which he described as a small, poorly-equipped county lower-primary school. Because it was the only school in the town, it had more than eighty students ranging in age from five or six to thirteen or fourteen. Including himself, there were four men teachers, and he had been looking for a woman teacher for singing classes and to be in charge of playground activities. But he had had trouble finding someone because the town was out of the way, the pay was low, and travel to and from Shanghai was not convenient. If I was interested and did not fear hardship, I could leave with him that very day. He added that I would not be lonely because the younger sister of one of the teachers was now living at the school, studying part-time and working part-time because she had missed out on school as a child. After I had heard what he had to say, I immediately answered that I would go with him that afternoon.

"Good." He smiled and looked at his wrist watch. "The steamboat leaves at two-thirty, so we don't have much time. Is your baggage ready?"

"I have very little. If you wait a bit, I'll be back." I hurried upstairs to the front room and took leave of An's uncle and aunt, thanking them for their hospitality. Then I went to my room and for my two pieces of luggage, which I took downstairs. Headmaster Sun had left to hire rickshaws, which arrived soon afterwards. An's uncle and aunt walked us to the gate. They urged me to consider their home my own and invited me to visit on holidays and festivals. An carried my luggage, and came with us to the bank of the river. He came onto the little boat with us and saw us onto the steamboat. When he bade us farewell, he took my hands tightly in his. With a slight smile on his face, he said he could now stop worrying about me and would write to Wei's sister as soon as he got back so that Wei and his sister would be reassured as well. He told me he himself would probably leave Shanghai before long, but that he would write to me as soon as he knew when he was leaving and where he was going. Finally, he told me to be calm and patient and to wait for the spring until Wei was released. Then everything would be possible.

For the previous ten days, I had been walking along a new road with An as my companion. He had treated me with the affection of a brother. I did not know when I would see him again. I felt sad and loath to part with him, and I wanted to thank him and to beg him to take good care of himself, but the whistle blew and he moved away before I had the chance. All I could do was stand at the rail and watch him climb into the little wooden boat as it bobbed back towards the shore and finally disappeared in the distance.

Chapter 50

THE steamboat stopped at every little market town along the swirling river, and the further we went the narrower the river became. Headmaster Sun appeared used to the journey and did not sit in the cabin but found a place in the bow, on the upper deck, where he spread a handkerchief and sat beside me. The water hissed alongside the boat and the villages and towns lay peacefully on both banks. The air was pleasant and the fields were green under the intense blue sky. The leaves on the trees were flame-colored or bright green. The autumn sun shone warmly. From time to time we could hear children's voices, happy laughter, the barking of dogs and the occasional crowing of a cock from the banks. Before I realized it, my anxiety began to fade away. The town where we were going was the last stop. By the time we got there the sun was already slanting down towards the west. I followed Headmaster Sun onto the jetty. A row of whitewashed houses with black-tiled roofs stood on the river bank. Fishermen's boats hugged the curve of the river. Their nets hung on poles nearby. It seemed to be a fishing town. The school was nearby, down two long, narrow dirt lanes. The people we met on the way saluted Headmaster Sun in a friendly, respectful way, saying, "Mr. Sun, you've been to Shanghai and back today." He would nod modestly to them and answer their greetings.

The school's buildings and equipment were as simple and poor as he had said. There were three brick buildings around a dirt courtyard and surrounded by a low wall of whitewashed brick. We entered through a little wooden gate. To the right was a small house. The blue-black smoke of a cooking fire spiralled from the short white chimney on the roof. Headmaster Sun took me inside and said, "Mother, I'm back." An old woman in her fifties, with a delicate face and wearing silver bracelets and earrings, was sitting beside the stove feeding the fire. She stood up and smiled at me. Headmaster Sun pointed to me and said, "This is our new young woman teacher." She nodded to me and dipped hot water from the iron water heater in the stove into a wooden pail so we could wash. Then she busied herself serving dinner.

There were six people at the table including me. Mr. Tang, who was about fifty, had been a traditional teacher. Mr. Wu and Mr. Yang were both under thirty. Mr. Wu's younger sister, Xiao Hui, was a year younger than I and was studying in the third year of lower-primary school. She also watched the small children during playtimes. They were all sincere, simple, and pleasant. They seemed happy to see me and insisted that I sit in the seat of honor. Fragrant steam rose from the two meat dishes and two vegetable dishes on the table. There was clear-steamed fish with scallions and ginger and pork broiled with soy sauce and dried bean curd. One of the vegetables was yellow and one green. Their color was fresher and their taste more delicious than the food in Shanghai. The rice was unpolished and tasted of the burning reeds over which it had been cooked. The water journey and the fresh country air had stimulated my appetite, and I filled my bowl a second time. After we ate we all helped Mrs. Sun clear the table and move it to one side. The dining room then became the teachers' living room and study. The house was quite large, with one room in front and another behind. Mr. Wu and Mr. Yang shared the back room. The front room already had four desks, but now that I had come they rearranged them and brought in another one, almost new, which they placed near the latticed door where the light was good. Soon Mrs. Sun came in with an oil lamp in one hand and a big pot of tea in the other. We all sat around drinking tea and chatting for a while and then Headmaster Sun suggested that we walk around the courtyard and look at the classrooms and the sleeping quarters.

It was late fall. The country air was cooler than in the city and the stars and moon seemed to shine more brightly. A huge tree loomed like a giant in the courtyard near the corner of the brick wall. Its branches waved gently in the night breeze. The classroom for the lower-primary classes was in a one-story building against the eastern wall. Rows of long, narrow tables with long benches in between filled the big room. Headmaster Sun said the three lowest grades used the same room. The classrooms for the fourth year of lower primary and the first year of upper primary were in a two-story building across the courtyard against the central section of the western wall. The first floor was divided into two rooms by thin wooden partitions. Each room contained about fifteen desks and chairs. The upstairs had been partitioned into three rooms. The easternmost one was Headmaster Sun's bedroom. His board bed, bedcurtains and quilts were neat and clean, and there were books all over. He had hung an *erhu* fiddle, a moon-shaped *yueqin* guitar, two bamboo flutes, and some other musical instruments on the walls. The central room was Mr. Tang's. It was all but empty except for the bed and a few paintings and sheets of paper covered with ideographs pasted on the partitions. The westernmost room contained two beds with blue and white linen curtains and the usual thin mattress covered with blue-stenciled cotton. This was Xiao Hui and Mrs. Sun's room. Now that I was there, Mrs. Sun moved into the little fuel storage room behind the kitchen and let me have her bed. There was a long table, with a stool on either side, in the middle of the room, and latticed windows ran across the whole south wall. One of the beds did not have a quilt, so I knew it must be mine. I wondered what I would do, now that the nights were getting cool, if I had no quilt. Because I had just arrived, it did not seem right to start out by borrowing things. But just then Mrs. Sun came in carrying a quilt covered with blue-stenciled white cotton which she had just finished making. She put it on the bed without saying anything and went back downstairs.

Everyone went to bed early. After we put out the lamp in our room only the light from Mr. Tang's shone through the cracks in the partition. We could hear him chanting softly, but could not tell whether he was reading the students' essays or poetry. After a while he also put out his lamp and went to bed. It was very quiet. Occasionally I could hear the chirping of crickets in the far fields. The cold, bright moonlight slanted in through the open lattices. There was a bed of rice straw under my thin mattress and when I first lay down it felt hard and prickly, but after a while it became smooth and soft.

It was the first night in many months that I felt peaceful, and I fell asleep almost at once. In the middle of the night the cold awakened me and I opened my eyes. The moonlight was shining on my pillow. I pulled the padded quilt around my shoulders and lay looking at the moonlight, unable to sleep. My thoughts could not help flying to Changsha, so many *li* away. The same moon was shining down on us both. I wondered if he was sleeping, or awake and looking at the moon as I was and if we were thinking of each other. This was the first time since we had parted that I felt we could send our thoughts to each other, that I felt close to him. I wanted to get up and go to the window and gaze at the moon, but I was afraid I might waken Xiao Hui.

The next day was Sunday. After breakfast, Headmaster Sun and the three men teachers put on clean, pressed gowns and said they would take me for a walk in the country. They led the way through the front gate and Xiao Hui and I followed. It was a warm, clear, almost cloudless day. The dirt road was rough, but we were wearing soft-soled shoes, so it did not tire us to walk. The town was surrounded by ponds, rice fields, trees and houses. The autumn scenery in this region had a delicate, beautiful quality. There were mulberry trees everywhere. Xiao Hui told me that the women of the area spent all spring and summer caring for the silkworms and all autumn and winter spinning.

Wherever we went, little boys and girls called out greetings in voices like sparrows chattering. "Good morning, Headmaster! Good morning, Mr. Tang! Good morning, Mr. Wu! Good morning Mr. Yang! Good morning Elder Sister Wu!" They all stared when they saw me, and Headmaster Sun would say, "This is Teacher Lu. She has just arrived." The children would look at me and smile but would not greet me. As we passed, women would poke their heads out through the gates and greet Headmaster Sun and the others. Then they would whisper to each other, "Look at the new woman teacher!" The news travelled through the whole town in no time. More and more children came out and followed us, always keeping a few feet behind us. Whenever we stopped, they stopped, whenever we walked, they followed. Dogs followed the children, jumping happily around them. The chickens by the side of the road scattered, the startled sparrows took wing, and everyone—men and women, old and young—laughed. I had not expected to become the center of attention and could not help smiling myself. On the way back to the school I noticed that the faces and figures of the women had a delicate beauty that matched the beauty of the landscape. Most of them wore blue homespun or stenciled coats and trousers and silver earrings and silver bracelets of old, beautiful design. Some of the little girls wore red and green homespun. Only a river separated this place from Shanghai, but here the customs and relationships among people were honest, sincere, and friendly—completely different from the crafty, self-serving ways of the people of the city.

415

I was worried about beginning to work the next day. After lunch I asked Headmaster Sun for my schedule. He had assigned me the upper-primary class in Chinese, which he had been teaching, and the history class in the fourth year of lower primary, which Mr. Wu had been teaching. I was also to teach all the singing classes and handicrafts and recreation for the lower-primary class. He said that if I could not manage all this he would help me mark the papers. I leafed through the textbooks and assured him that I would do my very best. I also said I hoped that he and the other teachers would not be too polite to give me advice. I then sat down at my desk and began preparing. Except for the history—I felt I needed to study reference books so I could make the lessons more interesting —the subjects presented no difficulties. I asked Headmaster Sun for some reference books on the last part of the Qing Dynasty, and he brought me several thick volumes dealing with the Opium Wars and the final disintegration of the dynasty. He told me that the students were still very young and that I did not need to go into matters too deeply. I was worried that the students would not understand me because of my accent, but he told me not to worry. He said that except for Mr. Tang, the teachers all used Mandarin in teaching. I sighed with relief.

Once I finished preparing my classes, I went up to my room and wrote to Biying. I told her that our trip on the river had been peaceful and that I had been fortunate enough to find work three days after reaching Shanghai. I told her about the school and the town and about my fellow teachers. I said everything was just as I would wish it and that she was not to worry about me. I also asked her to send me my blue homespun gowns because cotton clothes were more suited to the country. Then I asked whether she had set a time for her marriage and when my aunt and the little boy would return to Hankou. Finally, I asked her to write when she had time.

I also wrote to An to thank him for his concern and friendship. I told him that my arrival in Shanghai and my teaching job were all due to him and that I intended to make the most of my opportunities. I begged him to be careful and said that we all had great faith in the future of China. I added that I hoped we would meet again soon. I was about to start a letter to Wei's elder sister when Xiao Hui came up to tell me dinner was ready, so I put down my pen.

That evening after we had drunk our tea, Xiao Hui and Mr.

Yang both suggested that Headmaster Sun play the *erhu* for us. He made a few polite, modest excuses, but then went upstairs to fetch it. Xiao Hui took the lamp into the inner room. Headmaster Sun sat at the door looking out at the full moon and played some ancient melodies. I had not known that he could play so masterfully. Sometimes his playing sounded as if he were telling a mournful story, at other times, the music he played was light and gay. The moonlight was cold and the evening breeze was chilly, but we were so absorbed in the music that we were aware of nothing else. Mrs. Sun crept in and sat in the corner to listen to her son play. It was nine o'clock before we all went to bed.

The next day, I began my life as a schoolteacher. It was a day I would never forget. The students began arriving while we were still eating breakfast. The older ones wandered around the courtyard and smiled at me, giving me sidelong glances. My lower fourth and upper first classes were in the morning. The students were twelve to fourteen years old, and only three or four of the fourteen or fifteen students in each class were girls. I could not help feeling timid as I stepped up onto the teacher's platform. Headmaster Sun seemed to realize how I felt and introduced me to each class. He told them that I was the first woman teacher the school had ever had and that the other teachers were very glad to have me. He said he hoped all the students would behave and not think that because women teachers were gentle and sympathetic, they could do as they pleased. The students all sat at attention and listened quietly.

After he left I opened the book. I had planned to have the students discuss the previous lesson so I could learn about how well they understood things, but they all begged me to explain the new lesson to them. So I had to start explaining it to them word by word. After about two lines I looked up and saw that the girls all had their heads bent and were smiling with their hands over their mouths. The boys were exchanging glances and smiling. They were laughing at my accent, and none were paying any attention to the lesson. I felt confused. I did not want to stop explaining, but I could not go on that way, either. I did not know what to do. I remained silent for a moment, and they stopped smiling, so I went back to the lesson, keeping my eyes only on the book and not looking at them until the bell rang at the end of the period. When I looked up, I saw that they had all stood up respectfully and looked friendly. I stopped feeling anxious. When the second and the third periods began, both the students and I were unsure of ourselves, but after a while, as I concentrated on explaining the texts, my confidence grew. I felt the morning went smoothly.

In the afternoon I taught my three lower-primary classes. I had felt more confident because I thought the smaller children would be easier to teach than the older ones. My heart went out to them, all round, rosy and cheerful. As soon as the bell rang, I took a big pile of cut paper and went to the classroom without waiting for Headmaster Sun. There were more than fifty students in the three classes. They ranged in age from about five to nine, but there were many more of the little ones. They were all shouting and scrambling around for seats. I waited near the door for a while until they had all sat down before going to the desk. When the children saw me they scrambled out of their seats and bowed to me and there was more disorder before they all sat down again. The first class was handicrafts. I started handing out the paper I had brought, but when I was halfway through, I heard some of the little ones in front quarrelling. I ran back to them and saw that four or five of them were pushing each other on their seats. The children around them were watching the excitement with round, staring eyes. It took me some time to settle them down. Then I heard more quarrelling, this time from the back rows. I had to run back and forth five or six times before the classroom quieted down.

After I handed out all the paper, I showed the bigger children how to fold it into animals and the little ones how to make boxes out of it. But while I was talking to the big ones, the little ones started talking and playing among themselves, and when I tried to teach the little ones, the big ones played and talked. I could not pay equal attention to both groups at once. I would clap my hands and the children would be quiet, but only for a moment. Then their voices would rise again. I tried to talk louder, but my voice was just a squeak. Finally the bell rang and the children all dashed outside. Only a few brought their finished work to me. The second period was singing, and the third was recreation, out in the courtyard. Although I had Xiao Hui to help me, there were too many children and they were all very small. So it was difficult to keep order and get them to play games. I got confused and worried and could only try to outshout them. By the time the afternoon was over, I was hoarse and very upset. I had not realized that the lower-primary classes would be so difficult. I was so convinced that Headmaster Sun and the others would be disappointed in me that I could scarcely eat dinner.

But after dinner Headmaster Sun came over to me and said his school, like all the others in the region, had too many students and not enough classrooms. He told me he knew that the day had been very difficult, but reassured me by saying it would get easier after I knew the students better. Mr. Tang and the other teachers all told me they had had the same difficulties when they first started teaching and that it did indeed get easier. This made me feel better.

After we finished our tea we all began preparing for the next day's classes. In order to save oil, I sat across the table from Xiao Hui and we shared the lamp. I worked until after one in the morning before I went to bed, but I could not get to sleep. I kept hearing the students shouting and reliving the afternoon. I should not have assumed that the work would be easy. I had been too hasty. I had not had enough patience. I resolved that starting the next day I would be very careful to do what the headmaster and the others told me to and would overcome the difficulties I was facing.

Day by day I learned from the children and the children learned from me. Day by day our relationship grew and developed, and we learned to understand each other. The smaller children were lovable and eager to learn, and once they had learned something they never forgot. When I saw that they always rushed in and out of the classroom in great disorder and wasted too much time, I taught them two short songs:

When you come, go and sit in your seats.
When Teacher comes, stand upright in straight rows.
All together make a bow, then sit down.
All together make a bow, then sit down.

The other was:

The bell rings, all in line should walk out.
Make straight the line, keep in step, do not push.
Take your time, march, march, forward march, do not push.
Take your time, march, march, forward march, do not push.

The little ones did as they were told in the songs and acted much more orderly. Even when they were disorderly, I remained calm and was careful not to raise my voice. Even if they were being noisy, when they saw that I was talking quietly and calmly they would involuntarily lower their voices and listen to me. When they saw that I was happy, they too were happy and tried even harder to behave. I noticed that their hands were black with dirt and ink when they went home for lunch, so one day I poured out a basin of water and washed my own hands. I told them I always washed my hands before I ate. Before long, even the smallest children would hold out their clean little palms when they came back to the school after lunch. The older girl students gravitated to me and if I ran into any difficulties Headmaster Sun and the other teachers were all willing to discuss things and help me and each other. I found my work more interesting each day.

At the end of the month I found a large envelope on my desk. Inside was a six-month contract from Headmaster Sun. I was honored as a first-class teacher and my salary was twenty-two dollars a month. After subtracting the food money for the month—the sleeping quarters were provided by the school—I still had about sixteen dollars left. A first-class teacher and a salary of twenty-two dollars! It was more than I had ever expected. There were not many opportunities to spend money in the countryside. Pens, ink, and paper were supplied by the school, and although the first month I had to buy bed curtains, quilts and a mattress, every month that followed I had about fifteen dollars left. My colleagues were also careful in their spending. Except for Mr. Tang and Mr. Yang, who went by boat to nearby towns to visit their families each month, and the headmaster, who went to Shanghai once a month to buy supplies, magazines, and books for the school, we all preferred to remain in the countryside rather than go to the city, which was expensive and tiring. As I became more familiar with the lessons, I began to find time to read some of the classic and new novels as well as classic poetry.

The days were filled with the children's laughter and the buzz of their studying. The leaves fell from the Chinese parasol tree and the cassia's fragrance faded. Before we realized it the winter cold had come again. Just before winter vacation, Headmaster Sun gave us our contracts for the spring term. As usual, all the teachers were asked to come back, but when he handed me my contract he hesitated, as if he wanted to say something. I understood what was troubling him and said immediately that I was grateful that he wanted me to stay and that no matter what

happened I would like to teach until the summer. I promised not to leave in the middle of the term, which would create difficulties for him and for the school. He understood and smiled and nodded in relief.

Before we knew it, it was time for winter vacation. Mr. Tang and Mr. Yang packed and went happily to their homes to join their family circles for New Year's. Mr. Wu went to visit relatives. Xiao Hui stayed to be company for me and to make up her lessons. With her, Headmaster Sun, his mother, and her other son, a fifteen-year-old who came home from middle school to spend the vacation, our winter holidays were not lonely. We were very comfortable. Mrs. Sun was a kind, modest, traditional woman who never asked questions about school matters or talked much. She treated all the teachers with affection. She washed, starched, and mended the men's clothes, shoes and socks. Xiao Hui told me she had been widowed rather early and had raised her two sons by herself. Headmaster Sun spent only one year at Beijing University but had not been able to continue because the family was too poor. So he had returned and become headmaster of the primary school and was helping his younger brother study in middle school. Now his mother and younger brother helped us with preparations for New Year's. She pasted soft thick paper over all the cracks in the doors, windows, and partitions to keep out the cold north wind. The two braziers never lacked kindling or charcoal and burned red and warm all day long. After lunch she would often bring her sewing upstairs and sit in front of the brazier and chat with Xiao Hui and me.

It was the school's custom never to accept presents from the students' families, so the people in the town always selected the best rice and vegetables and the freshest fish and sold it to the school at the lowest possible prices. At New Year's, the parents banded together, took up a collection, and brought us an earthenware jug of the best Shaoxing wine, two fat hens, a basket of eggs, some pickled fish, fresh pork, and vegetables, with a piece of red paper pasted on each. To show even more respect, they chose two parents and two students as their representatives to bring it all to us. Headmaster Sun could not, of course, send it back. There was enough to feed the five of us for two weeks. It was too rainy and snowy for us to go out much, so I spent my holiday leisure time reading A Dream of Red Mansions and Outlaws of the Marsh. I enjoyed them so much I could not put them down. On sunny days I missed the children and would go out walking with Xiao Hui to see them. They often came to the courtyard to play, too. The days passed quickly and easily.

At last the kind spring wind began to blow, bringing green to the bare branches of the mulberry trees and to the dry grass. The hard ice on the ponds melted into soft ripples and soft threads of rain moistened the earth. The insects all awakened from their winter sleep and crept to the surface of the soft earth. Peach, pear, and apricot blossoms opened smiling. The mustard blossoms were like gold.

It was again time for the women to busy themselves with the silkworms. All the women, their heads wrapped in blue homespun, went out to gather mulberry leaves. The birds sang happy songs from the mulberry trees and the many-colored butterflies darted among the flowers. The earth had come to life again and was singing with joy.

The spring wind blew me the news of Biying's new happiness; her wish of so many years had at last been fulfilled and she and her childhood friend were married after New Year's. My aunt and Biying's little boy had already returned to Hankou from Jiujiang. Life was peaceful for them all. My aunt's spirits were high and she was planning to open another girls' school. They would write to me again as soon as everything was settled and they hoped I would return to Hankou to live with them.

The spring wind also blew me news from An. He reported that all was not peaceful in the country and that many people were struggling to survive because rents and taxes were exorbitant in the countryside. Though the peasants worked their farms year round, they could not produce enough to keep themselves warm and fed. Cold and hungry, they were rising up against the landlords and tax collectors. An was now with a group of friends who were devoting themselves to the unfinished work of the Northern Expedition. At the end of the letter he wrote, "The task is great and difficult, but we hope China's future will be great and bright. When our brother Wei is released, we hope you and he will continue to work hard for our country and our people. We also hope that we shall all meet again soon."

One morning in late spring I received a letter from Wei. How much deep emotion that thin letter in its thin envelope carried! My hands trembled, my heart throbbed with happiness, and my tears fell on the dozen or so lines in which he recounted his longings and anxiety of the previous year. His writing was strong

422

and vigorous; a year in prison seemed not to have lessened his courage and determination. He wrote that in a day or two he would go to see his parents and that he would come to Shanghai within another two weeks to be with me.

"My heart is white-hot," he wrote. "My trials have given me an even deeper love for our country, for my work, and for the one I love. Loved one, we are both young and have all our lives before us. Let all our plans wait until I have come to you. Once we see each other again we can plan everything...."

The bell for the morning class sounded. I folded the letter and hid it under my pillow. I took out a handkerchief and wiped my eyes. Even before my eyes were dry, I had a smile on my face.

I thought how warm his words were: "We are both young and have all our lives before us." "The days to come are many, my loved one—for you, for the country, and for all humanity. My heart is full of love." I picked up my schoolbooks and the students' compositions, turned and ran down the stairs and into my classroom.

But shortly after May Day I was shocked to receive a letter from Biying informing me that Wei and many other revolutionary youths had been executed by the warlord He Jian, governor of Hunan Province. She enclosed a scribbled note to me from Wei, who had written it right before his execution. A sympathetic jailer had brought it to Biying. The note read:

"Baowen,

I have been fighting for our country and the ideals of humanity. Soon I am to die for this great cause. Remember the calligraphy I wrote for you, that poem by a Hungarian poet, 'Life is precious / Love is all the more precious / But for the cause of freedom / I can lose either or both.' I wish you well. The liberation of China and the emancipation of humanity are bound to come, but they will come only through the dedication of many revolutionaries, some of whom must give their lives. Farewell! Don't grieve over me. Carry on the struggle to the end. I'll be happy in the afterlife."

The tears blinded me and streamed down my cheeks. I kept reading his last words to me over and over. That night as I lay in bed, I thought of them again and his face and our times together all came back to me like a film. I could not sleep for pondering over his words and the Hungarian poet's poem. The reactionaries had killed the man I loved, but I could not let myself be crushed by sorrow. I had to do as he had asked. I had to work for my country and the poor of the world, and carry on his unfinished cause.

Life is precious
Love is all the more precious
But for the cause of freedom
I can lose either or both.

从童养媳到电影明星

王 莹 著

*

外文出版社出版

（中国北京百万庄路 24 号）

邮政编码 100037

北京外文印刷厂印刷

中国国际图书贸易总公司发行

（中国北京车公庄西路 35 号）

北京邮政信箱第 399 号　邮政编码 100044

1989 年（36 开）第一版

1993 年第二次印刷

（英）

ISBN 7-119-00402-6 /I・38（外）

01500

10-E-2253P